C000075364

Northumberland p137

Cumbria p39

North Yorkshire p187

Lancashire p110

W. Yorkshire p196

ENGLAND

Isle of Anglesey p249

Mersyside p120

Conwy p243

Cheshire p27

Derbyshire p52

Lincolnshire p117

Nottingham-shire p139

Gwynedd p245

Staffordshire p162

Shropshire p148

Leicestershire p112

Rutland p147

Norfolk p121

Powys p254

Worcester-shire p180

Northampton-shire p135

Cambridgeshire p26

Suffolk p163

Ceredigion p241

Herefordshire p95

WALES

Bedford-shire p15

Pembrokeshire p252

Carmarthenshire p240

Monmouth-shire p250

Gloucestershire p82

Buckingham-shire p22

Hertfordshire p101

Essex p78

Swansea p255

Bridgend p238

Cardiff p239

Oxfordshire p141

Berkshire p16

Kent p105

Vale of Glamorgan p256

Bath & NE Somerset p10

Wiltshire p173

Surrey p166

Somerset p153

Hampshire p90

W. Sussex p169

E. Sussex p168

Devon p60

Dorset p73

Isle of Wight p103

Cornwall p30

Channel Islands p198

Guernsey

Herm Island

Sark

Jersey

CONTENTS

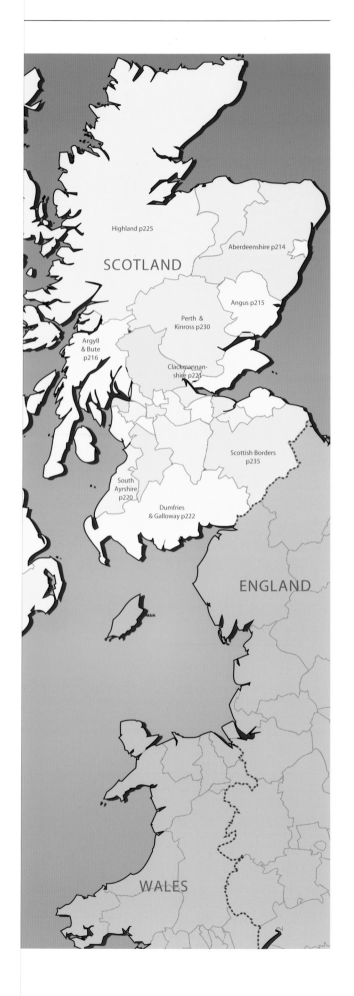

Highland p225

Aberdeenshire p214

SCOTLAND

Angus p215

Perth &
Kinross p230

Argyll
& Bute
p216

Clackmannan-
shire p221

Scottish Borders
p235

South
Ayrshire
p220

Dumfries
& Galloway p222

ENGLAND

WALES

INTRODUCTION

Andrew Warren, Managing Director, Condé Nast Johansens Ltd.

One of the most rewarding and enjoyable aspects of publishing this Guide is the rich variety of correspondence that we receive from you, our Guide users.

Of course it would be unrealistic to imagine that you are always full of praise for our recommendations. Your constructive observations are always appreciated and keep us all on their toes, not to mention the properties that we recommend!

We encourage your comments as they help us to compile a more useful Guide each year and they also contribute directly to the nominations for our Annual Awards. You may wish to complete a 'Guest Survey Report' printed at the back of this Guide or on our website www.johansens.com where you will also find some very attractive 'special offers'.

We very much hope that you enjoy using the 2005 edition of our Guide where you will find many favourites and a choice of new recommendations.

Above all please remember to mention 'Johansens' when you make an enquiry or reservation and again when you arrive. You will be especially welcome.

THE CONDÉ NAST JOHANSENS PROMISE

Condé Nast Johansens is the most comprehensive illustrated reference to annually inspected, independently owned accommodation and meetings venues throughout Great Britain, Europe and North America.

It is our objective to maintain the trust of guide users by recommending by annual inspection a careful choice of accommodation offering quality, excellent service and value for money.

Our team of over 50 dedicated Regional Inspectors visit thousands of hotels, country houses, inns and resorts throughout the world to select only the very best for recommendation in the 2005 editions of our Guides.

No hotel can appear unless it meets our exacting standards.

CONDÉ NAST JOHANSENS GUIDES

Recommending only the finest hotels in the world

As well as this Guide, Condé Nast Johansens also publishes the following titles:

RECOMMENDED HOTELS & SPAS, GREAT BRITAIN & IRELAND

Unique and luxurious hotels, town houses, castles and manor houses chosen for their superior standards and individual character.

RECOMMENDED HOTELS & SPAS, EUROPE & THE MEDITERRANEAN

A wonderful choice of properties including châteaux, resorts, charming countryside hotels and stylish city hotels.

RECOMMENDED HOTELS, INNS & RESORTS, NORTH AMERICA, BERMUDA, CARIBBEAN, MEXICO, PACIFIC

A diverse collection of properties across the region, including exotic ocean front resorts, historic plantation houses and traditional inns.

RECOMMENDED VENUES, GREAT BRITAIN & EUROPE

Venues that cater specifically for business meetings, conferences, product launches, events and celebrations.

When you purchase two Guides or more we will be pleased to offer you a reduction in the cost.

The complete set of five Condé Nast Johansens Guides may be purchased as 'The International Collection'.

To order any Guides please complete the order form on page 303 or call FREEPHONE 0800 269 397

Tanqueray®

HOW TO USE THIS GUIDE

To find a hotel or inn by location:

- Use the **county maps** at the front to identify the area of the country you wish to search.

- Turn to the relevant **county section** where hotels are featured alphabetically by location.

- Alternatively use the **maps** on pages 292-302 at the rear of the Guide. These maps cover all regions of Great Britain & Ireland and each hotel is marked.

There are over 40 properties which did not feature in our last (2004) edition and these are identified with a "NEW" symbol at the top of the page.

To find a hotel by its name or the name of its nearest town look in the indexes on pages 284-288.

The indexes also list recommended hotels by their amenities such as swimming pool, golf, etc.

If you cannot find a suitable hotel where you wish to stay, you may decide to choose one of **Condé Nast Johansens Recommended Hotels** as an alternative. These establishments are listed by place names on pages 258-261.

Once you have made your choice please contact the hotel directly. Rates are per room, including VAT and breakfast (unless stated otherwise) and are correct at the time of going to press but should always be checked with the hotel before you make your reservation. When making a booking please mention that Condé Nast Johansens was your source of reference.

We occasionally receive letters from guests who have been charged for accommodation booked in advance but later cancelled. Readers should be aware that by making a reservation with a hotel, either by telephone, e-mail or in writing, they are entering into a legal contract. A hotelier under certain circumstances is entitled to make a charge for accommodation when guests fail to arrive, even if notice of the cancellation is given.

All guides are obtainable from bookshops, by calling Freephone 0800 269397, by using the order coupons on page 303 or at www.johansens.com/bookshop

CONDÉ NAST JOHANSENS

Condé Nast Johansens Ltd., 6-8 Old Bond Street, London W1S 4PH
Tel: +44 (0)20 7499 9080 Fax: +44 (0)20 7152 3565
Find Condé Nast Johansens on the Internet at: www.johansens.com
E-Mail: info@johansens.com

Publishing Director:	Stuart Johnson
P.A. to Publishing Director:	Amelia Dempster
Hotel Inspectors:	Jean Branham
	Geraldine Bromley
	Robert Bromley
	Pat Gillson
	Marie Iversen
	Pauline Mason
	John O'Neill
	Mary O'Neill
	Fiona Patrick
	Liza Reeves
	John Sloggie
	Nevill Swanson
	David Wilkinson
	Helen Wynn
Production Manager:	Kevin Bradbrook
Production Controller:	Laura Kerry
Senior Designer:	Michael Tompsett
Copywriters:	Clare Barker
	Sasha Creed
	Norman Flack
	Debra Giles
	Rozanne Paragon
	Leonora Sandwell
Marketing Coordinator:	Siobhan Smith
Marketing Promotions Executive:	Niko Downie
Client Services Director:	Fiona Patrick
PA to Managing Director:	Siobhan Smith
Managing Director:	Andrew Warren

Copyright © 2004 Condé Nast Johansens Ltd.

Condé Nast Johansens Ltd. is part of The Condé Nast Publications Ltd.

ISBN 1 903665 19 1

Printed in England by St Ives plc
Colour origination by Arkima Ltd

Distributed in the UK and Europe by Portfolio, Greenford (bookstores). In North by Casemate Publishing, Havertown (Bookstores.)

2004 AWARDS FOR EXCELLENCE

The winners of the Condé Nast Johansens 2004 Awards for Excellence

The Condé Nast Johansens 2004 Awards for Excellence were presented at the Awards Dinner held at The Dorchester hotel, London, on November 10th, 2003. Awards were offered to those properties worldwide that represented the finest standards and best value for money in luxury independent travel. An important source of information for these awards was the feedback provided by guests who completed Johansens Guest Survey reports. Guest Survey forms can be found on page 304.

Most Excellent Country House Award

BALLACHULISH HOUSE – Argyll & Bute, Scotland, p216

"The welcome here is one of the warmest, elegant furnishings, a piper heralding dinner - spacious bedrooms and innovative fusion of classic French and local fayre."

Most Excellent Traditional Inn Award

THE BELL AT SKENFRITH – Monmouthshire, Wales, p250

"The Inn looks over the historic bridge of the river Monnow, carefully renovated retaining a classical style with roaring log fires, flagstone floors and stunning oak beams."

Most Excellent Coastal Hotel Award

YE OLDE BULL'S HEAD – Isle of Anglesey, Wales, p249

"The yachting town of Beaumaris is set in an area of "outstanding natural beauty". The hotel is a perfect balance between traditional and contemporary."

Most Excellent Value for Money Award

PEN-Y-DYFFRYN HALL HOTEL – Shropshire, England, p150

"Combining tranquillity, superb comfort, unobtrusive hospitality and good food within an unpretentious atmosphere."

The following award winners are featured within Condé Nast Johansens 2005 Guides to Hotels – Great Britain & Ireland, Hotels & Spas – Europe & The Mediterranean, Hotels – North America & Caribbean. See page 2 for details.

Most Excellent London Hotel
Number Sixteen – London, England

Most Excellent City House
Green Bough Hotel – Cheshire, England

Most Excellent Service
Riverside House – Derbyshire, England

Most Excellent Restaurant
The French Horn – Berkshire, England

Most Excellent Spa
Chewton Glen – Hampshire, England

Europe: Most Excellent City Hotel
J & J Historic House Hotel – Florence, Italy

Europe: Most Excellent Countryside Hotel
Le Domaine de Divonne Casino, Golf & Spa Resort – Divonne-les-Bains, France

Europe: Most Excellent Waterside Hotel
Château Eza – Èze Village, France

Europe: Most Excellent Value for Money Hotel
Ürgüp Evi – Ürgüp-Nevsehir, Turkey

Europe: Most Excellent Spa Hotel
Almenara Golf Hotel & Spa – Sotogrande, Spain

North America & Caribbean: Most Outstanding City Hotel
The Chase Park Plaza – Missouri, USA

North America & Caribbean: Most Outstanding Inn
The Lodge at Moosehead Lake – Maine, USA

North America & Caribbean: Most Outstanding Hotel
Coral Reef Club – Barbados, Caribbean

North America & Caribbean: Most Outstanding Spa
The Bishop's Lodge– New Mexico, USA

North America & Caribbean: Most Outstanding Resort
Spice Island Beach Resort – Grenada, Caribbean

www.hildon.com

Now all your guests can have a room with the best view. Philips offers a dedicated range of LCD and Plasma screen technology for the Hotel environment. With a wide choice of FlatTV's from 15" to 42" we have the right size screen for any room,and all models are designed to operate with interactive systems for in-room movies, games and internet connection. For the most discerning hotelier, Philips' unique Mirror TV creates a high quality video picture through a polarized mirror. You choose the frame to complement the decor of your establishment.Whether in a hallway, reception area, or as a guest-room centrepiece, Philips Mirror TV delivers high visual impact.

If you're not quite ready for FlatTV, there is a comprehensive range of conventional Philips Hotel TV's to choose from. All models incorporate a Welcome Message and give you the ability to lock the settings as you want them. The ProPlus range features a Digital Clock Alarm and FM Radio and the Smartcard range is designed to operate with interactive systems.

Isn't it time you upgraded to Philips Hotel TV?

For more information please contact your local Philips head office, or visit our website www.philips.com/itv

PHILIPS

Let's make things better

Images from www.britainonview.com

For further information on England, please contact:

Cumbria Tourist Board
Ashleigh, Holly Road, Windermere, Cumbria LA23 2AQ
Tel: +44 (0)15394 44444
Web: www.gocumbria.co.uk

East of England Tourist Board
Toppesfield Hall , Hadleigh, Suffolk IP7 5DN
Tel: +44 (0)1473 822922
Web: www.eastofenglandtouristboard.com

Visit Heart of England
Larkhill Road, Worcester, Worcestershire WR5 2EZ
Tel: +44 (0)1905 761100
Web: www.visitheartofengland.com

Visit London
6th Floor, 2 More London Riverside, London SE1 2RD
Tel: 0870 156 6366
Web: www.visitlondon.com

One North East Tourism Team
Aykley Heads, Durham DH1 5UX
Tel: +44 (0)191 375 3000
Web: www.visitnorthumbria.com

North West Tourist Board
Swan House, Swan Meadow Road, Wigan, Lancashire WN3 5BB
Tel: +44 (0)1942 821 222
Web: www.visitnorthwest.com

Tourism South East
The Old Brew House, Warwick Park, Tunbridge Wells, Kent TN2 5TU
Tel: +44 (0)23 8062 5400
Web: www.seetb.org.uk

South West Tourism
Woodwater Park, Exeter, Devon EX2 5WT
Tel: +44 (0)1392 360 050
Web: www.visitsouthwest.co.uk

Yorkshire Tourist Board
312 Tadcaster Road, York, Yorkshire YO24 1GS
Tel: +44 (0)1904 707961
Web: www.ytb.org.uk
Yorkshire and North & North East Lincolnshire.

English Heritage
Customer Services Department , PO Box 569, Swindon SN2 2YP
Tel: +44 (0) 870 333 1181
Web: www.english-heritage.org.uk

Historic Houses Association
2 Chester Street, London SW1X 7BB
Tel: +44 (0)20 7259 5688
Web: www.hha.org.uk

The National Trust
36 Queen Anne's Gate, London SW1H 9AS
Tel: +44 (0)20 7222 9251
Web: www.nationaltrust.org.uk

or see pages 263-265 for details of
local attractions to visit during your stay.

THE COUNTY HOTEL

18/19 PULTENEY ROAD, BATH, SOMERSET BA2 4EZ

Directions: From M4, junction 18 take the A46 and the A4 towards Bath. Just before the city centre turn left onto the A36 ring road and follow signs for Exeter and Wells. The hotel is on the right after the Holburne Museum.

Web: www.johansens.com/countyhotelbath
E-mail: reservations@county-hotel.co.uk
Tel: 0870 381 8455
International: +44 (0)1225 425003
Fax: 01225 466493

Price Guide:
single £80
double £110–£190

The County Hotel, winner of the AA Guest Accommodation of the Year Award 2001, the Little Gem Award by the RAC and the English Tourism Council's Gold Award, stands in the centre of Bath. It is an attractive stone-built building with a frontage enhanced by arched sash windows and twin balconies ornamented with open stone balustrades. Completely refurbished in 1999, décor and sympathetic modernisation have resulted in the creation of elegant, relaxing accommodation. The 22 exquisite en-suite bedrooms have every home comfort. Many have splendid views over the Cricket ground and Bath Abbey. Breakfast is served in an intimate dining room which opens onto a conservatory where morning coffee, afternoon tea and light lunches can be ordered. Dinner is not available but the hotel's owners will happily help select one of the many nearby restaurants for an evening out. Drinks can be enjoyed in the stylish bar or lounge. The hotel has a non-smoking policy apart from the bar area. Bath's attractions include the Roman Baths, pump room, Royal Crescent, the thriving theatres and fascinating museums. Ample parking is available.

Our inspector loved: The comfortable well appointed bedrooms.

DORIAN HOUSE

ONE UPPER OLDFIELD PARK, BATH BA2 3JX

Built in 1880, the charming Dorian House is built of historic Bath stone and retains many of its original features. Beautiful stained glass windows are a feature in the hallway of this fine example of Victorian architecture, where fresh flowers and antiques adorn each room. Spacious bedrooms have a restful ambience and views over the Royal Crescent or well-tended gardens. Some have traditional oak four-poster or cast-iron beds and are luxuriously decorated with opulent fabrics and stunning décor. Egyptian cotton sheets, tea/coffee making facilities and other modern amenities ensure a comfortable stay. The warm bar and lounge with its open fireplace have an intimate, relaxed atmosphere with large comfortable sofas and menus collected from all the excellent restaurants in town so that guests may plan their lunch or evening meal. A delicious breakfast includes homemade bread, fresh fruits or a scrumptious full English breakfast. The hotel's central location is perfect for those wishing to explore Bath, whose many attractions include the fascinating Roman Baths, Bath Abbey, Stourhead Gardens and the Royal Crescent.

Our inspector loved: *The cosy and informal feel – a home from home.*

Directions: From Bath take the A367 signposted Shepton Mallet. After about a minute's drive turn right into Upper Oldfield Park. Dorian House is the 3rd building on the left

Web: www.johansens.com/dorianhouse
E-mail: info@dorianhouse.co.uk
Tel: 0870 381 8650
International: +44 (0)1225 426336
Fax: 01225 444699

Price Guide:
single £52–£78
double/twin £72–150

OLDFIELDS

102 WELLS ROAD, BATH, SOMERSET BA2 3AL

Directions: From the M4, junction 18, follow signs for Bath city centre, then take the A367 (signpost for Radstock). Oldfields is situated on the corner of Upper Oldfield Park, the first turning on the right.

Web: www.johansens.com/oldfields
E-mail: info@oldfields.co.uk
Tel: 0870 381 8792
International: +44 (0)1225 317984

Price Guide:
single £55–£95
double/twin £75–£145

Oldfields is a large, elegant and traditional Victorian bed & breakfast with panoramic views of Bath. It is superbly positioned, only 8 minutes' walk to the city centre and is built from the honey-coloured stone for which Bath is famous. Although the house is equipped with every modern feature to ensure that visitors experience maximum comfort and convenience, it retains many of the elaborate cornices and artistry of its original character. The bedrooms are beautifully furnished with rich fabrics and antiques and offer a full range of amenities. A delicious choice of breakfast to include full English, fresh seasonal fruits and smoked salmon with scrambled eggs are served in the magnificent dining room overlooking the city of Bath. Newspapers are provided and for those with time to linger over breakfast, there is unlimited tea and coffee. There is also a drawing room, gardens and private car park, which make Oldfields the perfect choice for a visit to Bath. You are assured of a warm welcome from the resident hosts. Hot-air ballooning, golf and horse riding can be arranged. The famous Roman baths, pump room & spa and Royal Crescent are all within easy walking distance. Bath is the perfect centre to explore the Cotswolds, Glastonbury and Wells Cathedral, Stonehenge, Salisbury, Bristol and South Wales. Oldfields is a strictly non-smoking hotel.

Our inspector loved: The new beautifully decorated four-poster rooms.

TASBURGH HOUSE HOTEL

WARMINSTER ROAD, BATH BA2 6SH

The impressive, red brick Victorian façade can only hint at the warmth, style, comfort and excellent service provided in the 3 floors of its interior. A former gentleman's residence built in the 1890's this hotel, 5 times winner of the coveted RAC Little Gem award, majestically rises high over 7 acres of beautifully tended terraced gardens and meadow park just ½ mile from Bath's city centre. Guests can enjoy spectacular views over and beyond the Avon and a stroll through landscaped gardens and grounds featuring over 1,000 trees down to the Kennet and Avon Canal. The towpath provides a picturesque walk into the city. Personally run by the owner, Tasburgh offers traditional English elegance and tasteful décor with all modern comforts, fresh cut flowers and glossy magazines in all the rooms. The Reception Hall, with original floor tiling and stained-glass windows, is particularly attractive. The Drawing Room has typical Victorian features such as high ceiling, marble fireplace and large bay window and there is a lovely, light conservatory with a spectacular chandelier and French doors leading onto a terrace. Bedrooms are elegantly decorated, en suite and appointed to a high standard. Some have a four poster or half-tester bed and original marble surround fireplace. Many have scenic views. Excellent gourmet breakfasts are provided in a sunny Dining Room and in winter it is warmed by a large open fire.

Our inspector loved: The well-kept garden and views over the Avon valley.

Directions: Leave Bath by entering Warminster Road (A36) via Beckford Road with Sydney Gardens to the right. Tasburgh House is on the left after passing Trossachs Drive.

Web: www.johansens.com/tasburgh
E-mail: hotel@bathtasburgh.co.uk
Tel: 0870 381 8941
International: +44 (0)1225 425096
Fax: 01225 463842

Price Guide:
single £65
double/twin £95–£130

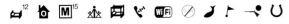

THE RING O' ROSES

STRATTON ROAD, HOLCOMBE, NEAR BATH BA3 5EB

Directions: From Bath, take the A367 towards Shepton Mallet. At Stratton-on-the-Fosse, turn left towards Holcombe. The hotel is on the left.

Web: www.johansens.com/ringoroses
E-mail: info@ringoroses.co.uk
Tel: 0870 381 9181
International: +44 (0)1761 232478
Fax: 01761 233737

Price Guide:
single £65-£75
double/four poster £75-£85

Situated in the old village of Holcombe, The Ring O' Roses country inn is a rural haven nestling high on the Mendip Hills yet is only a few miles from Bath, Wells and Bristol. The inn is steeped in history and is named after the well-known nursery rhyme reminiscent of the plague that devastated the village. An atmosphere of comfort and conviviality pervades the hotel, enhanced by oak panelling in the lounge, antiques and the rich textures and warm colours of the expertly chosen décor. Guests will love to read by the crackling log fire in winter or in the picturesque and sunny gardens that overlook Downside Abbey in warmer months. Elegant bedrooms are spacious and individually decorated in a traditional style. Sumptuous, freshly prepared dishes are created with imagination and flair, complemented by an extensive wine list. There is plenty to do for both history and nature lovers in the area. The ancient St Andrew's church retains impressive original features and has a beautifully tended churchyard surrounded by lovely woodland and hillside walks. Luccombe Pond, which was built by monks in medieval times still has plenty of fish and is a birdwatcher's paradise.

Our inspector loved: *The well-appointed, individually decorated bedrooms and delicious food.*

MILL HOUSE HOTEL & RESTAURANT

MILL HOUSE, MILL ROAD, SHARNBROOK, BEDFORDSHIRE MK44 1NP

This is a little gem in a riverside setting with gardens sloping down to the meandering waters of the Great Ouse where a mill pond and weir still exist to this day. Otters reside here alongside colourful kingfishers that entertain guests with their fluttering and flights. The Mill House Hotel & Restaurant is set amidst peace and tranquillity in a village 6 miles north west of the county town of Bedford, famed for its Norman castle, now only a mound, 4 old churches and John Bunyon, who lived here from 1655 - 1688. It is a welcoming, attractive hotel with foot-comforting flagstone floors and a warm Mediterranean colour décor. Vases of fresh flowers abound and in cooler months an open fire welcomes guests into the entrance hall. Service is of the highest standard, individual and attentive. Each of the bedrooms is a haven of country-style relaxation, individually decorated, furnished and equipped with every home comfort. The recently refurbished Colonial-style restaurant, with award-winning chefs Paul and Mathew leading a small dedicated team, offers exciting flavours and amazing desserts. The well balanced wine list compiled by a master of wine complements the cuisine. Woburn and Cambridge are within easy reach whilst the more energetic may wish to visit Grafham Water, Santa Pod Raceway or horseracing at Huntingdon.

Our inspector loved: The contrast of the warmly welcoming entrance and the cool beauty of the mill pond.

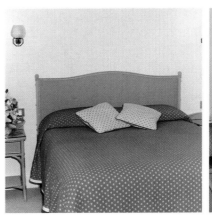

Directions: From Bedford take A6 north. Sharnbrook is signed.

Web: www.johansens.com/millhousesharnbrook
E-mail: info@millhousehotelandrestaurant.co.uk
Tel: 0870 381 9189
International: +44 (0)1234 781678
Fax: 01234 783921

Price Guide:
single £70-£90
double/twin £85-£110
Enquire about special breaks.

Bedford
Woburn
Leighton
Buzzard
Luton

15

THE COTTAGE INN

MAIDENS GREEN, WINKFIELD, BERKSHIRE SL4 4SW

Approached from a country lane, The Cottage Inn offers a welcoming feel as soon as you turn into its gravel drive. Red and white table-clothed tables shaded by umbrellas offer al fresco dining on a summer's day or evening, whilst the restaurant with its friendly bar is as conducive to a romantic twosome as it is to a larger party or business occasion. 2 private dining areas are available upon request, and a varied, freshly prepared menu is served. The gastronomy is simple yet delicious and comes in generous portions, along with a fantastic selection of wines and champagnes. The inn has been run by its owners, Bobby King and Jon Mee, for 17 years, and usually one or the other is on hand to ensure the very high standards for which it is renowned are maintained. Bedrooms are located to the rear of the cottage with their own entrance. They are very comfortable, well stocked and popular with corporate and leisure guests alike. Visitors can take advantage of nearby golf courses, and enjoy day trips to Windsor Castle, Legoland and Ascot. Weekend rates available.

Directions: Take J6 from the M4 and join the A330 towards Ascot. Just past the crossroads for the B3022 turn left into Maidens Green. The inn is 200 yards on the right.

Web: www.johansens.com/cottageinn
Tel: 0870 381 9234
International: +44 (0)1344 882242
Fax: 01344 890671

Price Guide:
(including continental breakfast)
single/double £87.50

Our inspector loved: The charming restaurant and pretty yet practical bedrooms.

THE LEATHERNE BOTTEL RIVERSIDE RESTAURANT

THE BRIDLEWAY, GORING-ON-THAMES, BERKSHIRE RG8 0HS

Uniquely situated on the banks of the Thames, surrounded by water meadows and rolling hills, The Leatherne Bottel offers peace and tranquillity with no distractions except for ducks and swans and the occasional rowing 8. Guests can enjoy the cosy and sunny restaurant or dine al fresco on the deck. Chef, Julia Storey, who has been at The Leatherne Bottel for 8 years, lovingly and passionately prepares meals from the finest of fresh ingredients, whilst guests unwind completely! Annie Bonnet, who runs the restaurant, grows her own herbs and salad leaves to create unusual salads which may include mustard, orach, miburna, lemon basil and pineapple sage. There is also an abundance of fish, shellfish and caviar in the summer and game in the winter. Much thought and time has been taken in the choosing of the wine list which includes hidden treasures in wooden boxes and wonderful armagnacs and cognacs. A lighter lunch menu is available from Monday to Friday and a set dinner menu costs £23.50 for 3 courses. A full à la carte menu is on offer every day and the restaurant is open for Sunday lunch but closes Sunday evenings. A river journey can also be arranged on board MV Dorothy.

Our inspector loved: A visit to this special restaurant is like going on holiday!.

Directions: Signed off the B4009 Goring–Wallingford road. From the M4, junction12: 20 minutes. From the M40, junction 6: 25 minutes. Oxford is 30 minutes drive and London is 60 minutes.

Web: www.johansens.com/leathernebottel
E-mail: leathernebottel@aol.com
Tel: 0870 381 8685
International: +44 (0)1491 872667
Fax: 01491 875308

Price Guide:
from £23.50

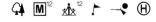

THE INN ON THE GREEN

THE OLD CRICKET COMMON, COOKHAM DEAN, BERKSHIRE SL6 9NZ

Directions: From the M4 take junction 8/9 towards Marlow. Follow the signs to Cookham Dean and turn right by the war memorial on the Old Cricket Common

Web: www.johansens.com/innonthegreen
E-mail: reception@theinnonthegreen.com
Tel: 0870 381 8639
International: +44 (0)1628 482638
Fax: 01628 487474

Price Guide:
single from £100
double from £130

With open views over the village green and beyond, The Inn on the Green is situated in the heart of the picturesque village of Cookham Dean near Maidenhead. A heartfelt welcome is warmly offered in this sophisticated restaurant and hotel, which is furnished to an extremely high standard, with attractive colour schemes, imaginative décor and comfortable furniture. A cosy bar is the perfect place to relax and the adjoining dining room opens onto a spacious terrace in the summer, a sunny spot for early evening dining. The inn is as ideal for a special stay or dinner with friends as it is for weddings, corporate meetings and exclusive use. Individually decorated bedrooms are beautifully appointed and benefit from all modern conveniences such as DVD players and surround sound, some with a marvellous four-poster bed. Guests can explore the local woods, which provide many excellent walks and the Thames, which is only 2 kilometres away, winds through the beautiful Thames Valley; an enchanting day out. Local attractions include Windsor Castle, the second home of the Royal family, Legoland and the pretty riverside town of Marlow, which has numerous unique shops and restaurants. The hotel is also within easy reach of Oxford, Eton, Henley and Heathrow.

Our inspector loved: The cosy bar and lovely bedrooms.

NEW

CROWN & GARTER

GREAT COMMON, INKPEN, BERKSHIRE RG17 9QR

The charmingly traditional English Crown & Garter is an extremely welcoming rural inn with an unpretentious, down-to-earth atmosphere. Set in beautiful Berkshire countryside, peacefully located near the attractive village of Inkpen, the old-fashioned 16th-century inn is reached driving through fairytale scenery of quiet lanes through fields and woodland and past cottages draped in honeysuckle. Its ancient charm can best be glimpsed in the bar area, which is the oldest part of the building. Featuring in the Good Pub Guide for 2004 and awarded AA Four Diamond Status, the Crown & Garter offers a deliciously interesting variety of dishes based on locally sourced meat and vegetables, which are served with flair in the separate dining area. Dotted around a pretty, peaceful cottage garden complete with pond, the well-equipped, comfortable en-suite bedrooms are light and airy and tastefully decorated in a contemporary style. The Crown and Garter is conveniently situated for the attractions of Southern England. London is easily reached, whilst Bath, Windsor and Oxford are less than an hour's drive away; the antiques centres of Marlborough and Hungerford are even closer. Special themed weekend breaks are available.

Our inspector loved: This down-to-earth "meet the locals" inn as well as the clean and spacious garden bedrooms.

Directions: Reached via the M4. Turn off A4 into Kintbury passing over Kennet and Avon Canal. Turn left at the opposite corner stores at the top of the hill into Inkpen Road. Straight ahead for 2 miles, do not turn off this road.

Web: www.johansens.com/crownandgarter
E-mail: enquiries@crownandgarter.com
Tel: 0870 381 9354
International: +44 (0)1488 668325

Reading
Windsor
Newbury

Price Guide:
single from £50
double from £70

THE ROYAL OAK RESTAURANT & HOTEL

YATTENDON, NEWBURY, BERKSHIRE RG18 0UF

The Royal Oak's team of friendly, courteous staff make sure that guests at this lovely old inn are warmly welcomed. Steeped in history, the inn played host to Oliver Cromwell and his generals. There are 5 elegant bedrooms overlooking the tranquil walled garden or historic village square. A delightful lounge offers country house comfort, whilst the friendly bar serves locally brewed real ale. For meetings, business lunches and dinner parties, there is a private room, which looks onto the walled garden – a picture in itself and ideal for dining on a balmy summer's day. The head chef produces menu after menu of delicious dishes, all cooked to order and complemented by fine wines from an extensive list. The à la carte menu in the brasserie and restauarant is approximately £25 for 3 courses. The Royal Oak 10 minutes from Reading and Newbury. Nearby attractions include Basildon Park, the Wyldecourt Rainforest and Newbury Racing.

Directions: From the west, leave M4 at Jct13 turning up the A34 (north) and take exit to Hermitage after 300 yards. At T-junction turn left and then right by the Fox Inn for Yattendon. From the east, leave M4 at Jct12 and head for Theale. Continue towards Pangbourne taking first left, signed Bradfield/Yattendon. Follow road into Yattendon village square.

Web: www.johansens.com/royaloaknewbury
E-mail: oakyattendon@aol.com
Tel: 0870 381 9346
International: +44 (0)1635 201325
Fax: 01635 201926

Price Guide:
single £95–£105
double/twin £110–£130

Our inspector loved: The attractive village setting and lovely feeling of this delightful property.

CANTLEY HOUSE

MILTON ROAD, WOKINGHAM, BERKSHIRE RG40 5QG

This fine Victorian building is reached from an impressive driveway and is surrounded by fields and open countryside. A traditional hotel with many homely and comfortable features, it also boasts some extremely modern elements such as high-speed broadband Internet access in all refurbished bedrooms. Rooms in the Clocktower Wing are large, bright and sunny, and most have access to their own patio leading onto the glorious landscaped grounds which include a sunken garden, lavender walk and peaceful ponds. The hotel is an excellent venue for meetings, conferences and private occasions, and its flexible facilities include The Briar, a 17th-century barn that seats up to 100 people. Miltons is the hotel's atmospheric restaurant, which is situated around its own courtyard and serves tasty and imaginative modern cooking for dinner and lunch. In winter an open fire adds to its cosiness. Another welcome addition is the beauty and pampering zone, which offers an array of tempting treatments. Windsor, Royal Ascot, Legoland and Oxford are all easily accessible from the hotel. Weekend packages are available.

Our inspector loved: *The eclectic mix of traditional amd modern in this character filled hotel.*

Directions: Follow the A329 into Wokingham. Keep in right hand lane through the town centre into Broad Street and take the right hand filter into Rectory Road. At traffic lights turn left into Glebelands Road, then bear right into Milton Road. The hotel is on the right after a mini-roundabout.

Web: www.johansens.com/cantley
E-mail: reservations@cantleyhotel.co.uk
Tel: 0870 381 9233
International: +44 (0)118 978 9912
Fax: 0118 977 4294

Price Guide:
single from £100
double/twin from £120

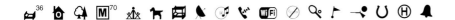

NEW

THE DINTON HERMIT

WATER LANE, FORD, AYLESBURY, BUCKINGHAMSHIRE HP17 8XH

Directions: Ford is between Aylesbury and Thame, off the A418. `15minutes from the M40.

Web: www.johansens.com/dintonhermit
E-mail: colinswooddeb@aol.com
Tel: 0870 381 9295
International: +44 (0)1296 747473
Fax: 01296 748819

Price Guide:
double £80–£100
four-poster £125

This interesting inn takes its name from the reputed executioner of Charles I, who after performing the deed, allegedly hid himself in a cave nearby. The names of the bedrooms and décor in the main building reflect this period in history. 400 years old and Grade II listed, The Dinton Hermit has been beautifully restored by new owners Debbie and John Colinswood. The attractive buildings do not disappoint upon entry with a cosy bar boasting an open log fire leading through to a welcoming restaurant that serves tasty, modern British cuisine. Each double bedroom is en suite and fully equipped with modern amenities; period rooms have been embellished with open wood beams and four-poster beds and have adjoining bathrooms; the contemporary rooms in the converted barn are refreshing. The property is surrounded by farmland and an expanse of fields gives visitors open views. Being easily accessible from major motorway networks and the towns of Aylesbury and High Wycombe make the Dinton Hermit an ideal stopover for a weekend walking break, a corporate stay or an evening of dining with friends and relaxation.

Our inspector loved: *The variety and uniqueness of this interesting inn.*

THE IVY HOUSE

LONDON ROAD, CHALFONT-ST-GILES, BUCKINGHAMSHIRE HP8 4RS

This lovely 200-year-old brick and flint Grade II listed building certainly makes an interesting and inviting first impression. It is set just off the road, but as soon as you step inside, peace descends and a feeling of relaxation takes over. Upon encountering the friendly owners and staff it comes as no surprise that The Ivy House is the recipient of many awards. In the bar, comfortable old armchairs surround open fireplaces, and below its wooden beams guests can enjoy wines from an extensive international wine list, a wide range of malt whiskies, a well-stocked bar and varied beer selection to make the most hardened of real ale enthusiasts proud. The Ivy House serves a menu that covers all tastes and requirements, from traditional English fayre to more exotic dishes and specials and its' fun children's menu comes complete with quizzes and puzzles. Set in the beautiful Chiltern countryside offering stunning views, the freehouse has recently been in the midst of a £500,000 development to include the addition of 5 individually furnished bedrooms, an extended bar and al fresco patio area. The Ivy House is as suitable for an evening with friends, a comfortable business stay, a walking weekend or special occasion.

Our inspector loved: *The newly added bedrooms and superb all round hospitality.*

Directions: The Ivy House is located between Amersham and Chalfont St Giles on the A413 (London Road). It is easily accessible from the M40, A40 and M25.

Web: www.johansens.com/ivyhousebucks
Tel: 0870 381 9236
International: +44 (0)1494 872184
Fax: 01494 872870

Price Guide:
single £70
double/twin £90

THE GREYHOUND

HIGH STREET, CHALFONT-ST-PETER, BUCKINGHAMSHIRE SL9 9RA

Directions: Take J16 off the M25 or J1 off the M40. Follow the A40, then the A413 to the village centre. The Greyhound is easily located. Alternatively, the train journey from London to Gerards Cross takes 20 minutes.

Web: www.johansens.com/greyhound
E-mail: reception@thegreyhound.net
Tel: 0870 381 9216
International: +44 (0)1753 883404
Fax: 01753 891627

Price Guide:
single £105
double/twin £140
master bedroom £170

Continuing a long tradition – the inn has stood at this site for over 600 years – The Greyhound offers superb warmth and hospitality to its guests, with a twist of 21st-century luxury. Recently refurbished, the ancient building revels in its wide brick fireplaces, flagged stone floors and polished wooden bar and panelling. Indeed, the bar is one of Buckinghamshire's oldest and most famous, and serves a huge range of premium beers, spirits and cocktails. The contemporary, understated interior displays fresh flowers throughout, and each of the spacious and attractive bedrooms has comfortable solid oak beds beneath beamed and vaulted ceilings, and sumptuous bed linen. En-suite bathrooms are furnished with designer toiletries, generous white suites and Italian marble walls and floors. Dining in the contemporary yet smart restaurant is a gourmet treat, and menus of succulent steak, fine fish and seafood are followed by classic desserts and complemented by an excellent wine list. Outside a little stream runs through the pretty garden and past the charming terraces. Many delightful villages are close by, as are Windsor, Marlow, Henley and the Chilterns.

Our inspector loved: Its' all round hospitality and excellent bedrooms.

THE NAGS HEAD

LONDON ROAD, GREAT MISSENDEN, BUCKINGHAMSHIRE HP16 0DG

This welcoming 16th-century inn was once a staging post between Aylesbury and London, and is entered through a small door that leads into the cosy bar. An old staircase takes you up to 7 characteristic bedrooms, which have cottage windows with open views. All rooms are en suite with televisions and video players and tea and coffee making facilities, and are furnished traditionally and comfortably. A bar menu is available, offering light meals, snacks and sandwiches, alongside a good selection of beers, guest ales and wines. The restaurant serves fine, tasty food such as soups, steaks, and tempting desserts from ice creams to pavlovas and fruit crumbles. Food and drink can also be enjoyed in the large garden, set off the main road. Amidst extremely pretty rolling Buckinghamshire countryside, beneath the central ridge of the Chiltern hills, the inn is an ideal base from which to explore numerous interesting finds and walks or to utilize for a business stay. Aylesbury and Amersham with their areas of historic interest are nearby, and there are many National Trust properties to visit. Within easy reach of the M40 and M25, Windsor, Oxford and London are all easily accessible.

Our inspector loved: *Discovering this Olde Worlde small coaching inn and its charm.*

Directions: Follow the London Road out of Great Missenden towards Amersham for approximately 1 mile. The Nags Head is on the right after a few bends. The M40 and M25 are nearby.

Milton Keynes

Aylesbury

High Wycombe

Web: www.johansens.com/nagshead
Tel: 0870 381 9237
International: +44 (0)1494 862945
Fax: 01494 862945

Price Guide:
single £70
double/twin £90
four poster/deluxe £120

THE MEADOWCROFT HOTEL

TRUMPINGTON ROAD, CAMBRIDGE CB2 2EX

Directions: From the M11, junction 11 follow signs to city centre for about 3 miles. The hotel is on the right in Trumpington Road.

Web: www.johansens.com/meadowcroft
E-mail: meadowcroft@meadowcrofthotel.co.uk
Tel: 0870 381 8651
International: +44 (0)1223 346120
Fax: 01223 346138

Price guide:
single from £100
double/twin from £120
four-poster from £140

Set in established gardens and surrounded by mature trees, the Meadowcroft Hotel is a calm oasis only a mile from Cambridge city centre and offers the highest standards of comfort with all the character of its Victorian traditions. Friendly staff create a hospitable and relaxed atmosphere and fresh flowers and original period details abound. Each bedroom benefits from plenty of light and a view of the pretty garden. They are beautifully furnished in peaceful tones, each with its own distinctive style - the upper rooms have high ceilings and windows whilst the lower rooms are full of character with interesting structure. A large, impressive wooden staircase dominates the hallway, and the cosy bar and relaxing lounge with open fireplace boast many antiques. There is no restaurant, but for residents, there is a substantial room service menu and a wide range of excellent restaurants nearby where reservations will gladly be made. Guests can explore Cambridge with its numerous attractions, such as punting on the Cam, the Botanical Gardens, the Fitzwilliam Museum, theatres, a traditional market and the historic university colleges. Enquire about weekend break availability.

Our inspector loved: The atmosphere of serenity surrounding the house.

FROGG MANOR HOTEL & RESTAURANT

FULLERS MOOR, NANTWICH ROAD, BROXTON, CHESTER CH3 9JH

A human sized frog with a polka dot tie points towards Frogg Manor, a beautiful Grade II listed Georgian manor house which, from its elevated position high in the Broxton Hills, affords a most spectacular view across Cheshire to the Welsh Mountains. Surrounded by 9 acres of woods and carefully tended gardens this original, eccentric and bourgeois Hotel is bursting with character and is home to several hundred frogs made from brass, wood and everything else you can think of. Plush surroundings, lavish décor and magnificent antique furniture set the scene; the Hotel has been excellently refurbished recently to maintain a high standard of comfort. The romantic conservatory restaurant serves delicious English style cuisine that is freshly prepared by proprietor, John Sykes and complemented by an extensive list of fine wines. After dinner the comfortable and cosy lounge is the perfect place to enjoy a fine scotch, coffee and chocolates. Luxurious bedrooms are individually and creatively decorated with attention to detail and quality such as fine Egyptian cottons and the best mattresses. Guests can explore the unspoilt local landscapes with rolling hills, sandstone cliffs, idyllic villages and ancient churches. Chester, the only completely walled city left in Britain, is nearby and features charming timbered houses and ancient Roman remains.

Directions: From Chester take the A41 towards Whitchurch for 8 miles, then the A534 towards Nantwich. The Hotel is on the right.

Web: www.johansens.com/froggmanor
E-mail: info@froggmanorhotel.co.uk
Tel: 0870 381 8534
International: +44 (0)1829 782629
Fax: 01829 782459

Price Guide:
single £60–£120
double/twin £80–£200

Our inspector loved: The eccentric charm of this Georgian country hotel.

BROXTON HALL

WHITCHURCH ROAD, BROXTON, CHESTER, CHESHIRE CH3 9JS

Directions: Broxton Hall is on the A41 Whitchurch – Chester road, eight miles between Whitchurch and Chester.

Web: www.johansens.com/broxtonhall
E-mail: reservation@broxtonhall.co.uk
Tel: 0870 381 8387
International: +44 (0)1829 782321
Fax: 01829 782330

Price Guide:
single £70–£85
double/twin £75–£130

Built in 1671 by a local landowner, Broxton Hall is a black and white half-timbered building set in five acres of grounds and extensive gardens amid the rolling Cheshire countryside. The mediaeval city of Chester is eight miles away. The hotel provides every modern comfort while retaining the ambience of a bygone age. The reception area reflects the character of the entire hotel, with its magnificent Jacobean fireplace, plush furnishings, oak panelled walls and carved mahogany staircase. On cool evenings log fires are lit. The small but well-appointed bedrooms are furnished with antiques and have en suite bathrooms as well as every modern comfort. Overlooking the gardens, the restaurant receives constant praise and AA and RAC Rosettes. French and English cuisine is served, using local game in season and freshly caught fish. There is an extensive wine list. Breakfast may be taken in the sunny conservatory overlooking the lawned gardens. The hotel is an ideal venue for business meetings and conferences. Broxton Hall is the perfect base from which to visit the North Wales coast and Snowdonia. There are a number of excellent golf courses nearby and racecourses at Chester and Bangor-on-Dee. Special breaks available

Our inspector loved: *The cosy antique filled rooms and pretty landscaped garden.*

WILLINGTON HALL HOTEL

WILLINGTON, NR TARPORLEY, CHESHIRE CW6 0NB

Built by Cheshire landowner Charles Tomkinson, Willington Hall was converted into a hotel by one of his descendants and in 1999 was bought by Stuart and Diana Begbie. Set in 17 acres of woods and parkland, the hotel affords wonderful views across the Cheshire countryside towards the Welsh mountains. There are both formally landscaped and "wild" gardens, which create a beautiful backdrop for the handsome architectural proportions of the house. The hotel is a comfortable and friendly retreat for those seeking peace and seclusion. Under the personal supervision of Diana and Stuart, Willington Hall has acquired a good reputation with local people for its extensive bar meals and à la carte restaurant, along with friendly and attentive service. The menus offer traditional English cooking with a French influence. Willington Hall is an ideal location for visiting the Roman city of Chester, Tatton Park, Beeston Castle and Oulton Park racetrack. North Wales is easily accessible. The hotel is closed on Christmas Day and Boxing Day.

Our inspector loved: The recently refurbished bedrooms overlooking the landscaped gardens.

Directions: Take the A51 from Tarporley to Chester and turn right at the Bull's Head public house at Clotton. Willington Hall Hotel is 1 mile ahead on the left.

Web: www.johansens.com/willingtonhall
E-mail: enquiries@willingtonhall.co.uk
Tel: 0870 381 8999
International: +44 (0)1829 752321
Fax: 01829 752596

Price Guide:
single £70–£95
double £110–£130

TREHELLAS HOUSE HOTEL & RESTAURANT

WASHAWAY, BODMIN, CORNWALL PL30 3AD

Directions: Washaway is located on the A389 half-way between the towns of Bodmin and Wadebridge. Approaching from Bodmin, Trehellas House is situated to the right, set back from the main road and accessed by a slip road.

Web: www.johansens.com/trehellas
E-mail: christico@btinternet.com
Tel: 0870 381 8953
International: +44 (0)1208 72700
Fax: 01208 73336

Price Guide:
single £50–£90
double £90–£100
suite from £140

This early 18th-century Grade II listed Cornish courthouse, steeped in history, is surrounded by 2 acres of grounds. Inside, its traditional features combine with attractive and comfortable modern furnishings. The beamed atmospheric restaurant, with its beautifully preserved Delabole slate floor and elegant décor, serves the best locally sourced fish, meat, poultry, vegetables and cheeses to create delicious English and European dishes. An extensive wine list includes selections from the local Camel Valley vineyard. Following a recent refurbishment the 11 bedrooms are all en suite and comfortably furnished with patchwork quilts and iron bedsteads. The chandelier-lit Courtroom Suite still retains the magistrates' dais and moulded cornice providing elegant and spacious accommodation. Outside, guests may wish to stroll in the pleasant gardens or enjoy the heated swimming pool (May - September) and for the more energetic there are many walks along the Camel trail. The village of Rock is a popular base for sailing and fishing and at nearby Daymer Bay is the little church where poet John Betjeman is buried. The Eden Project is just 12 miles away, tickets are available from the hotel.

Our inspector loved: The warm welcome and relaxed atmosphere.

Trelawne Hotel – The Hutches Restaurant

MAWNAN SMITH, NR FALMOUTH, CORNWALL TR11 5HT

A very friendly welcome awaits guests, who will be enchanted by the beautiful location of Trelawne Hotel, on the coast between the Rivers Fal and Helford. Large picture windows in the public rooms, including the totally refurbished spacious lounge/bar, ensure that guests take full advantage of the panoramic vistas of the ever-changing coastline. The bedrooms are charming, many with views of the sea. The soft colours of the décor, the discreet lighting and attention to detail provide a restful atmosphere, in harmony with the Wedgwood, fresh flowers and sparkling crystal in The Hutches Restaurant, which has been awarded an AA Rosette. The menu changes daily and offers a variety of inspired dishes, including local seafood, game and fresh vegetables. Ideally located for coastal walks along Rosemullion Head and the picturesque Helford Estuary. There are also a wealth of famous gardens within the area. "Slip Away Anyday" spring, autumn and winter breaks. Closed January. The Royal Duchy of Cornwall is an area of outstanding beauty, with many National Trust and English Heritage properties to visit and a range of leisure pursuits to enjoy.

Our inspector loved: The peaceful relaxing surroundings and the feeling of being made to feel so welcome.

Directions: From Truro follow A39 towards Falmouth, turn right at Hillhead roundabout, take exit signposted Maenporth. Carry on for 3 miles and Trelawne is at the top overlooking Falmouth bay.

Web: www.johansens.com/trelawne
Tel: 0870 381 8954
International: +44 (0)1326 250226
Fax: 01326 250909

Price Guide:
single £65–£85
double £90–£160

Newquay   Bodmin
Penzance   ● Falmouth
Isles of Scilly

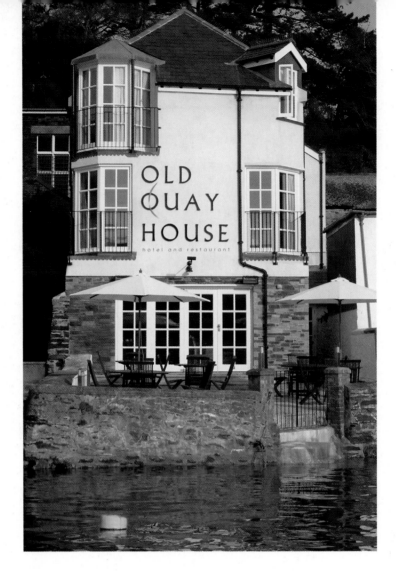

THE OLD QUAY HOUSE HOTEL

28 FORE STREET, FOWEY, CORNWALL PL23 1AQ

Directions: From the A390 take the B3269 to Fowey. Just before entering Fowey go across a mini-roundabout then continue until the bottom of the hill. Turn left into Lostwithiel Street, go past the church into Fore Street. The hotel is 200 yards on the right hand side.

Web: www.johansens.com/oldquayhouse
E-mail: info@theoldquayhouse.com
Tel: 0870 381 8783
International: +44 (0)1726 833302
Fax: 01726 833668

Price Guide:
single from £110
double/twin from £140
deluxe double from £170

Newquay
Bodmin
Penzance   Falmouth
Isles of Scilly

Built in 1889 as a Seaman's Mission, the Old Quay House has recently undergone an extensive refurbishment to transform itself into a highly desirable boutique hotel. Its 12 en-suite bedrooms are individually styled and sympathetically furnished to reflect the two distinctive styles of the building. Some are traditional with high ceilings and fireplaces, whilst others come complete with balconies, estuary views and contemporary yet comfortable custom-made furniture, incorporating natural materials from the Far East. All have high specification "future proof" technology and cosy goose down duvets. The decor in the open plan lounge and restaurant area has been designed so as not to distract from the fantastic views. Cream and beige muted tones act as backdrop to a collection of artwork. The food is contemporary, light and healthy, and seasonal menus include up to 90% Cornish produce. The bustling seaport of Fowey is an ideal base from which to explore Cornwall's beautiful coastline and numerous tourist attractions.

Our inspector loved: *The unique and tasteful presentation throughout -stunning.*

Cormorant On The River, Hotel & Riverside Restaurant

GOLANT BY FOWEY, CORNWALL PL23 1LL

Only 5 miles from the Eden Project, the Cormorant stands high above the beautiful Fowey Estuary with magnificent views over the shimmering waters and the Cornish countryside. The subject of an upgrading programme, this is a warm, friendly and inviting hotel with 11 entirely individual bedrooms. All have en-suite bathrooms, colour television, radio, direct-dial telephone and extensive views over the estuary and creeks. Guests can relax in an extremely comfortable lounge, which has full-length picture windows and a log fire in winter. The bar is small and welcoming. Guests can also enjoy lounging on the terrace near the hotel's heated swimming pool with its superb river views. This corner of Cornwall is a living larder of wholesome produce all made use of by the enthusiastic chef and served in a pretty candle-lit restaurant; a choice of good and imaginative menus is on offer. Guests can enjoy miles of walking along the coastline, fishing villages, Lanhydrock House and gardens and many National Trust properties. Fishing, riding and golf can be arranged locally. There is ample free parking within the grounds for all guests.

Our inspector loved: *The stunning location and relaxing warm atmosphere.*

Directions: From Exeter, take the A30 towards Bodmin and then the B3269 towards Fowey. After 6 miles turn left at a staggered junction to Golant. Bear right as you approach the estuary and continue along the water's edge. The hotel is on the right.

Web: www.johansens.com/cormorant
E-mail: relax@cormoranthotels.co.uk
Tel: 0870 381 8446
International: +44 (0)1726 833426

Price Guide: (including dinner)
single £85–£160 (winter months only)
double £160–£230

Newquay Bodmin
Penzance Falmouth
Isles of Scilly

TREHAVEN MANOR

STATION ROAD, LOOE, CORNWALL PL13 1HN

Directions: A38 over Tamar Bridge. Carry on until Trerulfoot roundabout and take exit for Looe.

Web: www.johansens.com/trehavenlooe
E-mail: enquiries@trehavenhotel.co.uk
Tel: 0870 381 8952
International: +44 (0)1503 262028
Fax: 01503 265613

Price Guide:
single £50
double/twin £80–£130

The Trehaven Manor Hotel, built of beautiful traditional Cornish stone, was originally a vicarage and stands serenely high above the picturesque seaside town of Looe. Approached along a sweeping driveway, this enchanting 19th-century house is a haven of tranquillity and commands wonderful views over the idyllic estuary and beyond to the Looe bridge. The spacious bedrooms are tastefully presented in a relaxed environment with comfortable furniture, bright colour co-ordinated fabrics and all modern conveniences. Homemade scones and delicious Cornish clotted cream are served in the lounge on arrival. A tasty breakfast is prepared using fresh local ingredients and served in the sunny restaurant with bay fronted windows. Dinner is by prior, arrangement, but many fine restaurants may be recommended in the area with pre-booking arrangements organised by Trehaven Manor. Looe, which is within a 3-minute walk, is an ideal base to explore charming Cornwall and its stunning sandy beaches. National Trust houses and gardens are in abundance or guests can visit the monkey sanctuary, Eden Project and Lost Gardens of Heligan. Tennis, bowling and boat trips for fishing or pleasure are available.

Our inspector loved: *The very friendly warm relaxed atmosphere.*

TREVALSA COURT COUNTRY HOUSE HOTEL

SCHOOL HILL, MEVAGISSEY, ST AUSTELL, CORNWALL PL26 6TH

Built overlooking the sea in the 1930s the Trevalsa was discovered by owners Klaus Wagner and Matthias Mainka in 1999, who lovingly set to work to restore the casual but elegant atmosphere of a country house. Blending traditional and modern styles, its oak-panelled hall and dining room, beautiful lounge and mullioned windows recall the ambience of a bygone age, whilst the newly refurbished en-suite bedrooms are simply and classically furnished. All principal bedrooms have splendid sea views and on the ground floor are 3 rooms particularly suitable for elderly or less able guests. The hotel's grounds are above the sheltered Polstreath Beach and access to its sloping sands and coves for swimming and fishing is directly available from the garden. A footpath also leads to the harbour and typically Cornish streets of Mevagissey, and St Austell, with its 18-hole golf course and modern sports centre, is just 5 miles away. Trevalsa Court can be reached by car without passing through Mevagissy's narrow roads and its location makes it an excellent base for touring all parts of Cornwall. The award-winning Lost Gardens of Heligan and the Eden Project, fast becoming a top visitor destination for the 21st century, are nearby.

Our inspector loved: Location and overall peace, tranquility and relaxation.

Directions: On approaching Mevagissey on the B3273 from St Austell go through Pentewan, climb the hill and turn left at the crossroads at the top. Trevalsa Court Hotel is ½ mile on the left.

Web: www.johansens.com/trevalsa
E-mail: stay@cornwall-hotel.net
Tel: 0870 381 8955
International: +44 (0)1726 842468
Fax: 01726 844482

Price Guide:
single £49–£98
double/twin £98–£150
suite £110–£170

35

NEW

HIGHLAND COURT LODGE

BISCOVEY ROAD, BISCOVEY, NEAR ST AUSTELL, CORNWALL PL24 2HW

Directions: From the A30 take the A391 to St Austell, then turn left onto the A390 through St Blazey Gate then right into Biscovey Road. The hotel is approximately 300 yards on the right.

Web: www.johansens.com/highlandcourt
E-mail: enquiries@highlandcourt.co.uk
Tel: 0870 381 9290
International: +44 (0)1726 813320
Fax: 01726 813320

Price Guide:
single £65–£85
double £120–£160

Newquay   Bodmin

Penzance   Falmouth

Isles of Scilly

Recently opened, this little hotel promises to be an absolute gem, awarded Five Diamond status from the RAC and AA and the recipient of the Diamond Sparkler Award from the RAC. Tucked away in 2 acres of beautiful grounds it offers total seclusion and privacy; an idyllic Cornish retreat. Each of the rooms is beautifully presented and has been carefully designed using luxurious fabrics to ensure the utmost in comfort. All of the guest rooms have patio doors with views of the gardens that are simply beautiful on a summer's evening, and the perfect setting for a leisurely drink. Local catch has a strong influence on the skilfully planned menu where light fish dishes such as Cornish scallops and crab patties are perfectly balanced by Cornish beef fillet and roasted lamb cutlets, finished by some wonderful desserts prepared by the hotel's very own dessert chef. This part of Cornwall offers many tourist attractions: the Eden Project can be reached on foot (just 1 mile away), the Lost Gardens of Heligan and pretty Fowey are nearby and the local beach is a 15-minute stroll away.

Our inspector loved: *The great welcome to this charming, tucked away little lodge.*

WISTERIA LODGE & COUNTRY SPA

BOSCUNDLE, TREGREHAN, ST AUSTELL, CORNWALL PL25 3RJ

Wisteria Lodge & Country Spa is an absolute gem peacefully tucked away on the outskirts of St Austell and within walking distance of the famous Carlyon Bay in the heart of Cornwall. This idyllic location offers the best of British hospitality with emphasis on comfort and relaxation. Stunning fabrics and first-class interior decoration within spacious surroundings provide an elegant respite from the stresses of day-to-day life, which is enhanced by extremely friendly and personalised service. Luxurious, individually styled bedrooms have all the amenities required of today's discerning traveller with wonderful features such as a four-poster bed, whirlpool bath or balcony. The ground floor suite has large French doors leading to a well-tended garden; fresh fruit and flowers, fluffy bathrobes and bathsheets add to guests' sense of wellbeing. Awarded the 5 Diamond ETC Silver Award and AA Dining Award, the candelit restaurant has a romantic atmosphere, and serves delicious dinner with freshly caught fish prominently on the menu. Each dish is personally prepared from guests' selection on the day. Guests will enjoy exploring Cornwall's dramatic coastline, historic buildings and castles in the proximity. The hotel is one mile from the Eden Project and 5 minutes by car from the Lost Gardens of Heligan. A 2-bedroom luxury apartment is available for a minimum 3 nights including breakfast for £250 per night.

Directions: On approaching St Austell on the A390 turn left opposite the garden centre, signposted to Tregrehan. Go left at Boscundle Close (the first turning to the left) and bear right.

Web: www.johansens.com/wisteria
E-mail: info@wisterialodgehotel.co.uk
Tel: 0870 381 9183
International: +44 (0)1726 810800

Price Guide:
double/twin £125-£190

Our inspector loved: This luxurious hotel offering just about everything.

TREDETHY HOUSE

HELLAND BRIDGE, BODMIN, CORNWALL PL30 4QS

Directions: From the A30, turn right signed Helland (approximately 4 miles before Bodmin). Follow the signs to Helland, pass through the village and over Helland Bridge. Tredethy is on the right just before brow of hill.

Web: www.johansens.com/tredethyhouse
E-mail: tredethyhouse@aol.com
Tel: 0870 381 9142
International: +44 (0)1208 841262
Fax: 01208 841707

Price Guide:
single from £72.50
double from £95
suite from £140

Set amidst 9 acres of grounds with views of the surrounding countryside, this elegant manor house is the perfect place to get away from the stresses of daily life. The property was formerly the home of Prince Chula of Thailand, the legal guardian of Prince Bira, famous motor-racing champion of the 1930s and 40s, and the house is filled with memorabilia. Many original features have been maintained, such as granite fireplaces, beautiful plasterwork and Victorian tiled floors. Owners Paul and Amanda and their small team of dedicated staff ensure that all guests have a truly enjoyable stay. Each of the 10 individually decorated en-suite bedrooms is furnished to a high standard; some have views of the surrounding countryside, others look onto the inner courtyards. A hearty Cornish breakfast is served in the conservatory, whilst dinner can be enjoyed in the dining room with its original stone fireplace and warming log fires. Seasonal local produce is used wherever possible to create mouth-watering dishes, accompanied by wines from the extensive wine list, including some from the award-winning local Camel Valley vineyard. The gardens provide ample opportunity for a relaxing stroll, and the secluded outdoor heated pool is perfect for a leisurely swim on a warm day. The house is ideally located for touring Cornwall; Padstow, the Eden Project and the Lost Gardens of Heligan are all within a 20-minute drive.

Our inspector loved: This relaxing away-from-it-all country house.

THE PHEASANT

BASSENTHWAITE LAKE, NR COCKERMOUTH, CUMBRIA CA13 9YE

Set in the staggering, unspoilt northern part of the Lake District only a few yards from Bassenthwaite Lake and surrounded by beautiful gardens and woodlands, this famous 17th-century coaching inn is renowned for its friendly hospitality and excellent service. It is an intimate venue with only 13 de luxe bedrooms, which have recently been refurbished to an extremely high standard with stunning fabrics, antiques and subtle colour schemes to create a light and airy atmosphere. Relaxing coffees over the morning newspaper or a mouth-watering afternoon tea Cumbria style with homemade specialities such as scones and brandy butter are served in the hotel's 3 quiet and comfortable lounges. The wood-panelled bar with polished walls and oak settles is a wonderful setting for pre-dinner drinks with its traditional and convivial atmosphere. Delicious traditional Cumbrian specialities to suit all tastes are served in the popular beamed dining room, which features a daily changing menu and a wide selection of fine wines. Guests can enjoy the peaceful solitude of the hotel's own gardens and woodlands whilst bird watching, fishing or walking, or explore the day trips around the magnificent Lake District. There are various sporting expeditions offered by the hotel.

Our inspector loved: The comfort and Old World ambience and charm of this traditional inn.

Directions: Just off the A66, The Pheasant is 6 miles east of Cockermouth and 8 miles north-west of Keswick. Signposted from A66

Web: www.johansens.com/pheasantcumbria
E-mail: info@the-pheasant.co.uk
Tel: 0870 381 9227
International: +44 (0)17687 76234
Fax: 017687 76002

Price Guide:
single £80–£90
double/twin £140–£160
suite £160–£180

UNDERWOOD

THE HILL, MILLOM, CUMBRIA LA18 5EZ

Andrew and Wendy Miller personally run this delightful non-smoking country house which was once a Victorian vicarage. Beautifully restored, it stands within 8 acres of landscaped gardens, meadows and paddocks, between the picturesque Whicham Valley and Duddon Estuary. The tranquil and elegant surroundings include 2 relaxing lounges, as well as an indoor heated swimming pool with steam room and a tennis court. Each of the 5 fully equipped bedrooms is en suite and individually furnished. Hosts Andrew and Wendy pride themselves on offering guests the utmost in comfort and hospitality, and every evening prepare and serve a 4-course dinner which combines the best in local ingredients, along with a carefully selected wine list. A hearty breakfast provides the perfect start for those wishing to explore the surrounding area. Lakes Coniston, Windermere and Wastwater are within easy reach, and there is plenty of opportunity to enjoy the attractions of Cumbria by car or on foot. The less adventurous can unwind with a relaxing swim, a stroll around the grounds or a game of croquet.

Directions: Leave M6 at Jct36. Follow A590 towards Barrow-in-Furness, at Greenodd turn right onto A5902 towards Millom until reaching A5093. Turn left here, go through 'The Green' and 'The Hill'. After ½ mile Underwood House is on the right.

Web: www.johansens.com/underwood
E-mail: enquiries@underwoodhouse.co.uk
Tel: 0870 381 8959
International: +44 (0)1229 771116
Fax: 01229 719900

Price Guide:
single £40–£70

Our inspector loved: Wendy's hospitality and Andrew's cuisine using mainly local and homegrown produce.

Carlisle

Penrith

Windermere

Kendal

CROSBY LODGE COUNTRY HOUSE HOTEL

HIGH CROSBY, CROSBY-ON-EDEN, CARLISLE, CUMBRIA CA6 4QZ

Crosby Lodge is a romantic country mansion that has been converted into a quiet, efficient hotel without spoiling any of its original charm. Grade II listed, it stands amid pastoral countryside close to the Scottish Lowlands and the Lake District. Spacious interiors are elegantly furnished and appointed to provide the maximum of comfort. The personal attention of Michael and Patricia Sedgwick ensures that a high standard of service is maintained. All of the bedrooms are beautifully equipped, most with antique beds and half-testers. 2 bedrooms are situated in the converted courtyard stables overlooking the walled garden and in these rooms guests are welcome to bring their pet dogs. In The Lodge restaurant, extensive menus offer a wide and varied choice of dishes. Traditional English recipes are prepared by Roger Herring and Gavin Irving, along with continental cuisine complemented by an extensive international wine list. Tables are set with cut glass and gleaming silver cutlery and in keeping with the gracious surroundings. Crosby Lodge, with its spacious grounds, is a superb setting for weddings, parties, business and social events. The 84 mile Hadrian's Wall walk passes by the hotel's woodland estate. Closed 24 December to 16 January. Special breaks available.

Our inspector loved: *Philippa Sedgwick's wine warehouse in the courtyard, selling quality wines and homemade produce.*

Directions: From M6 junction 44 take A689 Brampton road for 3 miles; turn right through Low Crosby. Crosby Lodge is on the right at High Crosby.

Carlisle

Penrith

Windermere

Kendal

Web: www.johansens.com/crosbylodge
E-mail: info@crosbylodge.co.uk
Tel: 0870 381 8461
International: +44 (0)1228 573618
Fax: 01228 573428

Price Guide:
single £89–£98
double £130–£170

41

THE QUEEN'S HEAD HOTEL

MAIN STREET, HAWKSHEAD, CUMBRIA LA22 0NS

Situated on the edge of Estwaite Water overlooked by Grizedale Forest, Hawkshead is a charming village in the centre of the Lake District with narrow cobbled streets and half-timbered cottages. The 16th-century Queen's Head Hotel is located in the centre of the village and boasts many period features such as low oak-beamed ceilings, panelled walls and large open fireplaces. A warm ambience is created in the cosy lounge bar, which serves hand-pumped ales and displays the famous Girt Clog, measuring a full 20 inches in length, which was worn by John Waterson. Extremely comfortable non-smoking bedrooms, some with four-poster beds, have en-suite bathrooms and lovely décor; 2 family rooms are available. Mouth-watering English cuisine, including Herdwick lamb, local venison, pheasant and mallard as well as delicious seafood specialities is accompanied by an extensive international wine list. 3 award-winning self-catering cottages with all modern conveniences are situated at the rear of the hotel and are ideal for longer stays. Guests can visit the Beatrix Potter Museum, Village Heritage Centre and Parish Church or explore the lush fells and Tarn Hows, the jewel of the Lakes.

Directions: Leave the M6, junction 36. Take the A590 to Newby Bridge then the second right and follow the road for 8 miles into Hawkshead. Drive through the village car park and turn right up the main street. The hotel is on the right.

Web: www.johansens.com/queenshead
E-mail: enquiries@queensheadhotel.co.uk
Tel: 0870 381 8844
International: +44 (0)15394 36271
Fax: 015394 36722

Price Guide:
single £48–£60
double/twin £65–£105

Carlisle

Penrith

Windermere

Kendal

Our inspector loved: The welcoming and friendly atmosphere of this traditional Lakeland village inn.

NEW

GRIZEDALE LODGE

GRIZEDALE FOREST, HAWKSHEAD, AMBLESIDE, CUMBRIA LA22 0QL

A very warm welcome and friendly service await guests at this charming, luxury country house, which offers a complete escape from stressful city life. Grizedale Lodge is set on the edge of the magnificent Grizedale Forest, the origins of which date back to Monastic times. Its name comes from the old Norse name for the wild boar, and guests can indeed glimpse a variety of wildlife from the balcony or patio, the ideal setting for a relaxing drink after a long day spent exploring the surroundings. The tastefully decorated bedrooms offer en-suite facilities, colour TV and tea and coffee making facilities, whilst the elegant Forest Suite has a superb four-poster bed and tranquil views. Guests can start the day with a hearty breakfast in the attractive breakfast room, snacks are available at lunchtime and early evening, and dinner is served upon prior arrangement. Being at the heart of the Lake District, the area has plenty of natural, historical and cultural attractions to offer; just 2 miles away is the picturesque village of Hawkshead and the grammar school that Wordsworth attended - his name is still to be seen scratched into the desk. Scenic roads lead to Lakeside with its preserved railway, the market town of Ambleside and Sawrey, and the car ferry to Windermere is close by. Trout fishing, cycling and golf can all be arranged nearby.

Our inspector loved: *The stunning location in the middle of the Grizedale Forest.*

Directions: M6 J36, take A591 past Windermere to Ambleside. B5286 to Hawkshead, then follow signs to Grizedale Forest hotel on the right before the Visitor Centre.

Web: www.johansens.com/grizedalelodge
E-mail: enquiries@grizedale-lodge.com
Tel: 0870 381 9342
International: +44 (0)15394 36532
Fax: 015394 36572

Price Guide:
single £45–£50
double £60–£95

43

SAWREY HOUSE COUNTRY HOTEL & RESTAURANT

NEAR SAWREY, HAWKSHEAD, AMBLESIDE, CUMBRIA LA22 0LF

Directions: Take junction 36 off the M6 and follow the A591 in the direction of Windermere and continue to Ambleside. Take the B5286 then the B5285 to Near Sawrey. Sawrey House is on the right.

Web: www.johansens.com/sawreyhouse
E-mail: enquiries@sawreyhouse.com
Tel: 0870 381 8886
International: +44 (0)15394 36387
Fax: 015394 36010

Price Guide:
(including 4-course dinner & coffee)
single £70–£85
double £140–£220

set in sculpted gardens designed for lazy indolence, Sawrey House is a totally non-smoking hotel and a quintessential English rural hideaway. Built in the 1830s with slate from the local quarry, it is one of the prettiest buildings in the pristine conservation hamlet of Near Sawrey. Next door is Hilltop, once the home of Beatrix Potter and visitors to Near Sawrey cannot fail to be captivated by the village's quaint tranquillity which so inspired her writings. Owners, Shirley and Colin Whiteside, are justifiably proud of their chef's dinners, which have received 2 AA Rosettes, and their comfortable dining room, which has spectacular views over Esthwaite water and the lush forests beyond. Guests can take afternoon tea in the spacious lounge or relax in the bar for pre-dinner drinks. The whole area is surrounded by National Trust land and is idyllic for walking. The hotel is centrally situated, with the Windermere ferry only minutes from the House and Hawkshead, Ambleside and Coniston are only a few minutes' drive away. For the more energetic, Sawrey House will organise horse riding, fishing, sailing and even hot-air ballooning. Langdale and the Grizedale Forest are amongst the many natural attractions in the near vicinity. Special breaks are available.

Our inspector loved: *Stunning views across the garden towards Esthwaite water.*

THE LEATHES HEAD

BORROWDALE, KESWICK, CUMBRIA CA12 5UY

The Leathes Head is an Edwardian country house set in a lovely location within the Borrowdale Valley. Log fires burn in the sitting room in winter and a delightful conservatory overlooks the Fells, affording guests the full benefit of the hotel's elevated position. Recently refurbished by owners Roy and Janice Smith it combines the charm and elegance of a bygone age with up-to-date standards of comfort. All bedrooms are en suite with a wide range of facilities, and 2 superior double aspect rooms boast magnificent views stretching across to Catbells and Maiden Moor. Downstairs there are rooms suitable for the less mobile. Food is excellent, and award-winning chef David Jackson has built a well-deserved reputation for his daily changing menus and dishes which, where possible, include locally sourced ingredients. This high standard is also reflected in the extensive wine list. Guests can choose from a varied collection of books and board games, enjoy a leisurely walk or cycle ride, or simply relax with a drink in the bar. This is a non smoking house. Special breaks available.

Our inspector loved: *While enjoying breakfast watching the Woodpeckers and Red Squirrels eating the bird nuts outside.*

Directions: From M6 Jct40 take A66 to Keswick, then B5289 to Borrowdale. The hotel is on the left, 3½ miles from Keswick. From the south, approach Keswick on A591.

Carlisle

Penrith

Windermere

Kendal

Web: www.johansens.com/leatheshead
E-mail: enq@leatheshead.co.uk
Tel: 0870 381 8686
International: +44 (0)17687 77247
Fax: 017687 77363

Price Guide: (including dinner)
single £65–£83
double/twin £110–£166

DALE HEAD HALL LAKESIDE HOTEL

THIRLMERE, KESWICK, CUMBRIA CA12 4TN

Directions: On the A591, halfway between Keswick and Grasmere the hotel is situated along a private driveway overlooking Lake Thirlmere.

Web: www.johansens.com/daleheadhall
E-mail: onthelakeside@daleheadhall.co.uk
Tel: 0870 381 8470
International: +44 (0)17687 72478
Fax: 017687 71070

Price Guide: (including dinner)
single £110–£125
double £170–£210

Carlisle

● Penrith

Windermere

Kendal

On the edge of Thirlmere, Cumbria's most central lake, with only the sound of the birds breaking the silence stands Dale Head Hall. It is a truly scenic gem. At the foot of Helvellyn, almost completely surrounded by lush woodlands, this glorious 16th-century house reigns alone on the shores of the lake and must surely command one of the most tranquil settings in the Lake District. Hosts, Alan and Shirley Lowe and family, having restored the 16th-century authenticity of the house, offer exceptional accommodation and service enhanced by Alan's hand-crafted and engraved furniture. The hotel was deservedly runner-up for the Johansens 1995 Most Excellent Country House Hotel. Bar and lounge are both delightful, sharing views over lake and mountains. The oak-panelled dining room is the ideal place to enjoy the hotel's superb cuisine (2 AA Red Rosettes). The bedrooms are extremely welcoming, warm and spacious and have all the things that one would expect to find, plus those little extras that make guests' stays so very special. Dale Head is one of those wonderful secrets one would like to keep selfishly quiet. Awarded the English Tourism Council Gold Award. Special offers are available.

Our inspector loved: *The feeling of total peace and quiet as this is the only house on Lake Thirlmere.*

TEMPLE SOWERBY HOUSE HOTEL

TEMPLE SOWERBY, PENRITH, CUMBRIA CA10 1RZ

Formerly the principal residence of the village, this delightful country house hotel is overlooked by Cross Fell, the highest peak in the Pennines. Set in a 1-acre walled garden, Temple Sowerby House Hotel offers its guests a peaceful and relaxing stay. Paul and Julie Evans provide a warm and hospitable welcome upon which the hotel prides itself. Awarded 2 Rosettes by the AA, the hotel has 2 dining rooms – the candle-lit Restaurant and the Garden Room, a lovely setting for private entertaining. The seasonally inspired à la carte menu might include a starter of terrine of pigeon, duck and chicken layered with pistachio nuts, followed by turbot with a parsley and parmesan crust with saffron rice and lime beurre blanc, rounded off with chocolate and raspberry tart. The individually furnished bedrooms, many just recently upgraded, all have private bathrooms including 2 de luxe rooms with aqua-massage baths. 4 of the rooms, including 2 on the ground floor, are situated in the Coach House, just a few steps from the main house. During the winter months, apéritifs are taken by the fireside, while in summer, guests can take drinks on the Terrace and enjoy views across the croquet lawn and garden. Special themed breaks are available including wine, antiques and activities.

Our inspector loved: Strolling through the secluded walled garden admiring the flowers, fruit and herbs.

Directions: On the A66, 7 miles from exit 40 off the M6, between Penrith and Appleby.

Web: www.johansens.com/templesowerby
E-mail: stay@temple–sowerby.com
Tel: 0870 381 8942
International: +44 (0)17683 61578
Fax: 017683 61958

Price Guide:
single £77–£80
double £110–£150

NEW

GILPIN LODGE

CROOK ROAD, WINDERMERE, CUMBRIA LA23 3NE

Directions: M6 exit 36. A591 Kendal bypass then B5284 to Crook

Web: www.johansens.com/gilpinlodge
E-mail: hotel@gilpinlodge.com
Tel: 0870 381 8546
International: +44 (0)15394 88818
Fax: 015394 88058

Price Guide: (including 5 course dinner)
single £160
double/twin £220–£290

This elegant, luxurious family-run country house hotel is set in 20 acres of woodland, moors and country gardens, 2 miles from Lake Windermere and 12 miles from the M6. The original building, tastefully extended and modernised, dates from 1901 and the long-standing staff, as much a feature of the house as the Cunliffe family, ensure a relaxed ambience alongside friendly, personal care and attention to detail. All the senses are delicately pampered; the profusion of fresh flower arrangements, picture-lined walls, antique furniture and log fires in winter, are all part of Gilpin hospitality. The sumptuous bedrooms have en-suite bathrooms and every comfort; some have patio doors, split levels and whirlpool baths. The exquisite food, created by a team of 8 chefs, has received 3 AA Rosettes and 4 RAC Dining Awards; the wine list contains 175 labels from 13 different countries. The beautiful gardens are the perfect place in which to muse whilst savouring the beautiful Lakeland scenery. This is Wordsworth and Beatrix Potter country and there are several stately homes, gardens and castles to visit nearby. Guests are entitled to free use of a nearby leisure club and Windermere golf course is ½ mile away. English Tourist Board Gold award, AA 3 Red Stars, RAC Gold Ribbon award, AA Ten Top Country Retreat, AA Ten Top Small Hotel. A Pride of Britain Hotel. (See website for guided tour.)

Our inspector loved: The superb service and new garden room.

FAYRER GARDEN HOUSE HOTEL

LYTH VALLEY ROAD, BOWNESS-ON-WINDERMERE, CUMBRIA LA23 3JP

Awarded The Cumbrian Tourist Board Hotel of the Year 2002, this lovely Victorian house overlooks Lake Windermere in spacious gardens and grounds. This very comfortable hotel, where guests can enjoy the spectacular views over the water, offers a real welcome and marvellous value for money. The delightful lounges and bar and the superb air-conditioned restaurant all enjoy lake views. There is an excellent table d'hôte menu in the award-winning restaurant, which changes daily and uses local produce such as fish, game and poultry whenever possible and also serves a small à la carte choice. The wine list is excellent and very reasonably priced. Many of the attractive bedrooms face the lake, some have four-poster beds and whirlpool baths en suite. There are also ground floor rooms suitable for the elderly or infirm. The nearby Parklands Leisure Complex has a an indoor pool, sauna, steam room, badminton, snooker and squash complimentary to hotel residents. Special breaks are available. The Windermere Steamboat Museum, boating from Bowness Pier and golf at Windermere Golf Club and The Beatrix Potter Attraction are all close by.

Our inspector loved: *The wonderful dining experience in the air-conditioned restaurant with stunning views of Lake Windermere.*

Directions: Take junction 36 off the M6 then the A590 past Kendal. Take the B5284 at the next roundabout and turn left at the end. The hotel is 350 yards on the right.

Web: www.johansens.com/fayrergarden
E-mail: lakescene@fayrergarden.com
Tel: 0870 381 8517
International: +44 (0)15394 88195
Fax: 015394 45986

Price Guide: (including 5-course dinner)
single £75–£120
double £130–£250

LINTHWAITE HOUSE HOTEL

CROOK ROAD, BOWNESS-ON-WINDERMERE, CUMBRIA LA23 3JA

Situated in 14 acres of gardens and woods in the heart of the Lake District, Linthwaite House overlooks Lake Windermere and Belle Isle, with Claife Heights and Coniston Old Man beyond. Here guests will find themselves amid spectacular scenery, yet only a short drive from the motorway network. The hotel combines stylish originality with the best of traditional English hospitality. Most of the superbly decorated en-suite bedrooms have lake or garden views. The comfortable lounge is the perfect place to unwind and there is a fire on winter evenings. In the restaurant excellent cuisine features the best of fresh, local produce, accompanied by a fine selection of wines. Within the hotel grounds, there is a 9-hole putting green and a par-3 practice hole. Fly fishermen can fish for brown trout in the hotel tarn. Guests have complimentary use of a private swimming pool and leisure club nearby, while fell walks begin at the hotel's front door. The area around Linthwaite abounds with places of interest: this is Beatrix Potter and Wordsworth country, and there is much to interest the visitor.

Directions: From the M6, junction 36 follow Kendal by-pass for 8 miles. Take the B5284, Crook Road, for 6 miles. 1 mile beyond Windermere Golf Club, Linthwaite House is signposted on the left.

Web: www.johansens.com/linthwaitehouse
E-mail: admin@linthwaite.com
Tel: 0870 381 8694
International: +44 (0)15394 88600
Fax: 015394 88601

Price Guide:
single £125–£150
double/twin £125–£270
suite £250–£295

Our inspector loved: Walking through the landscaped gardens up to the tarn with its spectacular views of Lake Windermere.

BROADOAKS COUNTRY HOUSE

BRIDGE LANE, TROUTBECK, WINDERMERE, CUMBRIA LA23 1LA

Tucked away in Troutbeck, one of the prettiest areas of the Lake District, Broadoaks is a wonderful retreat from which to explore this beautiful part of England. Views from the first floor are truly breathtaking, reaching over Lake Windermere and the Troutbeck Valley into the 10 acres of private grounds that belong to the hotel. Designed to be relaxing and luxurious, yet mindful of the graceful building's Victorian past, all bedrooms are furnished with four-poster or antique brass bedsteads, and are fully equipped with the latest Jacuzzi, spa whirlpool and sunken bath. Rich oak panelling runs from the entrance hall into the cosy music room with Bechstein piano and open fire, where guests can enjoy pre-dinner drinks or after-dinner coffee. Rich red damask complements the Victorian dining-room and is a splendid setting for the award-winning restaurant, which has a wide reputation and a choice of á la carte and house menus. All guests have complimentary use of a local private leisure club or can relax in the grounds trying their hand at pitch and put. Golf, fishing, croquet and clay pigeon shooting can also be arranged.

Our inspector loved: *The Victorian ambience of this hotel with beautiful views over Troutbeck Valley.*

Directions: M6 junction 36, A590/591 to Windermere. Go over small roundabout towards Ambleside, then right into Bridge Lane. Broadoaks is ½ mile on right.

Web: www.johansens.com/broadoaks
E-mail: trev@broadoaksf9.co.uk
Tel: 0870 381 8380
International: +44 (0)1539 445566
Fax: 01539 488766

Price Guide:
single £65–£160
double £90–£210

THE PEACOCK AT ROWSLEY

ROWSLEY, NEAR MATLOCK, DERBYSHIRE DE4 2EB

Directions: M1/exit 28, head for A6. Rowsley is midway between Matlock and Bakewell.

Web: www.johansens.com/peacockrowsley
E-mail: reception@thepeacockatrowsley.com
Tel: 0870 381 8805
International: +44 (0)1629 733518
Fax: 01629 732671

Price Guide:
single £75
double/twin £135

Once the Dower House for Haddon Hall, this superb 17th-century country inn has returned to the Haddon estate after nearly 50 years and remains a renowned historic fishing hostelry with a 3 Star AA rating. An exciting refurbishment has been overseen by Lord Edward Manners of Haddon Hall, and today the hotel's eclectic mix of ancient and modern are carried off with great style and charisma. Interiors have been created by the magnificent French designer India Mahdavi, and furnishings are bold, featuring contemporary colours and textures. Attractive gardens lead down to the River Derwent and fishermen are spoilt for choice as the River Wye is the only river in the country with wild rainbow trout and brown trout. Fishing reservations and tuition are available at the hotel, along with a purpose built drying room. The Peacock's 2 AA Rosette Awarded restaurant offers fine British cuisine, with a modern influence and a good selection of bar food is available. A warm welcome extends to dogs and children, however it is requested that children dine before 8 o'clock. Arrangements can be made for guests to use the nearby Woodlands Fitness Centre for gym and beauty treatments, and Haddon Hall, Chatsworth House and the Peak District National Park are all on the doorstep.

Our inspector loved: The transition from 1652 to present day - country chic with great charm.

DANNAH FARM COUNTRY HOUSE

BOWMAN'S LANE, SHOTTLE, NR BELPER, DERBYSHIRE DE56 2DR

Set amidst an area of rural and unspoilt countryside high above the Ecclesbourne Valley on the edge of the Peak District, Dannah Farm is an exceptional 18th-century Georgian farmhouse conversion on the Chatsworth Estate. In addition to obtaining 5 AA Red Diamonds, the hotel has won National Awards for Excellence and Tourism in the region and offers a unique service within a tranquil and relaxed environment. Bedrooms overlooking rolling pastures and large pretty gardens are beautifully furnished with antiques and old pine; some have four-poster beds, private sitting rooms, Japanese-style tubs, hot tubs and whirlpool baths. Aromas of freshly baked bread escaping from the kitchen whet the appetite and for breakfast there are free-range eggs and organic sausages. Dinner is by prior arrangement. Situated only 10 minutes from the World Heritage sites of Belper and Cromford, the countryside is criss-crossed with footpaths in all directions, whilst places of interest nearby include Chatsworth, Haddon Hall, Dovedale and water sports at Carsington.

Our inspector loved: Such contrasts! wonderful and still a farm. Telephone and go.

Directions: From Derby take A6 Matlock road. At Duffield turn left onto B5023 towards Wirksworth. At traffic lights at Cowers Lane turn right onto A517 towards Belper, then 1st left to Shottle. Bowman's Lane is 100 yds past crossroads in the village.

Web: www.johansens.com/dannah
E-mail: reservations@dannah.demon.co.uk
Tel: 0870 381 8476
International: +44 (0)1773 550273/550630
Fax: 01773 550590

Price Guide:
single £54–£95
double/twin £85–£99
suite £99–£150

BOAR'S HEAD HOTEL

LICHFIELD ROAD, SUDBURY, DERBYSHIRE DE6 5GX

Directions: The hotel is on A515, just south of A50 from Stoke on Trent to Derby

Web: www.johansens.com/boarsheadburton
E-mail: enquiries@boars-head-hotel.co.uk
Tel: 0870 381 8371
International: +44 (0)1283 820344
Fax: 01283 820075

Price Guide:
single from £45
double from £55

This 17th-century house was lost from the famous Vernon estate through a game of cards! It is now a well known local hostelry, having been run by the Crooks family for many years. Guests will be welcomed by the architectural beauty of this very old building. There is a bar, with natural brick walls, horse brasses and hunting horns. The residents' lounge looks onto a pretty patio where drinks are served in summer months. Much thought has been given to furnishing the delightful bedrooms which have every possible facility, including teletext and Sky television. Visitors enjoy a choice of real ales and excellent home-cooked dishes with the chef's specials listed on a blackboard. There are 2 restaurants, the elegant Royal Boar with an imaginative à la carte menu and the less formal Hunter's Table Carvery and Bistro offering fresh fish, pasta dishes and splendid roasts, both at lunchtime and in the evening. The Royal Boar is closed on Sunday evenings, but is famous for its Sunday lunch. A fascinating wine list covers vineyards worldwide, with 70 entries including 6 house wines and a selection of 10 half-bottles. Alton Towers and Uttoxeter Racecourse are attractions nearby. Other guests will enjoy Chatsworth House, Sudbury Hall, Tutbury Castle and the Bass Museum of brewing. Special weekend breaks available.

Our inspector loved: *The truly old fashioned menus - steak diane, tornedos rossini, lobster thermidore - a taste of the 1960's.*

LITTLEOVER LODGE HOTEL

222 RYKNELD ROAD, LITTLEOVER, DERBY, DERBYSHIRE DE23 7AN

A warm and friendly welcome by the Crooks family awaits guests at this busy country hotel, or 'restaurant with rooms'. Formerly a farmhouse, Littleover Lodge has been extended to provide modern and well-presented accommodation. In addition to the 13 recently refurbished, spacious bedrooms, which are equipped with every modern facility, there are three superb suites, all with upstairs balcony bedrooms and cosy day areas, offering the ultimate in relaxation and comfort. The Lodge Carvery is open lunchtimes and evenings and serves an extensive daily changing menu, whilst your choice from the exquisite à la carte menu in the restaurant offers an interesting variety of dishes to suit all tastes delightfully presented. Situated amid beautiful rural countryside, Littleover Lodge stands only minutes from Derby city centre with its Cathedral, Royal Crown Derby factories and Assembly Rooms, famed for snooker events. It is the perfect base from which to explore the numerous attractions nearby including Calke Abbey, Derbyshire Cricket Ground, Chatsworth House and Alton Towers. Sporting enthusiasts can visit Uttoxeter Race Course, which is also within easy reach. Special weekend breaks available.

Our inspector loved: *The buzz of this busy restaurant. Lobster thermidor and Barnsley chop, dishes from the past. Good memories.*

Directions: Leave M1 at junction 24, take A50 towards Stoke, then take A38 towards Derby, first slip road signed for Littleover.

Web: www.johansens.com/littleover
Tel: 0870 381 8695
International: +44 (0)1332 510161
Fax: 01332 514010

Price Guide:
single £45
double/twin £65
suites £75

THE CHEQUERS INN

FROGGATT EDGE, HOPE VALLEY, DERBYSHIRE S32 3ZJ

Directions: The inn is situated on the A625, which links Bakewell and Sheffield, 6 miles from Bakewell on Froggatt Edge.

Web: www.johansens.com/chequerscalver
E-mail: info@chequers-froggatt.com
Tel: 0870 381 8422
International: +44 (0)1433 630231
Fax: 01433 631072

Price Guide: (based on double occupancy)
single £55–£75
double/twin £55–£75
four poster £65–£85

Since February 2002, Jonathan and Joanne Tindall have worked hard to instil their pleasant personalities into this popular country inn. Its tradition for hospitality dates back to the 16th century when it was built on the old pack horse road. A Grade II listed building, the inn was originally 4 houses and has been extensively refurbished yet retains many of its charming period features including a horse mounting block and the old stables. Each of the 5 bedrooms has its own personality and is cosy with comfortable, characteristic furnishings alongside private bathroom and individually controlled heating. Gaining a Rosette the Chequers prides itself on its cuisine and chef, Michael Smith, creates a wide variety of European and British dishes comprising the freshest ingredients, including local game in season. Meals are available all day at the weekends and bank holidays. On cooler evenings guests can relax in the warmth of crackling open fires in the bar or enjoy breathtaking views of the setting sun from the elevated secret woodland garden. The surrounding Peak District area is ideal walking country and the inn is perfectly situated for exploring along the Derwent River or Peak trails. Nearby is the historic castle and caverns of Castleton, Haddon Hall, Chatsworth House and the lively market town of Bakewell, famous for its puddings.

Our inspector loved: The mix of menus in the dining room, excellent choice.

THE WIND IN THE WILLOWS

DERBYSHIRE LEVEL, GLOSSOP, DERBYSHIRE SK13 7PT

Situated 12 miles from the centre of Manchester, with good road and rail links, The Wind in the Willows is a delightful, family-owned early Victorian Country House, which has retained its original charm including oak-panelled rooms, traditional furnishings and open log fires. The hotel is situated within 5 acres of land with unspoilt views of the Peak District National Park, and surrounded by the heather-clad hills of the Pennines. The setting provides an escape from the pressures of modern day life into the atmosphere and elegant surroundings of a bygone era, with the dining room offering well priced traditional cuisine. The bedrooms with their splendid views are decorated predominantly with antique furniture and numerous personal touches. A small conference suite with its separate private entrance accommodates prestigious corporate meetings in peaceful, uninterrupted surroundings. Adjoining the grounds is a splendid 9-hole golf course, where guests can play within the beautiful scenery of the local countryside. Many activities can be arranged locally, including sailing, horse riding, hang gliding, fly fishing and pot holing. Places of interest nearby include Chatsworth, Haddon Hall, Castleton, Bakewell, Holmfirth, Hayfield, Kinder Scout with its panoramic views and the Lowry centre in Manchester.

Our inspector loved: The tranquility of this restful country house with such easy access to the surrounding towns.

Directions: A mile east of Glossop on A57, 400 yards down the road opposite the Royal Oak.

Web: www.johansens.com/windinthewillows
E-mail: info@windinthewillows.co.uk
Tel: 0870 381 9001
International: +44 (0)1457 868001
Fax: 01457 853354

Price Guide:
single £85–£100
double £115–£145

THE PLOUGH INN

LEADMILL BRIDGE, HATHERSAGE, DERBYSHIRE S30 1BA

Directions: From M1 exit 29 take A617 west, then via A619 and A623 shortly after north onto B6001 towards Hathersage. The inn is within proximity of Sheffield, Manchester and East Midland Airports.

Web: www.johansens.com/ploughinnhathersage
E-mail: theploughinn@leadmillbridge.fsnet.co.uk
Tel: 0870 381 8827
International: +44 (0)1433 650319
Fax: 01433 651049

Price Guide:
single £55–£89.50
double £75–£89.50
suite £110–£120

A 10-minute drive along the spectacular moorlands from Sheffield this beautifully restored 16th-century inn stands within 9 acres of grounds by the meandering River Derwent. Bob and Cynthia Emery and son Elliott, who has joined the family business, always ensure a warm and friendly welcome whether in winter by the roaring log fires or during summer in the garden, surrounded by an abundance of flower baskets. 3 double bedrooms in the main building are accessed by an external staircase and each of the 2 newly converted luxury suites offer en suite bathroom, sitting area, video player and hi-fi. They have been restored using local materials, leaving exposed beams and stonework. Meals are served daily, either in the cosy bar or in the intimate restaurant. The extensive Rosette Awarded menu offers something to please every taste. Bob, a former butcher, and head chef Robert Navarron, who trained in some of London's most prestigious restaurants, always strive to use the finest quality produce to create dishes ranging from home-baked pies to fine international cuisine complemented by a varied wine list and friendly informal service. Private dining and reception parties can be arranged. Castleton, with its world-famous Blue John mines, is only 10 minutes along the picturesque Hope Valley. Bakewell, Haddon Hall and 18th-century Chatsworth House are only a little further afield.

Our inspector loved: *This delightful hostelry offering excellent rooms.*

KEGWORTH HOUSE

42 HIGH STREET, KEGWORTH, DERBYSHIRE DE74 2DA

This is a Georgian town house at its best. Located on a quiet street off the main road in Kegworth village, Kegworth House is an extremely welcoming hotel offering luxurious accommodation, excellent cuisine and a friendly, relaxed atmosphere. Its proximity to major road links makes it an ideal venue for business meetings and small conferences, yet its tranquil setting appeals in equal measure to the leisure traveller. Parts of the building are over 350 years old. Its extensive cellarage even includes an extra one below all the others. The beautifully maintained, traditional English walled garden, holds a very special secret that owners Tony and Di Belcher may reveal; the ideal setting for a croquet match or simply for putting one's feet up with a book or newspaper. Guests can start their day with a hearty full English breakfast or choose a lighter option; all meals are freshly prepared using vegetables when possible from the garden. A 2 or 3-course dinner can be served upon prior request in the attractive panelled dining room with its polished oak floor. With adequate notice the hotel also arranges private functions for up to 12 guests. Kegworth House is just 5 minutes away from the Donington Park Raceway, and offers easy access to the Peak district with its numerous attractions.

Our inspector loved: *The true country house hospitality in this superb Georgian town house.*

Directions: 4 minutes from East Midlands International Airport and 3 minutes from the M1.

Web: www.johansens.com/kegworth
E-mail: tony@kegworthhouse.co.uk
Tel: 0870 381 9102
International: +44 (0)1509 672575
Fax: 01509 670645

Price Guide:
single from £75
double from £105
suite £195

        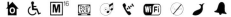

BICKLEIGH CASTLE

BICKLEIGH, DEVON EX16 8RP

Directions: Exit the M5 at junction 27 and take the A361 to Tiverton. Join the A396 south to Bickleigh Village, approximately 4 miles away. Follow signs to castle.

Web: www.johansens.com/bickleighcastle
E-mail: info@bickleighcastle.com
Tel: 0870 381 9316
International: +44 (0)1884 855363
Fax: 01884 855783

Price Guide: (excluding VAT)
single £55
double/twin £110
weekly let £450–£1250

Described as a film set Bickleigh Castle is a wildly romantic, rose-tinted, 14th-century fortification tucked away in 30 acres of lush green Devonshire countryside through which runs the tranquil, trout-filled River Exe. A square building with solid stone walls, listed gatehouse, great hall and armoury, this is one of the oldest inhabited castles in Britain whose first recorded owner in the Domesday Book was Alward the Englishman of the Court of Mortain. A succession of owners have added to the castle's charm with today's welcoming and hospitable incumbents, Robert and Sara Hay, are consistently updating facilities and comfort. A beautiful, 11th-century chapel, within an enclosure of cob walls, stands in the grounds, together with a clutch of thatched cottages that create a diverse and attractive complex of buildings. 4 of these delightfully decorated and furnished cottages offer peaceful and restful accommodation for guests seeking a bed and breakfast, short break or longer retreat to commune with nature or explore the surrounding countryside attractions. Delicious French-inspired cuisine can be enjoyed in the magnificent Baroque Hall, which also has a stylish wine bar and dance floor. The castle can offer accommodation by arrangement and is available for exclusive use.

Our inspector loved: *This tucked away corner of paradise along the River Exe.*

YEOLDON HOUSE HOTEL

DURRANT LANE, NORTHAM, NR BIDEFORD EX39 2RL

On arriving at Yeoldon House Hotel, guests are assured of two things: a generous and warm welcome, and a totally relaxing atmosphere. Set beside the river Torridge and with lawns sloping down towards the water's edge, the sense of serenity is instant, and enhanced by the heartfelt greetings of the proprietors. The ambience is one of home-from-home comfort – relaxed and casual, but with a little added luxury. Each bedroom has its own style whether it be a cosy single, a grand four-poster or a split level suite; some have balconies from which to admire the spectacular Devon scenery. Soyer's restaurant is a source of great pride for Yeoldon House – named after the Victorian chef Alexis Soyer, it has an air of casual elegance and offers an interesting table d'hôte menu of locally-sourced meat, fish and vegetables, catering for all palates. Breakfast too is served here, and it is a perfect setting from which to watch the sun rise over the river. This part of Devon boasts magnificent and unspoilt scenery, and the coastal path is a must for walkers. Guests can visit the picturesque village of Clovelly, Exmoor, Rosemoor Gardens, Lorna Doone country, Lundy Island and the North Devon beaches. 3 nights mini breaks available.

Our inspector loved: The newly refurbished top floor bedrooms and the overall relaxing, welcoming atmosphere.

Directions: Leave M5 at Jct27 and join A361 towards Barnstaple, then A39 towards Bideford. At Torridge Bridge roundabout follow signs for Northam.

Web: www.johansens.com/Yeoldon
E-mail: yeoldonhouse@aol.com
Tel: 0870 381 9019
International: +44 (0)1237 474400
Fax: 01237 476618

Price Guide:
single £60–£70
double/twin £100–£115.

GIDLEIGH PARK

CHAGFORD, DEVON TQ13 8HH

Directions: Approach from Chagford: go along Mill Street from Chagford Square. Fork right after 150 yards, cross into Holy Street at factory crossroads and follow lane for 2 miles.

Web: www.johansens.com/gidleighpark
E-mail: gidleighpark@gidleigh.co.uk
Tel: 0870 381 8545
International: +44 (0)1647 432367
Fax: 01647 432574

Barnstaple
Exeter
Sidmouth
Plymouth

Price Guide: (including dinner)
single £370–£470
double/twin £430–£550

Gidleigh Park enjoys an outstanding international reputation among connoisseurs for its comfort and gastronomy. It has collected a clutch of top culinary awards including 2 Michelin stars for its imaginative cuisine and the Gidleigh Park wine list is one of the best in Britain. Service throughout the hotel is faultless. The en-suite bedrooms – 2 of them in a converted chapel – are luxuriously furnished with antiques. The public rooms are elegantly appointed and during the cooler months, a fire burns merrily in the lounge's impressive fireplace. Set amid 45 secluded acres in the Teign Valley, Gidleigh Park is 1½ miles from the nearest public road. 2 croquet lawns, an all-weather tennis court, a bowling lawn and a splendid water garden can be found in the grounds. A 360 yard long, par 52 putting course designed by Peter Alliss was opened in 1995. Guests can swim in the river or explore Dartmoor on foot or in the saddle. There are 14 miles of trout, sea trout and salmon fishing, as well as golf facilities nearby. Gidleigh Park is a Relais & Châteaux member.

Our inspector loved: *The total peace and tranquillity surrounding this superb hotel.*

THE NEW INN

COLEFORD, CREDITON, DEVON EX17 5BZ

Those wishing to escape the hectic pace of everyday life will be delighted with this lovely 13th-century thatched inn, located in a truly secluded valley beside a babbling brook featuring newly designed gardens which are a delight. The New Inn, a Grade II listed building of cob, has been tastefully renovated and refurbished over the years. Today it retains the character and ambience of a past era. A warm welcome is extended to guests from owners Irene and Paul Butt and their talkative parrot, Captain! The resident ghost, Sebastian, is also reputed to be friendly... The AA 4 Diamond rated accommodation is excellent, with spacious and individually appointed bedrooms offering every comfort. In the winter months, the lounge is the place to sit and enjoy the cosy warmth of a log fire. 3 full-time chefs create memorable dishes, using the best and freshest local ingredients. The menu includes delicious starters, such as sherried kidney tart, cream of Devon crab soup or grilled goats cheese with walnuts and walnut oil salad, and a good selection of speciality dishes, grills, snacks and puddings. An extensive choice of drinks, including traditional ales, is served in the bars. The wine list has been awarded many accolades for its selection. The cathedral city of Exeter, Dartmoor and Exmoor are all close by.

Our inspector loved: The atmosphere, location and the mouth watering menus.

Directions: Take the A377 Exeter-Barnstable Road. Coleford is signed 2 miles from Crediton.

Web: www.johansens.com/newinncoleford
E-mail: new–inn@reallyreal-group.com
Tel: 0870 381 8757
International: +44 (0)1363 84242
Fax: 01363 85044

Price Guide:
single £60–£70
double £75–£85

THE EDGEMOOR

HAYTOR ROAD, BOVEY TRACEY, SOUTH DEVON TQ13 9LE

Bordering Dartmoor National Park, this elegant Victorian hideaway is nestled amidst 2½ acres of idyllic gardens and mature trees. Enthusiastic staff, who are dedicated to the well being of all guests, give a most friendly welcome and create a friendly, relaxed atmosphere. The hotel has been completely renovated and superb décor combines traditional and contemporary design to create an inspiring environment with plenty of light and space. Prize winning British and West Country specialities are served in the hotel's restaurant, which also boasts a wide range of enticing international wines. Guests will love the cosy bar, which has a roaring log fire on colder days for a warm, intimate evening with friends. Newly appointed bedrooms are stylish and comfortable with a contemporary, minimalist style and the Woodland Wing has pretty private patios on which to enjoy the fresh Devon air. With its proximity to Dartmoor, The Edgemoor is a paradise for nature lovers with an abundance of quiet riverside and easy Moorland walks. The breathtaking Devon coastline has many wonderful beaches and coves and there are picturesque villages, ancient castles and many places of historical interest nearby. The extraordinary Eden Project, with its unique collection of over 140,000 plants, is a short drive away.

Directions: On leaving the M5, join the A38 towards the direction of Plymouth. At Drumbridges roundabout, take the A382 towards Bovey Tracey. At the second roundabout turn left and after approximately ½ mile, fork left at the sign for Haytor.

Web: www.johansens.com/edgemoor
E-mail: reservations@edgemoor.co.uk
Tel: 0870 381 8499
International: +44 (0)1626 832466
Fax: 01626 834760

Price Guide:
single £75–£85
double/twin £120–£130

Our inspector loved: The delightful, peaceful location on the Dartmoor boundary.

COMBE HOUSE HOTEL & RESTAURANT

GITTISHAM, HONITON, NR EXETER, DEVON EX14 3AD

Combe House is a wildly romantic Grade I Elizabethan manor hidden in 3,500 acres of Devon's finest estates where magnificent Arabian horses and pheasants roam freely. Total peace and tranquillity together with generous hospitality can be enjoyed here in this warm and welcoming atmosphere created by the comfortable sofas, flamboyant flowers and roaring log-fires. 15 intimate bedrooms and suites, many with panoramic views, are decorated with style and individuality. The candle-lit restaurant serves innovative, contemporary British cuisine prepared by Master Chef of Great Britain, Philip Leach, perfectly complemented by a well-chosen wine list, including a specialist Chablis collection. The recently restored Georgian Kitchen is the ideal setting for a highly individual private lunch or dinner, dining by lamps and candlelight. Down Combe's mile-long drive is Gittisham, once described by H.R.H. Prince Charles as "the ideal English village", with its thatched cottages, Norman church and village green. The World Heritage Jurassic coast, from Lyme Regis to Sidmouth, Honiton antique shops, numerous historic houses and gardens, the cathedral of Exeter and the wide open spaces of Dartmoor can all be explored.

Our inspector loved: *The warmth and welcome of this beautifully located Elizabethan manor.*

Directions: From the M5 take exit 28 to Honiton and Sidmouth or exit 29 to Honiton. Follow signs to Fenny Bridges and Gittisham.

Web: www.johansens.com/combehousegittisham
E-mail: stay@thishotel.com
Tel: 0870 381 8440
International: +44 (0)1404 540400
Fax: 01404 46004

Price Guide:
single £125–£165
double/twin £138–£275
suites £275–£295

NEW

THE GALLEY RESTAURANT & ROOMS

41 FORE STREET, TOPSHAM, EXETER EX3 0HU

Directions: Exit the M5 at junction 30 and follow signs for Exmouth on the A376. Pick up signs for Topsham. Once in Topsham head for the High Street and follow the one-way system to the quay.

Web: www.johansens.com/galleyrestaurant
E-mail: fish@galleyrestaurant.co.uk
Tel: 0870 381 9307
International: +44 (0)1392 876078
Fax: 01392 876078

Price Guide:
single £62.50–£87.50
double £125–£175

One of Exeter's historic conservation areas is home to this Grade II listed building, which as The Galley Restaurant & Rooms has won numerous awards and accolades including an English Tourism Council silver award, a Five Diamond AA premier award, a prestigious Little Gem award for dining, and "Best Restaurant in Devon & South West" at the Westcountry Cooking Awards. Much of its success must be attributed to its directors and flamboyant Masterchef of Great Britain, Paul Da-Costa-Greaves, and their commitment to providing a unique and uplifting atmosphere along with the best and freshest produce available. Not only is the fish landed daily at Brixham, scallops are landed by divers. The restaurant itself has a great deal of character with its exposed brickwork, beams and open fireplaces and the 4 nautical cabins also boast 17th-century Olde Worlde features alongside panoramic river views, minibars, telephone and Internet connections, cable television and private bathrooms. The surrounding area is a haven for bird lovers and watchers, and for those wishing to explore the fascinating maritime history.

Our inspector loved: *Every aspect – will return as soon as possible!*

HOME FARM HOTEL

WILMINGTON, NR HONITON, DEVON EX14 9JR

Home Farm is an attractive thatched farmhouse, set in 4 acres of beautiful grounds. A small hotel since 1950, it has been tastefully restored by its owners to create a charming and relaxing ambience. The staff are friendly and children are made welcome. The public rooms have big bowls of flowers in summer and enchanting log fires in winter. Value for money is an important criterion. The Residents' Lounge is comfortable and there is a cosy, well-stocked bar serving light meals. The restaurant, oak-beamed and with an inglenook fireplace, offers a marvellous à la carte choice as well as a good, homemade table d'hôte menu using local produce. The wine list is extensive. Bedrooms are in the main building or across a cobbled courtyard. All have a private bathroom, telephone, colour television, hairdryer, radio alarm and tea/coffee making facilities. Wilmington is in the heart of 25 National Trust properties, 6 miles from the coast and there are 6 golf courses within 15 miles. Riding, water sports and fishing can be arranged. Honiton is known for its lace, as is Axminster for its carpets. A 2-bedroom lodge with stunning views is also available.

Our inspector loved: *The striking newly presented lounge.*

Directions: Take the A303 to Honiton, join the A35 signposted to Axminster. Wilmington is 3 miles further on and Home Farm is set back off the main road on the right.

Web: www.johansens.com/homefarm
E-mail: homefarmhotel@breathemail.net
Tel: 0870 381 8604
International: +44 (0)1404 831278
Fax: 01404 831411

Price Guide:
single £50–£60
double £75–£100

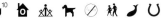

ILSINGTON COUNTRY HOUSE HOTEL

ILSINGTON VILLAGE, NEAR NEWTON ABBOT, DEVON TQ13 9RR

The Ilsington Country House Hotel stands in 10 acres of beautiful private grounds within the Dartmoor National Park. Run by friendly proprietors, Tim and Maura Hassell, the delightful furnishings and ambience offer a most comfortable environment in which to relax. Stylish bedrooms all boast outstanding views across the rolling pastoral countryside and every comfort and convenience to make guests feel at home. The distinctive candle-lit dining room is perfect for savouring the superb cuisine, awarded an AA Rosette, created by talented chefs from fresh local produce. The library is ideal for an intimate dining party or celebration whilst the conservatory or lounge is the place for morning coffee or a Devon cream tea. There is a fully-equipped, purpose-built gymnasium, heated indoor pool, sauna, steam room and spa. Some of England's most idyllic and unspoilt scenery surrounds Ilsington, with the picturesque villages of Lustleigh and Widecombe-in-the-Moor close by. Guests have easy access to the moors from the hotel. Riding, fishing and many other country pursuits can be arranged. Special breaks are available.

Directions: From the M5 join the A38 at Exeter following Plymouth signs. After approximately 12 miles, exit for Moretonhampstead and Newton Abbot. At the roundabout follow signs for Ilsington.

Web: www.johansens.com/ilsington
E-mail: hotel@ilsington.co.uk
Tel: 0870 381 8635
International: +44 (0)1364 661452
Fax: 01364 661307

Price Guide:
single from £86
double/twin from £126

Our inspector loved: The outstanding and beautiful location, and warm atmosphere within.

HEWITT'S - VILLA SPALDI

NORTH WALK, LYNTON, DEVON EX35 6HJ

This elegant, private 19th-century country house offers total peace and seclusion within 27 acres of gardens and woodlands. Once the home of the eminent Victorian, Sir Thomas Hewitt, it stands regally on high cliffs overlooking Lynmouth Bay and beyond, Wales. Approached by a meandering, residential driveway, the house sits just minutes from the centre of Lynton and is perfectly placed for walks along the Exmoor coastal path. The character of the house has been superbly retained with wonderful antiques, a sweeping oak staircase and beautiful stained glass windows by Burne-Jones. 2 self catering apartments are available all year round, and the warm, friendly "house party" ambience of Hewitt's means it lends itself perfectly to intimate gatherings. Exclusive use of the house is available on request. Dinner is available by prior arrangement and mouth-watering international dishes are created under the guidance of Italian chef and owner, Tito Spaldi. Local suppliers of venison, game, meats and cheeses are used to full advantage and the many fine wines on the accompanying list are truly first class. Guests can enjoy breakfast or a romantic dinner in the oak-panelled dining room, or in the summer, on the cliff terrace overlooking the bay.

Our inspector loved: The location of this little gem hidden away in north Devon – a must.

Directions: Leave the M5 at junction 23, signposted Minehead, follow the A39 to Lynton.

Web: www.johansens.com/hewitts
E-mail: hewitts.hotel@talk21.com
Tel: 0870 381 8593
International: +44 (0)1598 752293
Fax: 01598 752489

Price Guide:
single £70–£95
double/twin £140–£220

BROWNS HOTEL, WINE BAR & BRASSERIE

80 WEST STREET, TAVISTOCK, PLYMOUTH, DEVON PL19 8AQ

Directions: Tavistock is on the A386, a short distance from the M5 either via the A30 or the A38.

Web: www.johansens.com/brownstavistock
E-mail: enquiries@brownsdevon.co.uk
Tel: 0870 381 8386
International: +44 (0)1822 618686
Fax: 01822 618646

Price Guide:
single from £65
double/twin from £90
large double/four-poster £120–£150

Browns is situated in the ancient market stannary town of Tavistock. Originally an old coaching inn, it has been lovingly restored whilst retaining many period features such as stunning slate flag stones and massive beams. Guests are pampered with attentive service and crackling log fires whilst rich fabrics and cosy furniture create a pleasant atmosphere that is relaxed and intimate. The 20 beautifully decorated en-suite bedrooms are spacious and comfortable with chic décor and superb facilities for the discerning traveller. Delightful modern British cuisine is offered in the Brasserie-style restaurant, where an emphasis is placed on fresh fish and local produce, and the hotel's own well provides plenty of still and sparkling water of the purest quality. For leisure there is a gymnasium and soon to be indoor heated pool; outdoor enthusiasts may enjoy sailing, pony trekking, fishing, golf, bird watching and spectacular coastal walks. In Tavistock, there are the remains of an abbey, old-fashioned shops, a thriving market and a canal to visit; it is the ideal base for exploring the beautiful secluded coves and sandy beaches of Devon and Cornwall. The local church houses a breathtaking window designed by William Morris dating back to the 14th century. Dartmoor with its tors and wild ponies is within easy reach.

Our inspector loved: *This superb affordable chic hotel in the west country – a must.*

KINGSTON HOUSE

STAVERTON, TOTNES, DEVON TQ9 6AR

The Kingston Estate nestles amongst the rolling hills and valleys of the South Hams region of Devon, bounded by Dartmoor and the sea, with the focal point, Kingston House, commanding sweeping views of the moor. The Mansion, together with its superb cottages, have been restored by the Corfield family to their former glory and now offer some of the highest standard of accommodation to be found in the South West, boasting 3 period suites, reached by way of the finest example of a marquetry staircase in England. Dinner guests dine by candlelight in the elegant dining room at tables set with sparkling crystal, shining silver and starched linen. In winter, log fires crackle in the hearths, whilst in the summer pre-dinner drinks may be taken on the terrace overlooking the 18th-century gardens. For every visitor, hospitality and comfort are assured in this magnificent historic setting. Places of interest nearby include Dartington Hall, Dartmouth, Totnes, Dartmoor and Devon's famous coastline.

Our inspector loved: *The most wonderful feel and welcome of a genuine country house.*

Directions: Take A38 from Exeter or Plymouth, at Buckfastleigh take A384 Totnes Road for 2 miles. Turn left to Staverton. At Sea Trout Inn, take left fork to Kingston and follow signs.

Web: www.johansens.com/kingstonhouse
E-mail: info@kingston-estate.co.uk
Tel: 0870 381 8655
International: +44 (0)1803 762 235
Fax: 01803 762 444

Price Guide:
single £95–£105
double £150
suite £160–£170

PERCY'S COUNTRY HOTEL & RESTAURANT

COOMBESHEAD ESTATE, VIRGINSTOW, DEVON EX21 5EA

Directions: From Okehampton take the A3079 to Metherell Cross. After 8.3 miles turn left. The hotel is 6.5 miles on the left. See website for more comprehensive details.

Web: www.johansens.com/percys
E-mail: info@percys.co.uk
Tel: 0870 381 8817
International: +44 (0)1409 211236
Fax: 01409 211460

Price Guide:
single from £90
double from £150

A soft, tranquil ambience filters through every part of this stylish, charming Devon hideaway. Set amongst 130 acres of unspoilt countryside and with stunning wildlife that will enthrall and enchant, Percy's is ideal for those wishing to relax and unwind in a smoke and child-free environment. Against the backdrop of the breathtaking and striking wilds of Dartmoor and Bodmin Moor, Percy's combines modern architectural intelligence and traditional country house comfort with eye-catching results. The highly acclaimed and fully certified organic restaurant, winner of the 2003 Johansens Restaurant of the Year, only serves the freshest of ingredients. The fish bought at auction is only a few hours old, vegetables and a bespoke breed of lamb are nurtured on the estate and there is a choice of home produced eggs rich in natural flavour and colour. Guest rooms feature understated luxury with soothing colours, king-size beds, Jacuzzis, DVD players and freshly baked lavender and walnut shortbread to savour. Guests are welcome to explore the surrounding grounds with the company of any one of the 3 black resident Labradors.

Our inspector loved: The peaceful "away-from-it-all" location.

NEW

THE LORD BUTE

181/185 LYMINGTON ROAD, HIGHCLIFFE ON SEA, CHRISTCHURCH, DORSET BH23 4JS

Set in a peaceful area of Dorset, on the edge of the historic New Forest, this sophisticated hotel and restaurant offers first-class service in elegantly stylish surroundings. The entrance lodges were the original gate houses to historic Highcliffe Castle, which is presently being restored to its former glory in a £10m restoration programme. Beautifully appointed, the 12 bedrooms and suites are furnished with every modern amenity; several rooms in the main house offer air conditioning and spa baths. A separate family suite with small kitchenette is also available. The epitome of English sophistication, the Lord Bute Restaurant has won numerous awards and offers unrivalled service and the highest standards of cuisine. Jazz evenings are regularly held in the restaurant. The hotel is the perfect location for a special function or small conference, with a separate conference suite accommodating up to 30 delegates. Golf and horse riding can be arranged, and sailing facilities are also close by with Lymington and Cowes on the Isle of Wight a short drive along the coast. Bournemouth with its excellent shopping is only 8 miles away and several secluded beaches are within easy reach.

Our inspector loved: *The new owners' sense of style and the warmth of their hospitality.*

Directions: Leave the M27 at junction 1. Take the A35 and then the A337 to the hotel.

Web: www.johansens.com/lordbute
E-mail: mail@lordbute.co.uk
Tel: 0870 381 9341
International: +44 (0)1425 278884
Fax: 01425 279258

Price Guide:
single £65–£75
double £85–£105
lord bute suite £180
coach house £120

YALBURY COTTAGE HOTEL

LOWER BOCKHAMPTON, DORCHESTER, DORSET DT2 8PZ

Directions: Lower Bockhampton is a mile south of A35 between Puddletown and Dorchester.

Web: www.johansens.com/yalburycottage
E-mail: yalburycottage@aol.com
Tel: 0870 381 9015
International: +44 (0)1305 262382
Fax: 01305 266412

Price Guide:
single from £59
double from £94

Yalbury Cottage Hotel is a lovely thatched house dating back about 300 years. It offers guests a warm welcome and friendly, personal service in a pleasing Dorset hamlet close to Thomas Hardy's home. The 8 non-smoking en-suite bedrooms are furnished in a simple country style, in keeping with the building, whilst the comfortable lounge, complete with large Inglenook fireplace and low beamed ceiling, is the perfect place to relax or enjoy a drink before dinner. The hotel prides itself on the high standard of cuisine served in the attractive dining room. Head chef Ashley Dent Davies, has been awarded 2 AA Rosettes, and a variety of imaginative dishes is available, for example, seared scallops on a warm potato and caper terrine with saffron and tomato dressing; roast loin of lamb with a white bean casserole, fresh broad beans and thyme jus; raspberry shortcake crème brûlée. A programme of gourmet dining events can also be enjoyed and make unforgettable evenings. Places of interest nearby include Athelhampton House, Abbotsbury Swannery, Corfe Castle and Sherborne Castle. Yalbury Cottage, only 8 miles from the magnificent Heritage Coast, is an excellent basis from which to explore Dorset.

Our inspector loved: This haven of fine dining, now recognised with 3 RAC dining awards.

SUMMER LODGE

SUMMER LANE, EVERSHOT, DORSET DT2 0JR

Service is the mantra at this welcoming Georgian manor house, which lies tucked away amidst 4 acres in the village of Evershot. Built by the Ilchester family around 1789, Summer Lodge was extended in 1893, and has just undergone a programme of complete, sympathetic restoration. The 24 individually decorated bedrooms are fitted with the latest technology including flat-screen televisions and Internet access. Sumptuous Dorset Cream Teas are served every afternoon in the Drawing Room and lighter meals are available in the cosy bar. The stunning restaurant is the perfect place to enjoy international dishes and local specialities, created by award-winning chef Steven Titman and his team, and complemented by fine wines from the well-stocked cellar. The resident award-winning sommelier team are on hand to help with the choice. A brand new indoor heated swimming pool and spa area with several treatment rooms will be open from November 2004. Civil weddings, other functions, private dining and meetings can be held in the elegant Dorchester Suite, which accommodates up to 24 guests. Bikes and Wellington boots are available for guests to go exploring the surroundings, and the hotel is happy to provide information about local attractions. Riding stables and 12 golf courses are within easy reach.

Our inspector loved: This garden takes some beating! Bring notebooks and pencils to take home wonderful ideas.

Directions: The turning to Evershot leaves the A37 halfway between Dorchester and Yeovil. Once in the village, turn left into Summer Lane and the hotel entrance is 150 yards on the right.

Web: www.johansens.com/summerlodge
E-mail: summer@relaischateaux.com
Tel: 0870 381 8926
International: +44 (0)1935 482000
Fax: 01935 482040

Sherborne Shaftesbury

Bridport

Dorchester Bournemouth

Price Guide:
single from £152.50
double/twin from £185
suite/master bedroom from £330
ivy cottage from £510

THE GRANGE AT OBORNE

OBORNE, NR SHERBORNE, DORSET DT9 4LA

This 200-year-old house nestles peacefully in formal gardens, just 1½ miles from historic Sherborne. Guests are welcomed by owners Jennifer Mathews and Jon Fletcher, and can relax in each of the 10 well-appointed and spacious bedrooms, all with modern facilities. Dinner is served in a most pleasant ambience, overlooking the attractive floodlit gardens. As its AA Rosette attests, the restaurant specialises in both international and traditional cuisine. For those planning an event or occasion the hotel can provide a service for up to 120 guests, and is also suited to conferences and business meetings. This quiet haven is a most ideal escape from city life, and visitors will be able to unwind with horse riding, fishing or simply taking in the local scenery. Air enthusiasts are not to be left out and will be pleased to hear that the Fleet Aviation Museum can be found nearby. Keen golfers may use the golf course in close proximity to the hotel. Popular daytime excursions include visits to the impressive 8th-century abbey at Sherborne, and 2 castles, one built by Sir Walter Raleigh. The lovely Dorset coast and many National Trust properties are within easy reach.

Directions: Oborne can be found just off the A30 in between Sherborne and Milborne Port

Web: www.johansens.com/grangesherborne
E-mail: reception@thegrangeatoborne.co.uk
Tel: 0870 381 9240
International: +44 (0)1935 813463
Fax: 01935 817464

Price Guide:
single from £85
double from £98

Our inspector loved: *The very relaxing atmosphere created by the new owners.*

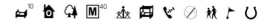

KEMPS COUNTRY HOTEL & RESTAURANT

EAST STOKE, WAREHAM, DORSET BH20 6AL

Small and welcoming Kemps Country Hotel is situated in unspoilt Dorset countryside, overlooking the Valley of the River Frome and the Purbeck Hills beyond. The hills provide the backdrop to the extraordinary Jurassic Coast, which now has World Heritage status. Once a Victorian Rectory, the hotel provides a comfortable and relaxed atmosphere in which to enjoy your stay. There are 2 lounges and a bar. Real log fires burn in winter, in summer the garden terrace is ideal for an aperitif. The bedrooms are set out in 3 locations: the Main House, the Garden Wing, where all the rooms are at ground floor level, and The Old Coach House. Superior rooms have Whirlpool Baths and 1 room has a Four Poster Bed. The pretty restaurant and conservatory has been awarded an AA rosette for excellent food. Most of the food produce is sourced locally with fish and seafood from the nearby coast and excellent local downland Lamb and Beef, whilst Dorset Dairy Products are legendary. Bargain Breaks are available all year. Places of interest nearby include Lulworth Castle, Corfe Castle, Athelhampton House and Gardens, Monkey World and The Tank Museum.

Our inspector loved: Delicious food in a delightful conservatory setting.

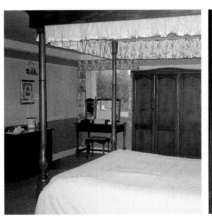

Directions: Situated in its own grounds on the A352 between Wareham and Wool.

Web: www.johansens.com/kemps
E-mail: stay@kempshotel.com
Tel: 0870 381 8647
International: +44 (0)1929 462563
Fax: 01929 405287

Price Guide:
single £69–£83
double/twin £94–£140

THE PUMP HOUSE APARTMENT

132 CHURCH STREET, GREAT BURSTEAD, ESSEX CM11 2TR

Directions: Leave M25 at Jct29 and join A127. Travel in direction of Southend, then turn onto A176 (Noak Hill Road) towards Billericay. Church Street is on the right, the Pump House on the left before the church.

Web: www.johansens.com/pumphouse
E-mail: johnwbayliss@btinternet.com
Tel: 0870 381 8842
International: +44 (0)1277 656579
Fax: 01277 631160

Price Guide:
£425–£950 per week
Short breaks available

Situated in picturesque rural South East England, the Pump House Apartment is an immaculate 2-storey apartment in the village of Great Burstead. Spacious and fully equipped it is an extremely comfortable home from home. Part of a modern house, Pump House is set in its own secluded gardens, with an oriental pond and paddocks. Visitors can avail of an outdoor swimming pool heated to 80 degrees from May to September, and a new, full-sized hot tub/spa set in a glazed Canadian Redwood Gazebo, located in a suntrap walled courtyard with a decorative fountain. The house is very flexible and the air-conditioned Apartment can be let as a 1, 2 or 3-bedroom residence. 2-beautifully appointed lounges are available in addition to an elegant dining room and well designed kitchen with views over the pretty gardens. The village of Great Burstead is steeped in history, and its 14th-century church has links with one of the Pilgrim Fathers and early settlers of the USA. London is 30 minutes by train; Cambridge, Canterbury, Colchester and the Constable Country are within a 1-hour drive. Country walks are a pleasure, and golf, tennis and badminton are among the many sports available nearby.

Our inspector loved: *The big hot tub in its gazebo in the suntrap walled garden.*

THE CROWN HOUSE

GREAT CHESTERFORD, SAFFRON WALDEN, ESSEX CB10 1NY

This Georgian hotel and restaurant, a restored coaching inn, or "restaurant with rooms", is set within beautiful gardens in the pretty village of Great Chesterford. The building is truly historic; the front is built on a 4th-century Roman wall and several priest holes have been preserved. Oak-panelled walls and flagstone floors enhance the warm and friendly atmosphere, and there is one of only two oriel windows in the area. Glowing fires add to the warmth in winter, whilst comfortable leather chairs in the lounge/bar create a welcoming ambience. The luxurious, individually designed bedrooms are all en suite and provide all modern comforts. The restaurant serves exquisite, innovative dishes, like the braised Scottish salmon with cucumber & ginger relish, herb polenta & cumin straw potatoes. Guests can enjoy the extensive menu, which is complemented by a carefully chosen wine list, in the intimate dining room or the vine-clad conservatory. The historic market town of Saffron Walden with its antiques shops, museum and castle is worth a visit, as are nearby Cambridge, Newmarket racecourse, Audley End and Duxford Air Museum. Stansted airport is within easy reach.

Our inspector loved: The double bath and big bathroom of The Crown Room.

Directions: Situated on B1383 leaving M11 at either Junction 9 or 10.

Web: www.johansens.com/crownhouse
Tel: 0870 381 8465
International: +44 (0)1799 530515 / 530257
Fax: 01799 530683

Price Guide: (per person)
single £55–£69.50
double/twin £39.75–£60

THE MISTLEY THORN

HIGH STREET, MISTLEY, COLCHESTER CO11 1HE

Directions: From Colchester (A12) take A120 in direction of Harwich, then follow signs for Manningtree.

Web: www.johansens.com/mistleythorn
E-mail: info@mistleythorn.co.uk
Tel: 0870 381 9347
International: +44 (0)1206 392821
Fax: 01206 390122

Price Guide:
single from £60
double from £70

This delightful, recently opened inn is located in the bustling Georgian port town of Mistley and welcomes guests with its friendly, relaxed atmosphere, which it owes to its new Anglo-Californian owners, Sherri Singleton and David McKay. Mistley was originally destined to be a spa town, and Robert Adam's designs are still evident in several buildings, one of them the Mistley Thorn. Reputedly built on the site where Mathew Hopkins held the famous witch trials, the recently completely restored inn is very much a meeting spot for locals and non-residents who appreciate the good food and excellent drinks menu. Sherri is an award-winning chef and uses only the best seasonal and local ingredients including fish from the East Coast. She also runs the "Mistley Kitchen", a series of hands-on culinary workshops. Classic Georgian colours enhance the elegant ambience of the public rooms, whilst more contemporary furnishings and excellent displays of work by modern artists add a modern feel. The 5 spacious bedrooms all offer large beds and every modern facility; 2 have lovely views of the Stour Estuary. The inn is ideally located for touring "Constable Country", and only a short drive from the Roman garrison town of Colchester. Guests can explore numerous artists' studios, walk along the waterside into Manningtree and go boating and birdwatching.

Our inspector loved: *The sculptural swan surveying the river view.*

THE CRICKETERS' ARMS

THE INN ON THE GREEN, RICKLING GREEN, SAFFRON WALDEN, ESSEX CB11 3YG

The epitome of an English country inn, the Cricketer's Arms is set on the boundary of the cricket pitch on the village green in Rickling Green. The 18th-century inn has been completely refurbished by its new owners, who have maintained the cosy, traditional ambience and authentic character but added a few contemporary touches. An open fire, beams and flagged floors blend with the sun streaming through onto pale walls, pine furnishings and leather sofas, and fresh flowers and original artworks abound. Guests can take a drink in the real ale bar, before enjoying dinner and fine wines from the excellent cellar in one of 2 restaurants, whilst in the warmer months, the Japanese-style terraced garden is the perfect setting for alfresco dining or a drink. There is a separate room for private dining, business meetings and small functions, accommodating up to 12 people. Individually decorated, ranging from colonial, quaint with beams, to sleek and modern, the newly refurbished bedrooms have superb handmade English beds and lavish polished chrome and porcelain fittings in the en-suite bathrooms. The inn is near to the market town of Saffron Walden and the Jacobean jewel Audley End House. The university city of Cambridge with its many attractions and horse racing at Newmarket are within half an hour's drive.

Our inspector loved: The decked patio with lots of plants and intimate seating areas.

Directions: From M11 J8 take A120 West to B1383. Go through Stansted Mountfitchet; carry on for another 5 miles. Only 8 miles from Stansted Airport.

Web: www.johansens.com/cricketersarms
E-mail: reservations@cricketers.demon.co.uk
Tel: 0870 381 9351
International: +44 (0)1799 543210
Fax: 01799 543512

Price Guide:
single £75
double £95–£125

81

BIBURY COURT

BIBURY COURT, BIBURY, GLOUCESTERSHIRE GL7 5NT

Directions: Bibury is on the B4425, 7 miles from Burford and 7 miles from Cirencester.

Web: www.johansens.com/biburycourt
E-mail: info@biburycourt.com
Tel: 0870 381 8360
International: +44 (0)1285 740337
Fax: 01285 740660

Gloucester
Cheltenham

Cirencester

Price Guide:
single from £125
double from £145
suite £220

Past visitors to Bibury Court are reputed to have included Charles II and during the reign of George III, the Prince Regent. This gracious mansion dates from Tudor times, but the main part was built in 1633 by Sir Thomas Sackville, an illegitimate son of the 1st Earl of Dorset. After generations of illustrious owners, it became a hotel in 1968. The great house is set on the outskirts of Bibury, which William Morris called "the most beautiful village in England". As a hotel, it is run on country house lines with one of the main objectives being the provision of good food and wine in informal and pleasurable surroundings. Log fires during the cooler months add to the comfort of guests. There are some lovely panelled rooms in the house, many containing antique furniture. Many of the bedrooms have four-posters, all have private bathrooms and for those who like greater privacy there is the Sackville suite. Trout fishing is available in the Coln, which forms the southern boundary of the hotel's 6 acres of grounds, and there are golf courses at Burford and Cirencester. Water sports and riding are available nearby. Bibury Court is ideally placed for touring the Cotswolds, while Stratford, Oxford, Cheltenham and Bath are all within easy reach.

Our inspector loved: *Comfortable and very relaxing. A real home from home in idyllic surroundings.*

CHARLTON KINGS HOTEL

CHARLTON KINGS, CHELTENHAM, GLOUCESTERSHIRE GL52 6UU

Surrounded by the Cotswold Hills, on the outskirts of Cheltenham but just a few minutes by car to the heart of town, stands Charlton Kings Hotel. If you seek instant peace and solitude, follow the footpath running alongside the Hotel into the beautiful Cotswold countryside. The famous 'Cotswold Way' escarpment walk passes just ½ mile away. Quality, comfort and friendliness are the hallmarks of this lovely Hotel. All of the rooms have been beautifully refurbished and most boast views of the Coltswold Hills and countryside. Standard rooms offer a high degree of comfort while deluxe rooms are much larger with many upgraded facilities ideal for a longer stay or that special occasion. The restaurant offers a variety of dishes to satisfy the most discerning of diners and requests from vegetarians or vegans can be readily accommodated. The enthusiastic and experienced staff have a great knowledge of the surrounding area which enables them to recommend and help plan guests' visits to places of interest, local events and entertainment. Cheltenham Spa is famous for its architecture, festivals and racing, there is also plenty on offer in the way of theatres, restaurants as well as a distinguished selection of shops. To the north, east and south lie numerous charming Cotswold villages and to the west the Forest of Dean, Wye Valley, Malvern Hills and much more.

Directions: The Hotel is the first property on the left coming into Cheltenham from Oxford on the A40 (the 'Welcome to Cheltenham' Boundary Sign is located in the front garden!). M5 junction 11, 5 miles

Gloucester
Cheltenham
Cirencester

Web: www.johansens.com/charltonkings
E-mail: enquiries@charltonkingshotel.co.uk
Tel: 0870 381 8416
International: +44 (0)1242 231061
Fax: 01242 241900

Price Guide:
single £58.50–£85
double £76–£120

Our inspector loved: *The well-appointed bedrooms and pretty garden.*

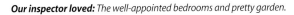

THE MALT HOUSE

BROAD CAMPDEN, GLOUCESTERSHIRE GL55 6UU

Directions: The Malt House is in the centre of the village of Broad Campden, which is just a mile from Chipping Campden.

Web: www.johansens.com/malthouse
E-mail: info@the–malt–house.freeserve.co.uk
Tel: 0870 381 8714
International: +44 (0)1386 840295
Fax: 01386 841334

Price Guide:
single £85
double £120–£130
suite £145–£160

This beautiful 17th-century Cotswold home stands in the idyllic, quintessential English village of Broad Campden. Behind its modest golden stone roadside face The Malt House hides beautiful gardens, an orchard, stream, croquet lawn and brook. The house boasts many awards for its standard of accommodation and meals, and the rooms, including residents' sitting rooms, feature comfortable, cosy furnishings and antiques together with fresh flowers in abundance throughout the house. All bedrooms and suites are individually decorated and most overlook the wide lawns. From the quaint summer house terrace croquet and quoits may be watched whilst enjoying a leisurely drink before taking dinner in one of the many restaurants, bistros and public houses within walking distance. Dinner for parties of 12 or more can be prepared by arrangement only. The Cotswold English breakfasts, which include local brown eggs, figs in season and home baked breads. dinner is by arrangement for exclusive use of the hotel. Nearby places to visit include Hidcote Manor Gardens (NT), Chipping Campden Church, the Cotswolds, Cheltenham, Stratford-upon-Avon, Oxford and Bath, plus many markets, galleries, antique and gift shops to visit.

Our inspector loved: *This beautiful Cotswold house with Judi as a welcoming host.*

THE WILD DUCK INN

DRAKES ISLAND, EWEN, CIRENCESTER, GLOUCESTERSHIRE GL7 6BY

Here is a typical, lovely little picture postcard hotel; warm, welcoming and rich in history. Built of mellow Cotswold stone in the 15th century when Queen Elizabeth I was instigating a network of coaching inns throughout the country, The Wild Duck is as attractive inside as it is outside. Décor and furnishings are rich and elegant, fine old oil portraits adorn the walls, large open log fires enhance the welcoming ambience in winter, windows look out over a secluded garden that is perfect for al fresco dining in summer. Though old in years, the inn has all modern comforts and amenities. Each individually decorated bedroom is en suite and has facilities to suit the most discerning visitor. Some of the rooms are on the ground floor, 2 have four-poster beds. Guests can enjoy a chat over drinks in a cosy bar or oak-panelled lounge before eating in style in the award-winning dining room. Traditional British and European menus offer superb seasonal dishes. In winter, specialities include game and fresh fish, which is delivered overnight from Brixham, Devon. All dishes are complemented by the extensive and excellent wine list. Within a mile of the inn is Cotswold Water Park with 80 lakes providing fishing and a range of water sports. Racing at Cheltenham and polo at Cirencester Park are nearby.

Our inspector loved: The superb selection of wines on offer at this lovely inn full of ambience and character.

Directions: Leave the M4 at junction 17 and follow Cirencester signs. Before the town turn right at Kemble and follow the signs to Ewen.

Web: www.johansens.com/wildduck
E-mail: wduckinn@aol.com
Tel: 0870 381 8997
International: +44 (0)1285 770310
Fax: 01285 770924

Price Guide:
single £70
double/twin £95
four poster £120
chinese suite £150

NEW INN AT COLN

COLN ST-ALDWYNS, NR CIRENCESTER, GLOUCESTERSHIRE GL7 5AN

Directions: From Burford (A40), take B4425 to Bibury, turn left after Aldsworth.

Web: www.johansens.com/newinnatcoln
E-mail: stay@new-inn.co.uk
Tel: 0870 381 8758
International: +44 (0)1285 750651
Fax: 01285 750657

Price Guide:
single £90–£104
double £120–£155

In days of yore, when Queen Elizabeth I was giving royal assent to the import of tobacco from the new-found Americas, she was also initiating a travel boom in England, by instigating a network of coaching inns after the pattern already set on the Continent. One of the Cotswold inns that her initiative helped to create was the New Inn At Coln St-Aldwyns on Akeman Street, the old Roman Road, leading east out of Cirencester. The New Inn At Coln, though old in years, is today utterly new in spirit, winning ever fresh awards for food and hospitality – its 2 Rosettes being in permanent flower as a second Queen Elizabeth reigns. Now under the ownership of Roger and Angela Kimmett, the New Inn At Coln has blossomed and the considerable skills of the kitchen add a gastronomic dimension to the charm and comfort of the ancient but cleverly modernised bedrooms – perfect accommodation for an idyllic week in the Cotswolds, a useful stopover or as a timely resting place after a fine dinner. For the business-minded, there is a charming meeting room. Close to this picturesque Cotswolds base are Stratford-upon-Avon, Bath, Oxford and Cheltenham and within healthy walking distance is Bibury with its photogenic Arlington Row.

Our inspector loved: The warm, friendly welcome and home from home feel.

LOWER BROOK HOUSE

BLOCKLEY, NR MORETON-IN-MARSH, GLOUCESTERSHIRE GL56 9DS

This delightful stone 17th-century house stands serenely in the heart of a beautifully kept village that is one of the Cotswolds best kept secrets. Blockley is a conservation area within a designated Area of Outstanding Natural Beauty that maintains the peace and quiet of a bygone era with its wisteria covered cottages, dovecotes in picturesque gardens and babbling brook meandering down to the village and through the garden of Lower Brook House. The brook once provided power for 12 mills, 6 of which are the names of the hotel's guest rooms. The caring owners have done everything imaginable to make these rooms as comfortable as possible; all are en suite, individually and tastefully furnished and offer every facility from television to fluffy bathrobes and homemade biscuits. 2 have four-poster beds and most have views over the village, with its 12th-century church, and onwards to the glorious countryside. A large, deep open fireplace is the centrepiece of the relaxing lounge, a favourite with guests who enjoy a social chat and apèritif before relishing the imaginative cuisine served in the highly acclaimed dining room. Local attractions include the Wildfowl Trust at Slimbridge and the Roman Villa at Chedworth. Blenheim, Warwick, Cheltenham and Bath are within easy reach.

Our inspector loved: This lovely Cotswold stone house with pretty garden and warm welcome from hosts Julian and Anna.

Directions: Located in the village of Blockley just off the A44, between Moreton-in-Marsh and Broadway.

Web: www.johansens.com/lowerbrookhouse
E-mail: info@lowerbrookhouse.com
Tel: 0870 381 9297
International: +44 (0)1386 700286
Fax: 01386 700286

Price Guide:
single £80–£145
double £80–£145

THREE CHOIRS VINEYARDS ESTATE

NEWENT, GLOUCESTERSHIRE GL18 1LS

Directions: From the A40 take B4215 to Newent. Follow brown heritage signs to vineyard.

Web: www.johansens.com/threechoirs
E-mail: ts@threechoirs.com
Tel: 0870 381 8946
International: +44 (0)1531 890223
Fax: 01531 890877

Price Guide:
single £75
double £95–£105

Three choirs is a 70-acre vineyard in the heart of the Gloucestershire countryside, and a rising star in English wine making. New this year are 8 beautifully appointed bedrooms in an idyllic location perched high on the vine terraces overlooking the estate below. Each has a private patio that catches the evening sun – a perfect spot to sip a chilled glass of wine chosen from the day's tasting. Comfortable beds and invigorating power showers will ensure a good night's sleep and refreshing start to the next day's lesson in vine cultivation! The emphasis at Three Choirs is on informality and the local staff offer the warmest of welcomes and cater for your every need during your stay. A wide-ranging menu of delicious and beautifully presented food accompanies the wines with tempting dishes like tartlet of avocado pear, tomato and cured ham with single Gloucester cheese and spiced fillets of black bream with marinated vegetables and coriander cream, and there is a good choice of vegetarian dishes. In addition to the wine tasting tour and exhibition on site, there is the Three Choirs Music Festival and Eastnor Castle to visit, and golf and riding can all be arranged nearby.

Our inspector loved: The comfortable rooms, all with a terrace overlooking the rolling vineyards .

NEW

THE SNOOTY FOX

MARKET PLACE, TETBURY, GLOUCESTERSHIRE GL8 8DD

Set in the heart of picturesque Tetbury in the Cotswolds, this quintessential 16th-century coaching inn exudes character and charm. The carefully restored mellow stone building has retained many of its original features yet has all the modern comforts one would expect from a luxurious country hotel. A traditional stone walled bar is cosy with a large inglenook fireplace and serves traditional cask conditioned ales and fine beers to locals and residents alike. Hearty, homegrown food is produced with flair and imagination in the informal Bistro restaurant. It is open all day and serves lunchtime snacks, evening meals and cream teas. Intimate bedrooms are delightful and individually appointed with wonderful attention to detail and period finesse. There are 2 four-poster rooms and all feature en-suite bathrooms. The Snooty Fox is an ideal base for visiting the many stately homes and beautiful villages in the Cotswolds. Tetbury is a pretty town of enormous historical interest with many antique shops and the royal Highgrove Estate of Prince Charles is located nearby. Cirencester, Cheltenham and Bath are a short drive away and well worth the visit.

Our inspector loved: The welcoming, informal atmosphere.

Directions: From junctions 17 or 18 of the M4, or junction 13 of the M5, follow signs to Tetbury. The Snooty Fox is in the market place within the centre of town.

Web: www.johansens.com/snootyfox
E-mail: mg@snooty-fox.co.uk
Tel: 0870 381 9306
International: +44 (0)1666 502436
Fax: 01666 503479

Price Guide:
single £69–£129
double £89–£199

THATCHED COTTAGE HOTEL & RESTAURANT

16 BROOKLEY ROAD, BROCKENHURST, NEW FOREST, HAMPSHIRE SO42 7RR

Directions: M27, Jct1, drive south on A337 through Lyndhurst, in Brockenhurst turn right before level crossing.

Web: www.johansens.com/thatchedcottagebrockenhurst
E-mail: sales@thatchedcottage.co.uk
Tel: 0870 381 8943
International: +44 (0)1590 623090
Fax: 01590 623479

Price Guide:
single from £70
double £90–£160
suite £160–£175

Basingstoke

Winchester

Southampton

Portsmouth

Lymington

The enchanting Thatched Cottage was built in 1627 and recently carefully transformed into this boutique hotel by the Matysik family, who have over a century's worth of experience in the hotel industry. Set in one of the prettiest villages in the New Forest, modernisation has not detracted from its original charm. The individually decorated double bedrooms have a unique Old World warmth, each room featuring either a four-poster bed, open hearth gas fire place or a Turkish steam shower. Breakfast includes 6 different options to choose from and is served until 11am. Lunch or award-winning afternoon tea can be enjoyed in the relaxing garden, whilst a cosy beamed lounge is the ideal place for an apéritif before entering into the exquisite dining room, offering delights from the New Forest such as wild mushrooms and New Forest venison. All dishes are freshly prepared in an open-plan kitchen starring "the chefs on show". An à la carte menu and set menus are presented with flair and imagination in a relaxing ambience by candlelight in what has aptly been named "A Cottage for the Happy Few". The cuisine has won numerous awards and is acclaimed by the British and international press. Nearby attractions include Beaulieu Motor Museum, Exbury Gardens, the Isle of Wight, Winchester and Salisbury.

Our inspector loved: *The stylish and hospitable provision for gusts' every need.*

    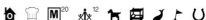

LE POUSSIN AT WHITLEY RIDGE

BEAULIEU ROAD, BROCKENHURST, NEW FOREST, HAMPSHIRE SO42 7QL

Set in 5 acres of secluded parkland in the heart of the New Forest, this privately owned Georgian house was once a Royal hunting lodge visited by the Queen Mother. Today it has the ambience of a true country house with the accent on relaxation. The bedrooms are individually decorated, and most have lovely views over open forest. The public rooms are similarly luxurious and elegant and log fires burn on cool evenings. Internationally acclaimed chef patron Alex Aitken has re-located his famous Le Poussin restaurant, awarded a Michelin Star and 3 AA Rosettes, in to Whitley Ridge whilst nearby Parkhill undergoes extensive refurbishment and expansion; his innovative, imaginative cuisine is a joy not to be missed. Guests can relax in the grounds or enjoy a game of tennis. Some of the country's best woodland walks are directly accessible from the gardens. Whichever pastime you choose, Whitley Ridge guarantees a restful and enjoyable stay. A number of stately homes, including Broadlands and Wilton House, are within easy reach. Lord Montague's Motor Museum, Buckler's Hard and historic Stonehenge are also within driving distance

Our inspector loved: The very tranquil setting at the heart of the New Forest. Attention to detail is a keynote here.

Directions: M27 junction 1. Situated on the B3055, Brockenhurst – Beaulieu.

Web: www.johansens.com/whitleyridge
E-mail: whitleyridge@brockenhurst.co.uk
Tel: 0870 381 8994
International: +44 (0)1590 622354
Fax: 01590 622856

Price Guide:
single from £65
double £110–£140
suite £140–£150

THE MILL AT GORDLETON

SILVER STREET, HORDLE, NR LYMINGTON, NEW FOREST, HAMPSHIRE SO41 6DJ

Tucked away in the verdant countryside between the New Forest National Park and the sea lies this idyllic ivy-clad 17th-century rural hideaway. Immaculately restored to its former glory, yet boasting every modern convenience, the Mill at Gordleton must now be considered one of the most tasteful of Hampshire's many fine inns. The landscaped gardens epitomise rustic charm, and visitors weary of their hectic urban lifestyles will surely find peace in the garden and mill pond with its charming sluice gates. The inn is no less immaculate inside. The intimate restaurant, overlooking the river and serving succulent fare, is simply a delight. Bedrooms are being refurbished in a most stylish way with quite delightful bathrooms. Nearby attractions include the Cistercian Abbey at Bealieu and and the more contemporary yacht ports of Hamble Point and Hythe Marina Village. The villages of Sway, Brockenhurst and Bucklers Hard - with their bustling pubs – are also worth a visit.

Directions: M27, junction 1. A337 south for 11 miles near Lymington after the railway bridge and mini roundabout turn sharp right before Toll House Inn, head towards Hordle and inn is on right after about 1½ miles.

Web: www.johansens.com/gordletonmill
E-mail: bookings@gordletonmill.co.uk
Tel: 0870 381 8558
International: +44 (0)1590 682219
Fax: 01590 683073

Price Guide:
single from £85
double/Twin £120
suite £175

Our inspector loved: *This fabulous New Forest hideaway and the abundant wild life in the gardens.*

THE NURSE'S COTTAGE

STATION ROAD, SWAY, LYMINGTON, NEW FOREST, HAMPSHIRE SO41 6BA

This remarkable little house is centrally situated in a quiet village on the southern edge of the New Forest. For nearly 70 years home to Sway's successive District Nurses, it is now a 4-bedroom hotel. The level of visitor provision cannot fail to impress, and chef proprietor Tony Barnfield's dedication to guests' comfort and enjoyment of their stay ensures an exceptional level of repeat visits. A worthy winner of the Best Breakfast in Britain Award, the hotel guarantees a good start to the day. At dinner, Tony and his young team offer both "Classic British" and "House Speciality" menu choices, served with style in the conservatory restaurant, overlooking the garden. The award-winning wine list with over 60 bins puts much larger hotels to shame and surprises with many in half bottles and no less than 13 by the glass. All bedrooms are on the ground floor and have CD and video players and refrigerators housing complimentary fruit juices, mineral water and fresh milk. Fruit, biscuits and Beaulieu chocolates add to the pampered feeling. The sparkling bright and warm bathrooms offer a generous array of toiletries. Non-smoking throughout. Places of interest nearby include the National Motor Museum at Beaulieu, Rothschild's Exbury Gardens and the yachting town of Lymington.

Our inspector loved: Tony Barnfield's never ending pursuit of perfection.

Directions: From M27 Jct1 take A337 to Brockenhurst and then B3055 signed to New Milton. The Nurse's Cottage is next door to Sway Post Office.

Web: www.johansens.com/nursescottage
E-mail: nurses.cottage@lineone.net
Tel: 0870 381 8774
International: +44 (0)1590 683402
Fax: 01590 683402

Price Guide: (including dinner)
single £75
double £140–£150
twin £150

LANGRISH HOUSE

LANGRISH, NR PETERSFIELD, HAMPSHIRE GU32 1RN

Standing in 12 acres of beautiful mature grounds including a picturesque lake, Langrish House combines the welcoming ambience of a traditional country house with the facilities expected from a modern hotel. Extended by the present owner's forbears in 1842, it opened as a hotel in 1979 and remains very much a family home. Today, new life is being breathed into the house by Nigel and Robina Talbot-Ponsonby, whose family portraits and heirlooms adorn the rooms. Each of the bedrooms overlooks the grounds, giving guests ample opportunity to savour Langrish's peace and tranquillity. All are fully equipped with en-suite bathrooms, direct-dial telephones, colour televisions and many thoughtful touches. Frederick's Restaurant, affords glorious views of the lawns and surrounding countryside. Fresh regional produce features in the superb cuisine, which has won the house AA recognition for fine dining. Langrish House is an ideal venue for wedding receptions and business conferences and offers dining facilities for up to 100 people. This is an excellent base for touring the Hampshire countryside: Gilbert White's Selbourne, Jane Austen's Chawton, Goodwood and Cowdray Park are close by.

Directions: Follow A272 from the M3/A31 at Winchester (16 miles) or from A3 at Petersfield (3 miles). Langrish House is signposted from the village on the road to East Meon.

Web: www.johansens.com/langrishhouse
E-mail: frontdesk@langrishhouse.co.uk
Tel: 0870 381 8679
International: +44 (0)1730 266941
Fax: 01730 260543

Price Guide:
single £65.70–£73
double £104–£124
suite £126–£140

Basingstoke

Winchester

Southampton

Portsmouth

Lymington

Our inspector loved: The ambience of this fine English manor house.

RHYDSPENCE INN

WHITNEY-ON-WYE, NEAR HAY-ON-WYE, HEREFORDSHIRE HR3 6EU

This 14th-century inn is set in the heart of Kilvert country and features several times in the works of the celebrated diarist. A striking half-timbered building, it has been tastefully extended to create an attractive dining room overlooking a well-kept garden. The bedrooms are individually furnished in time honoured style and all afford scenic views of the Wye Valley and the Black Mountains. The 2 welcoming bars have exposed beams and open fires typical of traditional inns and both serve draught ale and cider on tap. Closed for 2 weeks in January. An exceptionally well-balanced à la carte menu offers the best of country fare and international cuisine. Advantage is taken of the abundance of fresh local produce with Hereford beef, Welsh lamb, fresh fish and seasonally available game among the choices on the frequently changing menu. The sweet trolley offers a delicious array of puddings. Snacks, both the traditional and more unusual, are served in the bar. Private parties can be catered for. The area is a paradise for nature lovers; riding, pony-trekking, caving, wind-surfing and canoeing on the River Wye are all available, and Hay-on-Wye, famous for its second-hand bookshops, is close by. For walkers, Offa's Dyke Path passes near to the inn.

Our inspector loved: *The warm and cosy atmosphere of the traditional Inn with it's log fire glowing throughout the year.*

Directions: Located on the A483 Brecon to Hereford road just past Whitney - on- Wye on the Brecon side .

Web: www.johansens.com/rhydspence
E-mail: info@rhydspence-inn.co.uk
Tel: 0870 381 9156
International: +44 (0)1497 831262
Fax: 01497 831751

Price Guide:
single £45–£55
double £75–£85

THE VERZON

HEREFORD ROAD, TRUMPET, NR LEDBURY, HEREFORDSHIRE HR8 2PZ

Directions: 3 miles west of Ledbury on the A438.

Web: www.johansens.com/theverzon
E-mail: info@theverzon.co.uk
Tel: 0870 381 9348
International: +44 (0)1531 670381
Fax: 01531 670830

Price Guide:
single £60–£75
double £78–£110
suite £130

Conveniently located 3 miles west of the historic market town of Ledbury, this imposing Georgian country house dates back to 1790 and stands in over 4 acres of breathtaking rural countryside. New owners David and Gillian Pinchbeck took over the management in February 2004 and have since embarked on a programme of complete renovation with an emphasis on quality and comfort. The ambience is modern, yet welcoming and homely, and the friendly staff offer a personal, unobtrusive service. Guests can curl up with the paper on comfortable sofas in the lounge, which is warmed by an open fire on chilly days. The bedrooms, many of which have original fireplaces, have crisp white Egyptian percale sheets and luxurious goose down duvets and pamper guests with Molton Brown bath products. Guests can take a pre-dinner drink in the Mulberry Bar before sitting down to enjoy clean modern cuisine in the light and airy Terrace Brasserie. On sunny days the stunning new deck terrace with breathtaking views of the Malvern Hills provides the perfect setting for alfresco dining or a relaxing drink. The hotel is ideally located for exploring the cathedral cities of Hereford, Gloucester and Worcester, and is close to numerous areas of outstanding beauty. The Three Counties showground in Malvern is only a short drive away.

Our inspector loved: *The stunning deck terrace adjacent to the restaurant overlooking the hotel gardens.*

FORD ABBEY

PUDLESTON, NR LEOMINSTER, HEREFORDSHIRE HR6 0RZ

Set deep in the Herefordshire countryside and surrounded by beautiful landscaped gardens, Ford Abbey stands in 320 acres of private, sheltered land. Modern luxury and comfort are combined with the traditional framework of this former Benedictine Abbey, which still maintains its original timber beams and weathered stone. Ford Abbey's 4 de luxe barn lodges are perfectly located for couples or families wishing to explore the surrounding countryside, which is the least developed in England, and the homely accommodation provides a welcoming base to return to. Each lodge has its own kitchen with every cooking and washing facility required together with cutlery, glass, tableware and linen. Alternatively, guests may stay in the main residence and enjoy bed and breakfast service. All bedrooms feature en-suite bathroom and the Abbott Suite has been specifically designed for guests with disabilities. Ford Abbey's restaurant serves fresh organic produce from Ford Abbey Farm and prides itself on the high standard of its food and fine collection of wines and malts on offer. The fitness room is situated opposite the lodges where a heated swimming pool enables guests to relax and unwind after a day's treck around the grounds or visit to one of the many nearby places of interest.

Our inspector loved: *The attention to detail throughout and magnificent retsoration and furnishings.*

Directions: Take the A49 towards Hereford then the A44 to Bromyard. Ford Abbey is signposted off to the left.

Web: www.johansens.com/fordabbey
E-mail: info@fordabbey.co.uk
Tel: 0870 381 9144
International: +44 (0)1568 760700
Fax: 01568 760264

Price Guide:
double/twin from £115
suite from £210

THE PILGRIM HOTEL

MUCH BIRCH, HEREFORD HR2 8HJ

Directions: Located on the main road A49 midway between Hereford and Ross-on-Wye, and just 9 miles from J4 of the M50.

Web: www.johansens.com/pilgrimhotel
E-mail: stay@pilgrimhotel.co.uk
Tel: 0870 381 9335
International: +44 (0)1981 540742
Fax: 01981 540620

Price Guide:
single £65
double £85–£125

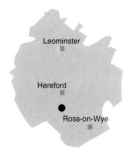

Surrounded by 4 acres of peaceful rolling parkland hills, this delightful Victorian country house is the ideal place for a relaxing break or a small meeting or conference. The house, which is set on the ancient pilgrims' route to the shrine of St Ethelbert in Hereford, was originally built as a vicarage in 1870, and later converted into a country house hotel and extended further in the 1970s. A cosy lounge with open fireplace and large windows invites guests to relax or have afternoon tea, whilst the bar with its beamed ceilings is ideal for a pre-dinner drink. 20 spacious en-suite bedrooms are equipped with all modern amenities; some have four-poster beds and views of the Herefordshire countryside towards the Black Mountains. Overlooking the gardens, the Pilgrim Restaurant is the perfect setting for a romantic dinner. 2 chefs create a varied and imaginative menu, based on fresh local produce, such as Herefordshire beef and salmon from the river Wye. The hotel offers a variety of short themed breaks, such as painting breaks and mind and body weekends. This is the ideal base for touring the Wye Valley, with the Royal Forest of Dean, the villages of Herefordshire and Symonds Yat all within easy reach.

Our inspector loved: *The very friendly welcome and the rolling parkland surrounding the hotel.*

Wilton Court Hotel
WILTON, ROSS-ON-WYE, HEREFORDSHIRE HR9 6AQ

Offering abundant peace and tranquillity on the banks of the River Wye, this property is a true gem, surrounded by walled gardens with mature shrubs, sloping lawns and an enchanting river. Leaded windows and stone mullions are some of the many vestiges of the hotel's 15th-century origins. Affording a view of either the gardens or the river, the recently refurbished en-suite bedrooms are well-appointed, complete with hardryer, alarm clock radio, tea and coffee making facilities, direct dial telephones and video teletext televisions. Guests may dine in the cosy bar, with its warm fire in winter, the light conservatory rosette awarded Mulberry Restaurant with its view of the gardens or enjoy meals alfresco. The very best of fresh local produce is used wherever possible. Sports enthusiasts will be pleased with the local facilities which include canoeing, salmon fishing on the River Wye, horse riding, ballooning, tennis, cycling, bowling and golf. The hotel has ample car parking and is within walking distance from the bustling streets of Ross on Wye with its 16th-century market place. Tintern Abbey, The Malvern Hills, the Forest of Dean and The Cotswolds are some of the many areas that are worth exploring.

Our inspector loved: A little gem in a fabulous setting right on the river.

Directions: From the M50, exit at junction 4 and turn into Ross at the junction of A40 and A49. Take the first right turning before the Wye River Bridge. The hotel is on the right facing the river.

Web: www.johansens.com/wiltoncourthotel
E-mail: info@wiltoncourthotel.com
Tel: 0870 381 9000
International: +44 (0)44 (0)1989 562569
Fax: +44 (0)1989 768460

Price Guide:
single £60–£85
double £80–£115
suite £115–£145

99

GLEWSTONE COURT

NR ROSS-ON-WYE, HEREFORDSHIRE HR9 6AW

Directions: From M50 junction 4 follow A40 signposted Monmouth. 1 mile past Wilton roundabout turn right to Glewstone; the Court is ½ mile on left.

Web: www.johansens.com/glewstonecourt
E-mail: glewstone@aol.com
Tel: 0870 381 8556
International: +44 (0)1989 770367
Fax: 01989 770282

Price Guide:
single £50-£68-£85
double £85-£104-£120

Leominster

Hereford

Ross-on-Wye

Glewstone Court is set in 3 acres of fruit orchards, lawns and flower beds. Although secluded, this refreshingly un-stuffy establishment is only 3 miles from Ross-on-Wye. Furnishings and an eclectic collection of antiques, bric a brac and books reflect the relaxed, hospitable personality of the owners, Christine and Bill Reeve Tucker. Most country pursuits can be arranged, including canoeing, fishing and riding. This is marvellous walking country, alternatively guests may wish to simply laze around in front of the log fires or on fine days, recline out in the garden. Christine's food is always innovative and reflects a love of good fresh local ingredients. Organic and free-range products are used as much as possible on the menu. Featuring both modern and traditional British dishes, the cuisine is always prepared and served with care and attention to detail. Now in their 19th year, accolades awarded include an AA Rosette for good food and the AA Courtesy & Care award. The bedrooms are comfortable and individually decorated. Each has en-suite facilities, a hospitality tray, soft bathrobes, direct dial phone and colour television. Closed Christmas Day and Boxing Day. Places of interest nearby include Ross-on-Wye, Hay-on-Wye, the Welsh Marches, Hereford Cathedral and the Brecon Beacons. Bargain breaks available all year round.

Our inspector loved: *An informal, cosy and welcoming house in lovely grounds.*

REDCOATS FARMHOUSE HOTEL AND RESTAURANT

REDCOATS GREEN, NEAR HITCHIN, HERTFORDSHIRE SG4 7JR

This 15th-century farmhouse has been owned by the Butterfield family for generations, and in 1971, Peter and his sister converted it into a hotel. Set in tranquil gardens, within rolling countryside, yet not far from the A1(M), traditional character with its original beams, exposed brickwork and inglenook fireplaces feature alongside comfortable, inviting furnishings. There are 3 dining rooms; the Oak Room with its beams, oak panelling and log fires in winter, oozing 15th-century charm and the elegant Victorian Room. This is the perfect location for intimate wedding parties and smaller conferences and business meetings requiring privacy. Largest of all is the Conservatory with its friendly bustle and views of the beautiful gardens. Redcoats has an excellent reputation for its cuisine, which uses predominantly local produce and a wine list that is as wide-ranging geographically as it is in prices. Fine wines are available by the glass and regular wine tasting sessions are held on the premises. Several historic houses nearby include: Knebworth House, Hatfield House, Wimpole Hall, Woburn Abbey, Wildlife Park and the Shuttleworth collection. The Roman city of St Albans, the traditional market town of Hitchin and Cambridge University are all within a 30-minute drive. Weekend breaks available.

Our inspector loved: The great character with so many of the orignal features retained, and spacious conservatory restaurant in contrast.

Directions: Leave the A1(M) at junction 8 for Little Wymondley. At the mini-roundabout turn left. At the T-Junction turn right and the hotel is on the left.

Web: www.johansens.com/redcoatsfarmhouse
E-mail: sales@redcoats.co.uk
Tel: 0870 381 8851
International: +44 (0)1438 729500
Fax: 01438 723322

Stevenage
Stansted
Bishop's
Stortford
Hertford
St Albans

Price Guide:
single £95–£105
double £107–£125

THE WHITE HOUSE AND LION & LAMB BAR & RESTAURANT

SMITHS GREEN, DUNMOW ROAD, TAKELEY, BISHOP'S STORTFORD, HERTFORDSHIRE CM22 6NR

This delightful 15th-century Grade II listed country manor house is set amidst an acre of lovely gardens and offers first-class accommodation. Recently completely refurbished, all bedrooms have state-of-the-art bathrooms and double aspect windows adding a light and airy feeling to the very attractive and comfortable furnishings. A high-speed wireless Internet connection is available. First-class dining is available at The Lion & Lamb; free transport is offered for the 2-minute drive. Welcoming open fires in the traditional restaurant provide warmth on chilly days, whilst soft lighting and beautiful old blackened oak beams stretching across the ceiling create an intimate atmosphere. Service is professional but relaxed, with an emphasis on the high quality of the food, prepared with fresh ingredients and fish from Billingsgate, and accompanied by fine wines. There are numerous cosy eating areas and a most unusual country-style room with its own terrace and garden available for functions and meetings for up to 25 people. On sunny days the beer garden offers plenty of seating. The White House is conveniently close to Stansted Airport and within easy reach of East Anglia's many attractions. Cambridge and horse racing at Newmarket are also within easy driving distance.

Directions: M11 J8, take B1256 (originally A120) in direction of Takeley. The House is about ¼ mile beyond the traffic lights on the left hand side.

Web: www.johansens.com/whitehousestansted
E-mail: info@whitehousestansted.co.uk
Tel: 0870 381 9334
International: +44 (0)1279 870257
Fax: 01279 870423

Price Guide:
single from £60
double from £75

Our inspector loved: The originality and ingenuity of the bathrooms.

RYLSTONE MANOR

RYLSTONE GARDENS, SHANKLIN, ISLE OF WIGHT PO37 6RE

Neil Graham and Alan Priddle are the proud owners of this hidden gem uniquely located in 4¹/₂ acres of tranquil gardens on the fringe of Shanklin. Just two minutes walk away through the gardens are the promenade and beach and the manor gardens enjoy stunning views out across Shanklin Bay. An atmosphere of comfort and relaxation is engendered in the stylish day rooms where afternoon tea and a good book are just the thing on inclement days. In the restaurant, Neil prepares a nightly table d'hôte menu with an eagle eye on the best available produce and an expert's touch in its preparation. Poached fillet of salmon, roast loin of lamb and breast of duck are served with imaginative, simple sauces. The entire hotel is totally non-smoking; no children under 16 are taken; and dogs are not permitted. Rylstone Manor is truly a haven of peace, in a delightfully protected environment. For the more active, water sports, fishing, riding and golf can all be arranged. In addition to being a walkers' paradise, the island has many other manor houses and gardens to visit. Nearby are the thatched cottages of Shanklin Old Village, Queen Victoria's Osborne House, Carisbrook Castle and Rylstone Gardens Countryside Centre.

Our inspector loved: The very pampered feeling yjat every guest here enjoys.

Directions: Just off the A3055 Sandown to Ventnor road in Shanklin Old Village, follow signs directly into Rylstone Gardens.

Web: www.johansens.com/rylstonemanor
E-mail: rylstonemanor@btinternet.com
Tel: 0870 381 8882
International: +44 (0)1983 862806
Fax: 01983 862806

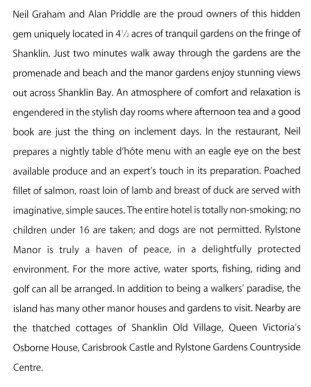

Price Guide:
single from £48
double from £96
half board single from £64
double from £128

THE WELLINGTON HOTEL

BELGRAVE ROAD, VENTNOR, ISLE OF WIGHT PO38 1JH

Directions: Ferry from Portsmouth, Lymington or Southampton to Fishbourne, Yarmouth. Ryde, East or West Cowes. A3054 to Newport, A3055 to Sandown, A5056 to Arreton/Sandown, B3327 to Ventnor.

Web: www.johansens.com/wellington
E-mail: reservations@thewellington.net
Tel: 0870 381 9320
International: +44 (0)1983 856600
Fax: 01983 856611

Price Guide:
single £60–£95
double/twin £90–£135

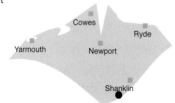

Facing due south and affording stunning views over Ventnor Bay, The Wellington Hotel is a chic, relaxing and intimate hotel. The property dates back to the Victorian period when Ventnor emerged as a popular seaside resort. The attractive building has been patiently renovated, restoring many of the original features to their former glory. Guests unwind in modern, well appointed rooms, all of which boast en-suite bathrooms and breathtaking panoramic sea views. A delicious menu featuring cuisine from around the globe, coupled with an attentive service, makes dining in the restaurant a memorable experience and the well stocked bar offers an extensive selection of fine wines. Enjoy drinks on the terrace, taking in the fresh sea air and watching the boats sail by - pure relaxation! The Wellington is only a short stroll from shops, entertainment and local transport and the beach is conveniently reached through the hotel gardens. Other places of interest in Ventnor include the Botanic Gardens, The Isle of Wight Coastal Visitor Centre and St Boniface Down, the highest point on the island.

Our inspector loved: The staff's desire to please each guest in this very stylish hotel.

THE GEORGE HOTEL

STONE STREET, CRANBROOK, KENT TN17 3HE

History, character and true Kentish hospitality go hand in hand at this charming inn in the heart of a pleasant and busy little town, which features many 18th-century houses and a medieval church with the honorary title of "Cathedral of the Weald". The George is a Grade II* Listed Building with references back to 1300 when it is reputed that Edward I stayed here. Queen Elizabeth I was also entertained at the George when she visited the town in 1573. She was presented with a silver cup bearing the arms of the Cinque Ports by the townsfolk in the upstairs beamed Big Room. This is still in use today and reached by a magnificent oak staircase. An excellent refurbishment, has culminated in an agreeable combination of modern facilities with traditional furnishings. Guests have the choice of 8 en-suite bedrooms, each tastefully and comfortably furnished. Some have four-poster beds and one a Jacuzzi. The Restaurant offers atmosphere and charm. Its centrepiece is a huge, beautifully preserved 600-year-old open fireplace that was once the "workhorse" of this former kitchen. Fresh local produce is used in the preparation of delicious menus. Sissinghurst Gardens, Leeds, Hever and Bodiam Castles are all close by.

Our inspector loved: *The ancient beamed interior and splendid staircase. Ghost hunters could be lucky here.*

Directions: Exit the M20 at Junction 7 and take the A229 south.

Web: www.johansens.com/georgecranbrook
E-mail: georgehotelkent@aol.com
Tel: 0870 381 8540
International: +44 (0)1580 713348
Fax: 01580 715532

Price Guide:
single from £60
double/twin from £90

WALLETT'S COURT HOTEL & SPA

WEST CLIFFE, ST MARGARET'S-AT-CLIFFE, DOVER, KENT CT15 6EW

Directions: From A2 roundabout immediately north of Dover take A258 signposted Deal. After 1 mile turn right and the Court is on the right.

Web: www.johansens.com/wallettscourt
E-mail: wc@wallettscourt.com
Tel: 0870 381 8966
International: +44 (0)1304 852424
Fax: 01304 853430

Price Guide:
single £79–£119
double £99–£159

This listed Grade II house, recorded in The Domesday Book as "The Manor of Westcliffe", was transformed by the Oakley family, who discovered it in ruins in the late 70s. The result is a charming property, enveloped in a relaxing atmosphere and set in landscaped grounds near to The White Cliffs of Dover. The beautifully appointed bedrooms are comfortable and well-equipped with an array of modern conveniences. They are located in either the main house or barn conversions, the most recent of which also features an indoor swimming pool and leisure facilities. Fitness enthusiasts may use the steam room, sauna, spa pool, tennis courts and croquet lawn. The attractive restaurant, awarded 2 AA Rosettes, offers imaginative lunch and dinner menus. The dishes change every month to incorporate the fresh seasonal produce. Try the St Margaret's Bay lobster served with pilaff rice and roasted vegetables, Dover Sole Meuniere or Romney Marsh lamb. The extensive wine list includes a good selection of half-bottles, all acceptably priced. Breakfast is another feast, with farm eggs, sausages made by the nearby butcher and homemade preserves.

Our inspector loved: *The unique treatment room in its woodland setting, all part of the excellent little spa facilities.*

RINGLESTONE INN AND FARMHOUSE HOTEL

'TWIXT HARRIETSHAM AND WORMSHILL, NR MAIDSTONE, KENT ME17 1NX

Truly traditional is the welcome that awaits visitors as they step back in time into this delightfully unspoilt, medieval, lamplit tavern. Built in 1533 as a hospice for monks, the Ringlestone became one of the early Ale Houses around 1615 and little has changed since. Its delights include original brick and flint walls and floors, massive oak beams, inglenooks, old English furniture and 8 acres of idyllic gardens. There are 3 en-suite bedrooms and a separate cottage at a charming farmhouse just opposite the inn, all furnished in a style totally in keeping with expectations for a stay in this beautiful escapists' spot. Spacious farmhouse dining and reception rooms are also available for private and corporate functions. Full of character and candlelight ambience with sturdy, highly polished tables made from the timbers of an 18th-century Thames barge, the Ringlestone has a reputation for excellent English cooking and features in many food guides. A wide range of options from sandwiches to hot dishes is available at lunchtimes and a traditional roast is served on Sundays. The diverse evening menu includes unusual and interesting pies, complemented by their extensive wine list and a wide range of English country fruit wines. Leeds Castle is nearby.

Our inspector loved: The unbelievably quiet and remote setting in unspoilt countryside.

Directions: Leave M20 at Jct8. Head north off A20 through Hollingbourne, turn right at water tower crossroads to Doddington.

Web: www.johansens.com/ringlestoneinn
E-mail: bookings@ringlestone.com
Tel: 0870 381 8856
International: +44 (0)1622 859900
Fax: 01622 859966

Price Guide: (room only)
single from £89
double from £99

        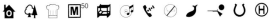

ROMNEY BAY HOUSE HOTEL

COAST ROAD, LITTLESTONE, NEW ROMNEY, KENT TN28 8QY

This spectacular house was built in the 1920s for the American actress and journalist, Hedda Hopper, by the distinguished architect, Sir Clough Williams-Ellis. The gracious drawing room overlooks the English Channel, panoramically surveyed through the telescope in the first-floor library. There is access to the beach, a tennis court, croquet lawn and golf course. A 5-minute drive to Lydd airport and you can fly to Le Touquet for lunch. Upstairs, designated non-smoking, the charming en-suite bedrooms are furnished with antiques. Wonderful cream teas can be enjoyed on the terrace in the sun-lit sea air. The new chef-patron and his wife, both with London hotel/restaurant backgrounds, now offer an outstanding dining experience. There is so much history in Romney Marsh, renowned years ago for its smuggling. Caesar landed here in 55BC at Port Lympne and the famous Cinque Ports stretch along the coast. Canterbury Cathedral is within easy driving distance. Littlestone Golf Courses adjoin the hotel and windsurfing is popular. Less than 20 minutes' drive from the Channel Tunnel Terminal.

Directions: From New Romney head for the coast by Station Road leading to Littlestone Road – pass the miniature railway station – at the sea, turn left and follow signs for Romney Bay House for about a mile.

Web: www.johansens.com/romneybayhouse
Tel: 0870 381 8863
International: +44 (0)1797 364747
Fax: 01797 367156

Price Guide:
single from £60
double £80–£150

Our inspector loved: This delightful country house by the sea with its opportunities for cycling around the Romney Marsh – cycles are available at the hotel.

HEMPSTEAD HOUSE

LONDON ROAD, BAPCHILD, SITTINGBOURNE, KENT ME9 9PP

Surrounded by 4 acres of beautiful gardens and overlooking rural Kentish countryside, Hempstead House's comfortable ambience of open log fires and antique furnishings is the epitome of classic Victorian charm. Situated between Sittingbourne and Faversham, it was a private home until being purchased by the Holdstock family in 1990 and renovated and extended into a delightful small country hotel with a high reputation for friendly and attentive service. The interior reveals many fine rooms with graceful features and elegant proportions enhanced by tasteful décor and fine furnishings. Tradition blends with modern comforts throughout. Each guest room has been individually designed and exudes its own special character. The reception rooms, with their elegant marble fireplaces, crystal chandeliers, antique and period pieces of furniture encapsulate the relaxed atmosphere, and the stylish restaurant tempts visitors to an array of English and French culinary delights. An ornately furnished private dining room caters for special occasions. Pre and after-dinner drinks can be enjoyed in the exquisite drawing room, smoking room or outside on the flood-lit terraces by the pool, which is also a popular venue for summer dining. Full conference, business and function facilities are available.

Our inspector loved: The stunning new Heritage Suite created from the old stable buildings to host conferences, weddings and private parties.

Directions: Approximately 1 mile east of Sittingbourne on the A2 to Faversham. Nearest motorway M2, junction 5.

Web: www.johansens.com/hempstead
E-mail: info@hempsteadhouse.co.uk
Tel: 0870 381 8649
International: +44 (0)1795 428020
Fax: 01795 436362

Maidstone
Canterbury
Tunbridge Wells
Dover

Price Guide:
single from £75
double/twin from £85

TREE TOPS COUNTRY HOUSE RESTAURANT & HOTEL

SOUTHPORT OLD ROAD, FORMBY, NR SOUTHPORT, LANCASHIRE L37 0AB

Directions: From M6 take M58 to Southport to end of motorway. Follow signs to Southport on A565. Bypass Formby on dual carriageway; as it changes to single carriageway, turn right at traffic lights to Tree Tops.

Web: www.johansens.com/treetopscountryhouse
E-mail: sales@treetopsformby.fsnet.co.uk
Tel: 0870 381 8950
International: +44 (0)1704 572430
Fax: 01704 572430

Price Guide:
single £60–£85
double £100–£160

The former Dower House of Formby Hall, Tree Tops, still retains the elegance of a bygone age, set in 5 acres of lawns and woods. Over the last 22 years, Lesley Winsland has restored the house to its true glory and has installed all the modern conveniences sought after by today's visitor. Spacious accommodation is available in well-appointed en-suite lodges with all the facilities a discerning guest would expect. An outdoor heated swimming pool has direct access to the sumptuously decorated Cocktail Lounge. Rich, dark leather seating, onyx-and-gilt tables and subtle lighting all contribute to the overall ambience, complemented by a truly welcoming and efficient staff. The restaurant and conservatory have been totally refurbished, cleverly incorporating some 21st-century ideas. A new menu offers a wonderful blend of traditional and modern, English and international cuisine. Table d'hôte, à la carte and lunchtime snacks are available, using only the freshest of local produce. Southport with its sweeping sands and famous Lord Street shopping centre is nearby. 10 golf courses including 6 championship courses are within a 5-mile radius.

Our inspector loved: *The light and airy restaurant with the modern international dining experience.*

110

THE INN AT WHITEWELL

FOREST OF BOWLAND, CLITHEROE, LANCASHIRE BB7 3AT

An art gallery and wine merchant all share the premises of this friendly, welcoming inn, the earliest parts of which date back to the 14th century. It was at one time inhabited by the Keeper of the "Forêt" – the Royal hunting ground, and nowadays it is not uncommon for shooting parties to stay or drop in for lunch. Set within grounds of 3 acres, the inn has a splendid outlook across the dramatically undulating Trough of Bowland. All bedrooms, including the luxury rooms in the coach house, have been attractively furnished with antiques and quality fabrics. All have hi-tech stereo systems and most have video players. The high-quality à la carte menu, created by head chef Jamie Cadman, features predominately English country recipes such as seasonal roast game, homemade puddings and farmhouse cheeses. Good bar meals and garden lunches are also offered. 8 miles of water is available to residents from the banks of the River Hodder, where brown trout, sea trout, salmon and grayling can be caught. Other sports can be arranged locally. Browsholme Hall and Clitheroe Castle are close by and across the river there are neolithic cave dwellings.

Our inspector loved: *The luxury antique baths and the wine shop in the reception.*

Directions: From M6 take Jct32; follow A6 towards Garstang for ¼ mile. Turn right at first traffic lights towards Longridge, then left at roundabout; follow signs to Whitewell and Trough of Bowland.

Web: www.johansens.com/innatwhitewell
Tel: 0870 381 8638
International: +44 (0)1200 448222
Fax: 01200 448298

Price Guide:
single £69–£87
double £94–£120
suite £140

111

ABBOTS OAK COUNTRY HOUSE

ABBOTS OAK, WARREN HILLS ROAD, NEAR COALVILLE, LEICESTERSHIRE LE67 4UY

Directions: Take the M1, then the A511 towards Coalville. Take the Loughborough exit at the roundabout. At the traffic lights, turn left. The hotel is opposite the Bulls Head. Alternatively, take the M/A42, then the A511 towards Coalville and along the bypass, then left to the hospital. Turn at Greenhill Road and right at the T-junction.

Web: www.johansens.com/abbotsoak
Tel: 0870 381 8303
International: +44 (0)1530 832 328
Fax: 01530 832 328

Price Guide:
single £55–£75
double £65–£95

Burton-Upon-Trent

Melton Mowbray

Leicester

Hinckley

This Grade II listed building is on the edge of Charnwood Forest, is set in 19 acres of mature gardens and woodland giving rise to a number of picturesque walks among areas granite outcrops. The grounds also include a tennis court and croquet lawn. The house interior features a 3 storey staircase carved in oak, also featured are several oak panelled rooms including the drawing room and elegant dining room. When it comes to meal time in the candle-lit atmosphere watched over by Queen Elizabeth I and Sir Walter Raleigh, a memorable culinary experience awaits. After dinner guest can relax in front of one of the open fires, or enjoy a game of snooker. Mid-week is ideal for people conducting business in the area, the house being convenient for the M1 and M42 motorways. There is excellent golf nearby and shooting can be arranged, alternatively guests may wish to use the hotel's mini-gym or relax in the sauna. Abbots Oak is ideally situated for visits to Stratford-Upon-Avon, Warwick Castle and Rutland Water. Donington Park race circuit is 15 minutes away.

Our inspector loved: Sitting in the tranquil gardens drinking coffee and admiring the trees and the building.

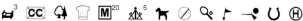

NEW

ROTHLEY COURT HOTEL

WESTFIELD LANE, ROTHLEY, LEICESTERSHIRE LE7 7LG

Set amidst 6 acres of beautiful landscaped grounds and bordered by a cricket ground, yet only a few miles from the centre of Leicester, this stunning manor house hotel is a tranquil oasis of rural England. Rothley Court is steeped in over 900 years of history. Its coat of arms is that of the Babington family, who bought Rothley Temple and its land around 1550 and held them for nearly 300 years. The motto, translated as "Faith is all", was said to Henry V on the eve of the Battle of Agincourt in 1415 by Thomas Babington, a squire on the King's personal staff. A steady programme of modernisation and extension has created an ambience of relaxed elegance, combined with personal service and a high standard of facilities in the bedrooms. The Honeymoon Suite has a four-poster bed and offers wonderful views over the grounds. Traditional bar food, morning coffee and afternoon tea are served in the Babington Bar with its magnificent fireplace, whilst the oak-panelled Babington restaurant offers a fine wine list and an extensive menu. Comprehensive function and meeting facilities for up to 85 persons are available. The Great Central Steam Railway at Loughborough and Rockingham Castle in Market Harborough are only a few of the many local attractions.

Our inspector loved: The unique 13th-century Templar chapel with its memorials to the Babington family

Directions: From M1 J21A, take A46, then A6. After ½ mile take first turn off onto B5328. From M1 J23, take A6 through Loughborough following Leicester signs. Follow signs to Rothley. From A47 join Leicester outer ring; at Redhill roundabout the outer ring joins the A6, turn right towards Loughborough. Rothley is signposted. The hotel is 200 yards out of the village.

Web: www.johansens.com/rothleycourt
E-mail: 6501@greeneking.co.uk
Tel: 0870 381 9339
International: +44 (0)116 237 4141
Fax: 0116 237 4483

Price Guide:
single £90
double £110–£125
feature £150

Burton-Upon-Trent
Melton Mowbray
Leicester
Hinckley

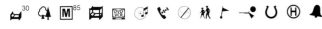

HORSE & TRUMPET

OLD GREEN, MEDBOURNE, NEAR MARKET HARBOROUGH, LEICESTERSHIRE LE16 8DX

Directions: Between Uppingham and Market Harborough.

Web: www.johansens.com/info@horseandtrumpet.com
E-mail: info@horseandtrumpet.com
Tel: 0870 381 9340
International: +44 (0)1858 565000
Fax: 01858 565551

Price Guide:
single £70
double £70

Set in the picturesque traditional English village of Medbourne, fronting onto an immaculate bowling green, the Horse & Trumpet dates back to the 18th century. It has been lovingly restored and converted into a restaurant with rooms by Gill Pemberton and her team and offers a relaxed atmosphere in peaceful surroundings. The Grade II listed main building has been built from mellow local stone and the reconstructed roof made of local straw thatch. In winter guests can enjoy the blaze of an open fireplace in the main building. Gill has created 4 superb en-suite bedrooms in the outbuildings, recycling many original features and materials such as an old Saloon bar window that has been incorporated into one of the bedroom doors. An old iron bedstead forms part of the décor of the secluded rear courtyard, which, on sunny days, provides the setting for alfresco dining. There are 3 attractive dining rooms in the main building. Chef David Lennox and his team create imaginative, modern British cuisine, which has won 2 AA Rosettes. Private dining for parties from 8 - 25 people can be catered for. On the last Friday of each month a multi-course tasting menu is available, affording guests the opportunity to sample a range of menu items, complemented by individually matched wines.

Our inspector loved: *Sitting in the courtyard, in the deep silence of the countryside, looking at the stone, the thatch and the slate.*

NEW

SYSONBY KNOLL HOTEL

ASFORDBY ROAD, MELTON MOWBRAY, LEICESTERSHIRE LE13 0HP

Surrounded by 1.5 acres of Edwardian landscaped gardens overlooking the river Eye, on the edge of the attractive market town of Melton Mowbray, Sysonby Knoll has been owned and run by the same family since 1965. Originally a 6-bedroom house, it has been gradually transformed into the superb 30-bedroom hotel it is today. The original building houses the reception and lounge areas, decorated in period style, and forms part of a courtyard, with the bar, restaurant and conservatory overlooking the gardens and fields beyond. Furnished to a high standard, the bedrooms have en-suite facilities and all modern comforts; 9 are single, and the rest are either twin- or double-bedded. The 2 stunning four-poster rooms overlooking the gardens are ideal for a honeymoon or special break. A wide choice of menus is available in the restaurant, featuring excellent, freshly prepared food and fine wines from a comprehensive wine list. A 12-hole par 3 golf course is within 500m of the hotel, and Melton Mowbray has a golf club for those who prefer a more serious game. The hotel has a total of 5 acres of grounds with course fishing on the River Eye. Guests with pets are always welcome. Superb riding facilities are available nearby. The hotel is a 15-minute walk from the centre of Melton Mowbray with its 12th-century church and busy street markets on 3 days each week.

Directions: From South: M1 J21a, follow A46 (Newark), ignore A607 to Melton, turn off at Six Hills on A6006 for Melton. Or: from A1 onto A606 (Oakham), pass through Oakham and continue to Melton. From North: M1 J24, follow A6 (Loughboro), turn left onto A6006 for Melton (just after dual carriageway ends). Or: from A1 onto A607 (Melton).

Web: www.johansens.com/sysonby
E-mail: reception@sysonby.com
Tel: 0870 381 9352
International: +44 (0)1664 563563
Fax: 01664 410364

Price Guide:
single from £60
double/twin from £75
four poster £98

Our inspector loved: A massive antique four-poster bed in one of the rooms.

NEW

THE RED HOUSE

23 MAIN STREET, NETHER BROUGHTON, LEICESTERSHIRE LE14 3HB

Directions: Situated 15 minutes east of Nottingham and 15 minutes north of Leicester on the A606 to Melton Mowbray.

Web: www.johansens.com/redhouse
E-mail: bookings@the-redhouse.com
Tel: 0870 381 9350
International: +44 (0)1664 822429
Fax: 01664 823805

Price Guide: (per person)
single/double from £50

Burton-Upon-Trent
Melton Mowbray
Leicester
Hinckley

Set in the charming village of Nether Broughton in the heart of rural Leicestershire, this pub, restaurant and hotel offers the perfect combination of traditional ambience and luxury with a modern edge. The warm and welcoming pub with its open fireplace and comfortable leather seating provides a relaxed environment in which to enjoy restaurant meals and a wide range of real ales, wines and spirits, whilst the contemporary restaurant is a more refined dining venue, with excellent food prepared by executive chef John Molnar from the house's sister restaurant bluu in Nottingham. The courtyard to the rear with teak decking and flowerbeds is a relaxing setting for a drink, lunch or dinner. On sunny days, the garden bar and grill, set in the old stables, offers yet another culinary experience. A more rustic, deli style menu is served here, prepared in an open plan kitchen. There are 8 individual bedrooms, furnished to a high standard with extremely comfortable, large king-sized beds dressed in fine Egyptian cotton. Each has its own bathroom complete with steel fittings, Crabtree & Evelyn toiletries and thick white towels. A dedicated room for private dining, functions and meetings is available. The idyllic surroundings including a marquee facility make the Red House ideal for wedding breakfasts and receptions for small to medium sized parties, with a dedicated team on hand.

Our inspector loved: *The impressive staircase and the tall period window.*

THE LEA GATE INN

LEAGATE ROAD, CONINGSBY, LINCOLNSHIRE LN4 4RS

Possibly the oldest inn in Lincolnshire, the Lea Gate dates back to 1542. With an abundance of oak beams, inglenook fireplaces, and even a priest hole, it has lost none of its Olde Worlde charm and has a welcoming atmosphere with as many as 5 fires blazing on chilly days! The 8 light and spacious bedrooms have a refreshing, airy feel with attractive furnishings and elegant canopied beds, and there is one four-poster. All bathrooms – some with Jacuzzi baths – are stylish and modern. Some of the bedrooms overlook the charming gardens, which have been recently re-designed around a large Koi pool and waterfall, whilst the gardens still retain features from the past like the ancient Yew tree – said to be as old as the inn itself. The Lea Gate Inn has a reputation for its fine food, which guests may take in any of the bars or in the restaurant. A wide variety of traditional and continental dishes are availabe, including some "Lea Gate Specialities", and local Lincolnshire sausages. RAF Coningsby's Battle of Britain Flight Aircraft is within striking distance, as is the National Trusts's Tattershall Castle and Lincoln Cathedral; or guests can explore the beautiful Lincolnshire wolds and local historic towns.

Our inspector loved: The real comfort and character together with excellent bedrooms.

Directions: From Lincoln take the A153 towards Horncastle and Skegness. At Coningsby take the B1192.

Web: www.johansens.com/leagateinn
E-mail: theleagateinn@hotmail.com
Tel: 0870 381 8684
International: +44 (0)1526 342370
Fax: 01526 345468

Price Guide:
single £49.50
double £65–£95

WASHINGBOROUGH HALL

CHURCH HILL, WASHINGBOROUGH, LINCOLN LN4 1BE

Directions: From Lincoln city centre, drive down Broadgate and over Pelham Bridge. Take the B1188 towards Branston then left along the B1190 to Washingborough. In Washingborough turn right at the mini-roundabout along Church Hill. Washingborough Hall is on the left-hand side.

Web: www.johansens.com/washingboroughhall
E-mail: washingboroughhall@btopenworld.com
Tel: 0870 381 8971
International: +44 (0)1522 790340
Fax: 01522 792936

Price Guide:
single £65
double/twin £90–£135

With its solid stone walls, white framed windows and grand pillared entrance door this majestic, listed Georgian manor house is one of the most attractive hotels in the county. Washingborough Hall was built circa 1700 as a private house - the first reference discovered is that of George Fairfax, Rector of Washingborough, and his family. Standing in splendid seclusion at the heart of 4 acres of wooded grounds and lawned gardens 2 miles from the centre of historic Lincoln, it is an ideal and comfortable retreat for those wishing to escape the bustle and noise of a busy outside world. Behind the Hall's delightful façade there is every traditional and modern comfort. The en-suite bedrooms are beautifully decorated and stylishly furnished with many offering superb views over the grounds. A spacious, delightfully decorated lounge is a comfortable and cool venue for summer guests seeking relaxation and a quiet chat and, with its large York stone open fireplace, a warm, welcoming haven in winter for guests following a cheek-chilling walk. Mouth-watering cuisine is enjoyed in the superbly decorated Wedgwood dining room, which overlooks the gardens. Places of interest nearby include Lincoln's 11th-century cathedral and castle and the Aviation Heritage Centre.

Our inspector loved: *The peaceful village location, yet only approximately 3 miles from the historic city of Lincoln.*

THE CROWN HOTEL

ALL SAINTS PLACE, STAMFORD, LINCOLNSHIRE PE9 2AG

Owned and run by a lively and enthusiastic brother and sister team, The Crown Hotel is being transformed and upgraded. An informal, friendly and comfortable blend of traditional and modern styles is omnipresent. In the public areas, many original features including stone walls have been retained. Each of the 20 bedrooms has its own individual character yet all display a range of good facilities and spotless white linen. Guests and local patrons alike may sample the appetising menu, offering the best of British traditional dishes, based on fresh local produce and cooked to order. Landlord Timothy Taylor offers 3 real ales and 1 guest ale, including Champion Beer of Britain, and a selection of fine wines by the glass. Hotel residents can have local membership of the nearby health club. The hotel is set in the town centre and there are ample facilities for parking. 3 superior luxury bedrooms are available in an elegant, period town house close by - "not to be rivalled in the Stamford area". Stamford is an attractive stone-built town with most of the properties hailing from the Medieval and Georgian eras and favoured by film makers and producers of costume dramas. Historic properties abound and include Peterborough Cathedral and Burghley House.

Our inspector loved: The entrance porch, which was decked with Hyacinths and fresh spring flowers.

Directions: The town is signed from the A1.

Web: www.johansens.com/crownstamford
E-mail: thecrownhotel@excite.com
Tel: 0870 381 8464
International: +44 (0)1780 763136
Fax: 01780 756111

Price Guide:
single £65
double £80–£145

NEW

RACQUET CLUB

HARGREAVES BUILDING, 5 CHAPEL STREET, LIVERPOOL L3 9AA

Directions: From the A59 take a right turn onto Leeds Street 5053. Follow this road onto Newquay 5036. Turn right at the church then follow the road round. Stay in the middle lane then head up Chapel Street. The hotel is on the right just after the Thistle hotel.

Web: www.johansens.com/racquetclub
E-mail: sales@racquetclub.org.uk
Tel: 0870 381 9287
International: +44 (0)151 236 6676
Fax: 0151 236 6870

Price Guide:
single £111–£120
double £117–£130

The Racquet Club reopened its doors in June, 2004 and offers 8 individually designed bedrooms, function rooms, member's area, restaurant, gym, health and beauty rooms and 2 squash courts. Located in the heart of the business area of the city, close to the pier head of Liverpool, guests can catch the ferry across the Mersey or stroll along the front of the Albert Dock. The Club is decorated with antiques and artefacts with modern and traditional influences and guests receive a warm welcome before they are led to their bedrooms on the second floor. All bedrooms have been carefully designed and feature every modern facility such as tea and coffee making facilities, hair dryers and power showers. Ziba restaurant is renowned for its attentive service and is inspired by French classic and modern English cusines accompanied by one of Liverpool's largest wine lists with over 150 wines. A private dining room, which can accommodate up to 24, is available and the Gallery Room can cater for private parties of up to 30. Guests may enjoy a dip in the plunge pool, Jacuzzi, sauna or steam, and even take part in a vigorous workout in the well equipped gym. A range of treatments and massages is available in the beauty rooms.

Our inspector loved: *This small hotel in the centre of Liverpool with its own racquet club and excellent facilities.*

THE WHITE HORSE

BRANCASTER STAITHE, NORFOLK PE31 8BY

Winner of the Condé Nast Johansens Most Excellent Coastal Award 2003, this welcoming inn commands dramatic views of the tidal marshland of the Norfolk coast; an ideal base for walkers, sailors, birdwatchers and sea-lovers alike. Its friendly atmosphere is perfectly complemented by excellent service, good food and a charming seaside ambience. The interior features scrubbed pine furniture and sepia prints of days gone by. The spacious, airy bedrooms are innovatively designed and located in total harmony with the landscape. 8 guest rooms can be accessed from outside, and each has its own patio with flowerbeds. 7 en-suite rooms are situated in the main building, including "the room at the top" which boasts the split-level accommodation and a viewing balcony with telescope. A new guest lounge and dining area adjoin the Conservatory restaurant with its stunning tidal-marsh views. The award-winning restaurant is gaining quite a reputation in the area for its imaginatively prepared food with freshly caught mussels and oysters being the seasonal speciality of the house. The grounds of the hotel adjoin the Norfolk Coastal path and amazing tidal marsh, which, with its many rare species of sea birds, is a paradise for ornithologists. Stately Homes at Sandringham, Holkham Hall and Houghton Hall are all nearby. Seasonal breaks are available.

Our inspector loved: The views across the salt marshes to the sea.

Directions: The White Horse is situated on the A149 coast road between Hunstanton and Wells.

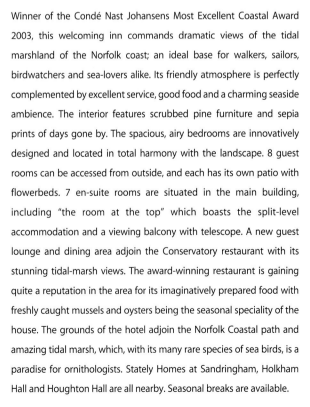

Web: www.johansens.com/whitehorsebrancaster
E-mail: reception@whitehorsebrancaster.co.uk
Tel: 0870 381 8986
International: +44 (0)1485 210262
Fax: 01485 210930

Price Guide:
single £45–£90
double £90–£210

IDYLLIC COTTAGES AT VERE LODGE

SOUTH RAYNHAM, FAKENHAM, NORFOLK NR21 7HE

Directions: From Swaffham take A1065 towards Fakenham. After 11 miles enter South Raynham. 100 yards past village sign turn left and continue 400 yards.

Web: www.johansens.com/verelodge
E-mail: major@verelodge.co.uk
Tel: 0870 381 8961
International: +44 (0)1328 838261
Fax: 01328 838300

Price Guide: (excluding VAT)
£273–£1269 per week

Quietly scattered amidst 8 acres of grounds, Vere Lodge offers a selection of spacious, comfortable and well-equipped self-catering cottages that suit any sized family. Some cottages have open fireplaces and their own private garden areas, while all offer microwaves, dishwashers, fridges and electrical appliances. A great deal of care has gone into making the cottages as homely as possible, with pictures and floral arrangements adding thoughtful finishing touches. There is a superb indoor leisure centre with a large heated swimming pool, sauna, solarium and games room, whilst the peaceful surroundings are a paradise for children. Each morning everybody gathers on the lawn for the animals' breakfast time, offering the opportunity to feed tame rabbits, goats, donkeys and ponies, then throughout the day they can enjoy the toddlers' playground, croquet lawn, football area, tennis court and Enchanted Wood. Further afield the delightful, unspoilt landscape of Norfolk has much to offer with its beaches, innumerable castles and stately homes, bird and wildlife sanctuaries and racing at Fakenham. Upon return to Vere Lodge, the availability of home-cooked frozen dishes takes the stress out of the evening meal. Short breaks available.

Our inspector loved: *That home from home with an excellent indoor leisure centre.*

THE MANOR HOUSE

BARSHAM ROAD, GREAT SNORING, NORFOLK NR21 OHP

Exclusively yours for up to 16 guests, The Manor House is an ideal venue to join with friends, family or business, weddings, baby naming ceremonies or the new ceremony of commitment between adult couples, whatever the occasion, for 1 night or longer. Relaxed informality and friendly, personal service are the ideals behind this gracious country house, which has welcomed guests since 1978, and allows you to get away from the stresses of modern life whilst offering high modern standards. The Manor House nestles behind the village church, standing in 1.5 acres of mature gardens amidst the unspoilt countryside of North Norfolk, only 15 minutes from the Heritage coast, Burnham Market and Holt. The magnificent architecture of this Grade II* listed building provides an impressive sense of history. The dining room is a wonderful example with its heavy oak beams and original stone mullion windows. Norfolk is a haven for wildlife and rare birds on the marshes and inland waterways; it boasts the most beautiful skyscapes and bright starry nights across the villages and beaches, and it harbours a wealth of history in a plethora of hidden houses, mansions, halls and churches. Golf, sailing and horse riding also feature highly on the agenda. Facilities for small conferences are available.

Our inspector loved: *The chance to live like the Lord of the Manor, whether it be a celebration or business.*

Directions: Great Snoring is 3 miles north-east of Fakenham from the A148. The Manor House is on Barsham Road, behind the church.

Web: www.johansens.com/manorgreatsnoring
E-mail: gtsnoringmanorho@aol.com
Tel: 0870 381 8716
International: +44 (0)1328 820597
Fax: 01328 820048

Price Guide: (fully staffed)
house rate from £950 per night

FELBRIGG LODGE

AYLMERTON, NORTH NORFOLK NR11 8RA

Directions: Please ring the Lodge for detailed directions and a brochure.

Web: www.johansens.com/felbrigglodge
E-mail: info@felbrigglodge.co.uk
Tel: 0870 381 8520
International: +44 (0)1263 837588
Fax: 01263 838012

Price Guide:
single from £88
double £116
suite £148

Jill and Ian Gillam have created this charming lodge with the aim of providing the highest possible standards of accommodation in North Norfolk in a setting of total quiet and relaxation. Evoking an informal and welcoming ambience, the Lodge provides complete freedom for guests to mix with others or to seek solitude. Here, time has stood still. Nothing disturbs over 50 different species of birds and other wildlife amongst rolling lawns and specimen trees and shrubs. Felbrigg Lodge enjoys an unrivalled position just outside the Felbrigg Hall estate, a 17th-century house owned by the National Trust. Approached by a long drive, the 8 acres of grounds are totally secluded. The rooms, which are all at ground level, are situated around the gardens in order to take the greatest advantage of the view and landscape. All are sumptuously decorated with flair and imagination and have luxurious en-suite bathrooms. Full English breakfasts and candle-lit dinners are served in the converted stables. Jill is an enthusiastic cook and uses the best local produce. Guests may relax in the privacy of their own rooms, wander at leisure through the gardens, play croquet, take afternoon tea in the summer house or swim in the heated indoor pool. A small, well-equipped gym is available for use by the more energetic.

Our inspector loved: *The comfort and careful attention to detail of the bedrooms and their location in the garden.*

THE GREAT ESCAPE HOLIDAY COMPANY

DOCKING, KINGS LYNN, NORFOLK PE31 8LY

The north-west Norfolk coast, sweeping towards the Wash consists mainly of a long stretch of sand and low cliffs, exposed saltings and tidal inlets. There are picturesque little harbours and villages, an abundance of birdlife and marshland stretching from King's Lynn westwards into Lincolnshire. It is a place of peace where one can believe that time stands still. Scattered along the coastline are a variety of unique and charming Great Escape holiday homes, all of which can help the visitor unwind from the pressures of everyday life. There are grand country houses, particularly attractive for corporate gatherings, charming and secluded little cottages, fascinating period houses and airy barn conversions. Some have large gardens leading down to the marshes, and boats are available for use. Others have a sunny patio, a studio or stables waiting for riding guests. The common denominator is the quality and style of décor, furnishings and service. After a personal welcome guests are provided with wine and the ingredients for a simple meal. White bed and bath linen together with first-class maid service ensure a perfect home-from-home environment. Daily staffing can be arranged. Ready to serve meal service and wine delivery. Short breaks available.

Directions: All properties are within easy reach of A149 coast road.

Web: www.johansens.com/greatescape
E-mail: bookings@thegreatescapeholiday.co.uk
Tel: 0870 381 8568
International: +44 (0)1485 518717
Fax: 01485 518937

Price Guide:
per week £300–£3,000

Our inspector loved: The personal service, which is superb.

Beechwood Hotel

CROMER ROAD, NORTH WALSHAM, NORFOLK NR28 0HD

Directions: Leave Norwich on the B1150 and drive 13 miles to North Walsham. Pass under the railway bridge, then left at the first traffic lights and right at the next set. The hotel is 150m on the left.

Web: www.johansens.com/beechwood
E-mail: enquiries@beechwood–hotel.co.uk
Tel: 0870 381 8353
International: +44 (0)1692 403231
Fax: 01692 407284

Price Guide:
single £65–£90
double £90–£160

Recipient of VisitBritain's Hotel of the Year 2003 for England, this elegant, spacious, ivy-clad house is surrounded by well laid-out gardens, dating back to 1800. For many years residents in North Walsham knew the hotel as the doctor's house; during these years an enviable society guest list was headed by Agatha Christie, a regular visitor during a 30-year period, and the Sheikh of Iraq. Individually decorated bedrooms are delightful, filled with traditional and antique furniture and feature magnificent large windows. The new Garden Wing comprises additional spacious and luxurious guest rooms, which boast Victorian-style bathrooms with freestanding "Mae West" style slipper bath. The comfortable garden lounge is well supplied with books and magazines and the lounge/bar is a relaxing haven. The exquisite "Ten-Mile Dinner" menu is served in the 2 AA Rosette awarded restaurant, which features locally reared meat and locally produced vegetables, prepared by head chef, Steven Norgate. When in season, expect to see Sheringham lobster, Cromer crab, Thornham oysters, mussels from Morston and even Norfolk cheese. One of the AA's Top 200 Hotels in Britain and Ireland and winner of the 1999 Johansens Most Excellent Value for Money Award.

Our inspector loved: *The personal welcome from the owners Don and Lindsay and their staff.*

ELDERTON LODGE HOTEL & LANGTRY RESTAURANT

GUNTON PARK, THORPE MARKET, NR NORTH WALSHAM, NORFOLK NR11 8TZ

Quietly grazing red deer, proudly strutting pheasants and cooing wood pigeons provide memorable awakening viewing to guests gazing from their bedroom windows over the vast and tranquil Gunton Park that is the scene of this 18th-century, Grade II listed hotel. Standing in the heart of unspoilt countryside yet only 4 miles from the coast, the impressive Elderton Lodge Hotel & Langtry Restaurant, with its own 6 acres of mature gardens, was once the Shooting Lodge and Dower House to Gunton Hall Estate. Gunton Hall, home of the Barons of Suffield, was a favoured retreat for Lillie Langtry, the celebrated Victorian beauty, who according to legend entertained Edward VII here when he was Prince of Wales. Bedrooms are attractive and comfortable, the bar informal and welcoming and the excellent cuisine featuring local game and seafood specialities – fit for a King, not only the Prince of Wales. This is an ideal venue for civil weddings and dinner parties. The cathedral city of Norwich, National Trust properties including Blickling Hall, Felbrigg Hall, Sheringham Park and the Heritage Coast and Norfolk Broads National Park are nearby. Midweek breaks are available.

Our inspector loved: The red deer, which really are an inspirational sight.

Directions: Leave Norwich on B1150. Join A149 towards Cromer and the hotel is on the left prior to entering Thorpe Market.

Web: www.johansens.com/eldertonlodge
E-mail: enquiries@eldertonlodge.co.uk
Tel: 0870 381 8502
International: +44 (0)1263 833547
Fax: 01263 834673

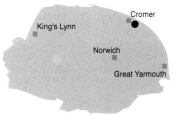

Price Guide:
single £50–£70
double £80–£115

THE NORFOLK MEAD HOTEL

COLTISHALL, NORWICH, NORFOLK NR12 7DN

Directions: On reaching Norwich take outer ring road to B1150 signposted North Walsham. After Horstead/Coltishall bridge, bear right on the B1354, signposted Wroxham. Entrance signposted on right just before church.

Web: www.johansens.com/norfolkmead
E-mail: info@norfolkmead.co.uk
Tel: 0870 381 8764
International: +44 (0)1603 737531
Fax: 01603 737521

Price Guide:
single £70–£95
double £85–£150

This elegant Georgian manor house, dating back to 1740, sits on a quiet edge of the Norfolk Broads, standing in 12 acres of lovely gardens and rolling lawns which sweep down to the River Bure. Guests can stroll down to the water to catch a glimpse of a kingfisher or heron and enjoy the variety of birdlife. The owners Don and Jill Fleming have added a host of personal touches to create a homely atmosphere; the fragrance of fresh flowers pervades the hotel. The delightful restaurant, overlooking the gardens and the river, offers a constantly changing menu thoughtfully selected by the chef to utilise the abundance of local produce, which includes fish caught off the Norfolk coast, game from the local estates, vegetables and herbs from the gardens. An extensive wine list has been carefully selected. Relax with a drink before dinner in the bar, where a log fire burns in winter and French windows open onto the old walled garden in the summer. Sport facilities include a well-stocked fishing lake, off-river mooring and a 60ft pool. Situated only 7 miles from the centre of Norwich and 12 miles from the coast, the Norfolk Mead is well situated for both business and leisure.

Our inspector loved: The welcome from Sybil the "resident cow".

THE STOWER GRANGE

SCHOOL ROAD, DRAYTON, NORWICH, NORFOLK NR8 6EF

The Stower Grange, built of mellow Norfolk bricks under Dutch pantiles, dates back to the 17th century. In former times it was a gracious rectory. Today it offers travellers a peaceful retreat – the gardens have fine lawns with inviting shade provided by the mature trees – yet the property is only 4½ miles from the commercial and historic centre of Norwich. The Stower is owned by Richard and Jane Fannon; the atmosphere is friendly and informal and in cooler months open fires add to the welcome. There are 8 spacious individually-decorated bedrooms with en-suite facilities, including 2 with a pine four-poster bed for those in a romantic mood. The Blue Restaurant, locally renowned as a "special place" to dine and looks directly on to the gardens. The imaginative cooking of chef, Mark Smith, ensures good eating from the individually priced menus. The restaurant closes on Sunday evenings, however, residents can enjoy a steak and salad in the Lounge Bar. Places of interest nearby include Norwich, Norfolk Broads, various historic houses including Sandringham, the Norfolk Coast and horseracing at Fakenham. Seasonal breaks are available.

Our inspector loved: *The excellent blend of the professional welcome and family friendliness.*

Directions: From the A11, turn left on to the inner ring road, proceed to the ASDA junction with A1067 Norwich–Fakenham Road. Approximately 2 miles to Drayton turn right at the Red Lion public house. After 80 yards bear left.

Web: www.johansens.com/stowergrange
E-mail: enquiries@stowergrange.co.uk
Tel: 0870 381 8921
International: +44 (0)1603 860210
Fax: 01603 860464

Price Guide:
single £70
double £90
suite £105

NEW

THE MOAT HOUSE

RECTORY LANE, HETHEL, NORWICH NR14 8HD

Directions: Leave Norwich on A11 signposted Newmarket/Thetford. Then take road to East Carlton and turn right onto Wymondham Road. After approximately 400 yards turn left into Water Tower Road. Rectory Lane is on the right shortly after passing a row of white cottages on your left.

Web: www.johansens.com/moathousehethel
E-mail: colles@hethelmoat.freeserve.co.uk
Tel: 0870 381 9317
International: +44 (0)1508 570149
Fax: 01508 570149

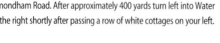

Price Guide:
single from £60
double from £90
suite from £105

Quietly grazing deer, slow paddling wild ducks and strutting geese provide memorable viewing to guests gazing over the 50 acres of secluded grounds, gardens and moat surrounding this idyllic country hotel. Situated just a few minutes' drive from the cathedral city of Norwich this elegant, non-smoking Georgian residence was once a rectory, a section added to the original 14th-century house in 1866. It is the ultimate, away-from-it-all romantic venue. The interior of The Moat House is delightful: spacious and airy, sunny in summer, cosy by open fires in winter. Relaxing décor, rich furnishings, fine pictures and fascinating collections reflect the interests of the hospitable owners, Colin and Lesley Rudd. There are 3 bedrooms, each a comfortable gem with all modern facilities. The apartment is en suite and the Blue and Four Poster rooms have a large luxurious bathroom across the landing. Breakfast and evening meals, by arrangement, are served in the Sitting Room. Large parties can enjoy the more formal, elegant dining room, which is also ideal for discreet business meetings. An unusual glass-sided passageway bridges the moat from the house to a superb leisure area with a large, heated swimming pool, bathed by light through floor to ceiling arched windows, sauna and Jacuzzi.

Our inspector loved: *The peacock sculpture by the poolside and the door leading into the leisure room.*

CATTON OLD HALL

LODGE LANE, CATTON, NORWICH, NORFOLK NR6 7HG

Tucked away from the busy centre of Norwich in the peaceful village of Old Catton, this small, family-run hotel offers an attractive blend of traditional charm, fine dining and superb accommodation. Originally built as a Gentleman's House in 1632 from reclaimed Caen stone and local flint, the Hall has been extended since the Victorian era. It has been carefully preserved to maintain its original character with many old timbers, mullioned windows, wide inglenook hearths and an abundance of pictures and objects reflecting both history and the family. Comfortable furnishings and generously proportioned rooms ensure all the needs of today's demanding visitors are met. The elegant, individually designed bedrooms feature superb beds, Egyptian cotton sheets and fresh flowers, whilst the bathrooms, some with Jacuzzi baths, boast powerful showers and large baths. Owner Anthea Cawdron prepares creative and unusual cuisine, based on old family recipes, fresh local produce and herbs from the garden. All meals are complemented by fine wines, carefully selected by the patron from reasonably priced award-winning shippers. Catton Hall overlooks its own attractive gardens and is only 2½ miles from the centre of Norwich. Both the Norfolk and Suffolk coastlines and Norfolk Broads are an easy drive away, and numerous historic houses and gardens are well worth a visit nearby.

Directions: From A11 turn left onto Norwich Ring Road (A140) following airport signs. Turn onto B1180 North

Web: www.johansens.com/cattonoldhall
E-mail: enquires@catton–hall.co.uk
Tel: 0870 381 9353
International: +44 (0)1603 419379
Fax: 01603 400339

Price Guide:
single £70
double £70–£120

Our inspector loved: The wide inglenook hearth in the sitting room.

THE OLD RECTORY

103 YARMOUTH ROAD, NORWICH, NORFOLK NR7 OHF

Directions: Follow the A47 Norwich bypass towards Great Yarmouth. Take the A1042 exit and follow the road into Thorpe St Andrew. Bear left onto the A1242 and the hotel is approximately 50 yards on the right after the first set of traffic lights.

Web: www.johansens.com/oldrectorynorwich
E-mail: enquiries@oldrectorynorwich.com
Tel: 0870 381 8784
International: +44 (0)1603 700772
Fax: 01603 300772

Price Guide:
single £68–£78
double £85–£110

Chris and Sally Entwistle extend a warm and hospitable welcome and the promise of fine personal service to guests at the Old Rectory. Dating back to 1754, their delightful Grade II listed Georgian home, clad with Wisteria and Virginia Creeper, stands in an acre of mature gardens on the outskirts of Norwich overlooking the River Yare. The spacious and well-furnished bedrooms, both in the hotel and the adjacent Coach House, offer quality, comfort and style. After a busy day, guests may unwind over a pre-dinner drink in the elegant Drawing Room, enhanced by a roaring log fire during the winter and choose from a prix-fixe menu. The tempting AA Rosette awarded dishes are changed daily and are freshly prepared to order. The Wellingtonia Room and the Conservatory, overlooking the sun terrace and gardens, are excellent venues for business meetings and private luncheons or dinners. Included in the top 200 by the AA and Johansens Most Excellent Service Award winner in 2001, The Old Rectory is an ideal base from which to explore the historic city of Norwich, the Norfolk Broads, the beautiful Broadlands countryside and the Norfolk Coast.

Our inspector loved: *The friendly hospitality from Chris and Sally, and the very comfortable accommodation.*

BROVEY LAIR

CARBROOKE ROAD, OVINGTON, THETFORD, NORFOLK IP25 6SD

Brovey Lair offers a totally innovative dining experience – it is a true new age gastro-destination. Among only a handful in East Anglia to be recommended by the Harpers and Queen Restaurant Directory, The Café at Brovey Lair has received the BMW Owners' Club endorsement as one of their "20 Great British Restaurants". Dinner is a four-course epicurean feast of exotic fish and seafood, intense vegetarian soups and delicious desserts. With an emphasis on healthy eating, chef-owner Tina Pemberton's signature dishes are based on fusing spices from distant countries with fresh local and Mediterranean produce. Weekenders are in for a real surprise. Starting at around 10am, the Californian/ Mexican brunch is likely to last until noon. On warm summer days guests will swim, have brunch on the terraces then sunbathe by the heated pool. This relaxed life style is reflected in Brovey Lair's contemporary junior garden suites that have all the luxuries and accessories of a 5-star hotel. Both suites afford restful views of the beautifully landscaped lawns and water features against a backdrop of tall trees and open country. Here is where hedonism and fabulous food combine to create an atmosphere of clandestine sensuality – a magic formula you may wish to keep to yourselves.

Our inspector loved: *The new artwork, especially the "Cherries" – luscious!*

Directions: Allowing 2 hours from north London take the M11 to jct.9 then A11 towards Norwich. Just north of Thetford turn left onto the A1075 towards Watton. Ovington is a right turn ½ mile north of Watton.

Web: www.johansens.com/broveylair
E-mail: champagne@broveylair.com
Tel: 0870 381 8385
International: +44 (0)1953 882706
Fax: 01953 885365

Price Guide:
single £115
double £125

BROOM HALL COUNTRY HOTEL

RICHMOND ROAD, SAHAM TONEY, THETFORD, NORFOLK IP25 7EX

Directions: ½ mile north of Watton on B1077 towards Swaffham.

Web: www.johansens.com/broomhall
E-mail: enquiries@broomhallhotel.co.uk
Tel: 0870 381 8384
International: +44 (0)1953 882125
Fax: 01953 885325

Price Guide:
single from £60
double £95–£160

Situated in 15 acres of mature gardens and parkland Broom Hall is a charming Victorian country house offering peace and tranquillity. The airy and spacious bedrooms, most of which have lovely views, are individually furnished and provide guests with both comfort and a range of modern amenities. A feature of the public rooms are the ornate ceilings and in the lounge a large open fire can be enjoyed in the winter months. An indoor heated swimming pool is available for guests' use. Fresh vegetables, from Broom Hall's own garden when in season, and many old-fashioned desserts ensure that dinner, overseen by the head chef, in the dining room overlooking the garden is an enjoyable occasion. Small conferences can be arranged and the entire house can be "taken over" for your family reunion or celebration. Seasonable breaks are available. Places of interest nearby include Norwich, Cambridge, Ely and Bury St Edmunds. Sandringham and many National Trust properties, Thetford Forest, Norfolk Broads and coastline offering nature reserves and bird sanctuaries are also within easy reach

Our inspector loved: *The fragrant gardens.*

THE WINDMILL AT BADBY

MAIN STREET, BADBY, DAVENTRY, NORTHAMPTONSHIRE NN11 3AN

The Windmill Inn Hotel was first established as an inn in the 17th century and is situated in the heart of the pretty village of Badby. A traditional thatched country pub, complete with log fires, The Windmill offers good food and a range of cask-conditioned ales. The owners, with their extensive experience of hotel and pub management, have plenty of ideas for regular activities. Winter Sportsmen's Dinners and theme nights with entertainment are popular events. The en suite bedrooms provide comfortable accommodation and the whole hotel is ideally suitable for house party weekends from 12–14 guests. Under the skilled eye of Gavin Baxter the award-winning kitchen prepares a varied range of freshly cooked dishes. The sumptuous menu includes a delicious traditional Sunday Luncheon, which offers excellent value for money. Stilton mushrooms, chargrilled Cajun chicken, steak and kidney pie and poached salmon with new potatoes are amongst the many highly recommended specialities. Weddings, functions and business meetings and conferences are catered for with ease. Places to visit include Althorp, Sulgrave Manor (home of the Washingtons), Blenheim Palace, Silverstone Circuit, Warwick and Stratford-upon-Avon.

Our inspector loved: *The delightful light and airy Henry Spencer bedroom in the Bluebell Cottage annexe.*

Directions: Situated in the centre of Badby, a village located off the A361, 2 miles south of Daventry on the Banbury road.

Web: www.johansens.com/windmillatbadby
E-mail: info@windmillinn-badby.com
Tel: 0870 381 9002
International: +44 (0)1327 702363
Fax: 01327 311521

Market Harborough

Northampton

Towcester

Price Guide:
single £62.50
double £65–£79
family room £79.50

THE FALCON HOTEL

CASTLE ASHBY, NORTHAMPTONSHIRE NN7 1LF

Directions: Exit M1 junction 14 northbound or 15 southbound. Follow the signs to A428 where Castle Ashby and The Falcon are clearly signposted, 6 miles south-east of Northampton.

Web: www.johansens.com/falcon
Tel: 0870 381 8512
International: +44 (0)1604 696200
Fax: 01604 696673

Price Guide:
single from £95
double/twin from £120
premier £139.50

6 miles south of Northampton, in the heart of the Marquess of Northampton's estate, The Falcon is a delightful country cottage hotel, secluded and tranquil, minutes away from the rambling acres of Castle Ashby House. The owners have invested energy and enthusiasm into transforming this once modest place into a haven of comfort, excellent food and attentive service. Bedrooms are beautifully furnished, cosy cottage style and the bathrooms have been recently upgraded. Lunch and dinner, which are created where possible from seasonal, home-grown produce, are served in the intimate restaurant which overlooks a lawn with willow trees. The excellent value-for-money cuisine, modern English in flavour, is prepared by chef Harvey Jones. A fixed-price menu costs £27.50, there is also an interesting à la carte selection. The extensive wine list can be studied by guests at their leisure over preprandial drinks by a glowing log fire. Walk in the grounds of Castle Ashby estate. Further afield, visit Woburn, Althorp, Silverstone, Bedford and Stratford.

Our inspector loved: *The welcoming atmosphere and open fire.*

WAREN HOUSE HOTEL

WAREN MILL, BAMBURGH, NORTHUMBERLAND NE70 7EE

"To visit the North East and not to stay here, would be foolish indeed". So says one entry in a visitors book that is filled with generous and justified praise for this delightful traditional country house, which lives up to all its promises and expectations and beyond. The hotel is set in 6 acres of gardens and woodland on the edge of Budle Bay Bird Sanctuary overlooking Holy Island and 2 miles from the majestic Bamburgh Castle. The owners, Anita and Peter, do not cater for children under 14, so they are able to offer a rare commodity of peace and tranquillity even during the busy summer months. Throughout the hotel, the antique furnishings and the immaculate and well-chosen décor evoke a warm, friendly and charming ambience. Seated in the candle-lit dining room, surrounded by family pictures and portraits, guests can select dishes from the daily changing menu and wines from over 250 bins. There is a boardroom for executive meetings. Dogs by prior arrangement. Special short breaks available all year. The Farne Islands are just a boat trip away; Bamburgh, Alnwick and Dunstanburgh Castles and Holy Island are nearby. Waren House is open all year. Special breaks available.

Our inspector loved: *This delightful small hotel on the heritage coast overlooking Budle Bay.*

Directions: There are advance warning signs on the A1 both north and south. Take B1342 to Waren Mill. Hotel (floodlit at night) is on south-west corner of Budle Bay just 2 miles from Bamburgh.

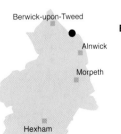

Web: www.johansens.com/warenhouse
E-mail: enquiries@warenhousehotel.co.uk
Tel: 0870 381 8967
International: +44 (0)1668 214581
Fax: 01668 214484

Price Guide:
single £79–£115
double £98–£150
suite £132–£205

THE OTTERBURN TOWER

OTTERBURN, NORTHUMBERLAND NE19 1NS

Directions: The hotel is situated in the village of Otterburn on the A696, the major road between Newcastle and Edinburgh.

Web: www.johansens.com/otterburntower
E-mail: reservations@otterburntower.com
Tel: 0870 381 8796
International: +44 (0)1830 520620
Fax: 01830 521504

Price Guide:
single £75–£110
double £120–£190
suite £190

With its thick stone walls, shoulder high ramparts and arrow-slit windows looking out over the beautiful Northumberland countryside, this magnificent fortress is steeped in history. Founded in 1076 as a defence against marauding Scots by a cousin of William the Conqueror, Otterburn Tower is now a welcoming hotel with all modern comforts. Elegant public rooms are luxuriously furnished and warmed by log fires in winter, whilst the en-suite bedrooms, some with four-poster beds and open fireplaces, are individually designed and offer views over the grounds. Dining at the Otterburn Tower is a delight, with all ingredients for the imaginative dishes supplied by either Longwitton Farm, covering over 2000 acres to the south-east of the hotel and run by the hotel owner's son, John Goodfellow Junior, or other locally accredited sources. The hotel's chefs personally oversee the journey from field to table to maintain the highest standards of freshness, preparation and cooking. A wide variety of vegetables, salad leaves and herbs is grown in the hotel gardens. Guests can go fishing along the hotel's 3-mile stretch on the north bank of the river Rede. Places of interest nearby include Hadrian's Wall, Holy Island and Bamburgh Castle.

Our inspector loved: *The delicious dinner of home-farmed lamb and home-grown vegetables.*

COCKLIFFE COUNTRY HOUSE HOTEL

BURNT STUMP COUNTRY PARK, BURNT STUMP HILL, NOTTINGHAMSHIRE NG5 8PQ

This is Robin Hood country and Cockliffe is situated in the heart of it, 6 miles north of Nottingham. A lovely, unusually designed 17th-century house with turreted-style corners it stands in 3 acres of colourful, mature gardens adjacent to the open spaces of Burnt Stump Country Park. Dane and Jane Clarke rescued the house from disrepair 10 years ago and are proud of their renovations and refurbishments, many of which are in keeping with original features. Décor and furnishings throughout are elegant and tasteful and most rooms afford splendid views over the garden. The 10 bedrooms are individually designed and comfortably appointed to reflect the needs of discerning guests. Most are Jacuzzi en suite, with thoughtful touches, period furniture and adorned with beautiful curtain fabrics carefully chosen by Jane Clarke. Head chef Andy Coleman produces an excellent and imaginative menu using local produce and game when in season, served in the attractive restaurant, adjoining the cocktail bar which is popular with guests for pre-meal drinks and after dinner coffee. A conference room with high-tech facilities is available. Golf, fishing, riding and fitness and leisure can be arranged locally. Places of interst nearby include Nottingham and its castle, Sherwood Forest, 12th-century Newstead Abbey and Southwell Minster with its medieval carvings, the earliest of their kind in England.

Our inspector loved: The striking interior decor throughout .

Directions: Exit the M1 at junction 26 and take the A60 north from Nottingham towards Mansfield, passing through Arnold. At the Seven Mile pub turn right then right again at the top of the hill into a hidden turning. The hotel is ½mile on the right.

Web: www.johansens.com/cockliffe
E-mail: enquiries@cockliffehouse.co.uk
Tel: 0870 381 8435
International: +44 (0)1159 680179
Fax: 01159 680623

Price Guide:
single from £95
double £105–£150

THE SARACENS HEAD HOTEL

MARKET PLACE, SOUTHWELL, NOTTINGHAMSHIRE NG25 0HE

Directions: In the centre of Southwell. Follow Queen Street past the Post Office on the left, then turn left for the hotel car park.

Web: www.johansens.com/saracenshead
E-mail: ccsaracenshead@aol.com
Tel: 0870 381 9337
International: +44 (0)1636 812701
Fax: 01636 815408

Price Guide:
single £75
double/twin £95–£130
four poster £150

Worksop

Mansfield

Nottingham

Set in the busy market town of Southwell, opposite the Norman Minster and close to the town of Newark, this charming former coaching inn dates back to 1460. Restored to its former glory after a complete refurbishment programme, the Saracen's Head Hotel reopened in June 2002 to offer modern comfort in elegant, relaxed surroundings. Many famous and historic people have enjoyed the hotel's hospitality, from Charles I, who spent his last night of freedom here in 1646, to Lord Byron and D H Lawrence. Numerous original features can be found throughout the hotel, including Elizabethan wall paintings, four-poster beds and a traditional "Magpie" façade. The 27 en-suite bedrooms are tastefully decorated and offer every modern comfort. Guests can while away a relaxing afternoon in the beautiful flower-filled courtyard, which is also the ideal setting for alfresco dining. The cosy bar and lounge areas with their log fires provide warmth on chilly days, and exquisite cuisine is served in the oak-panelled Byron restaurant. This is the perfect venue for meetings, conferences and private functions; the Bramley Room is ideal for up to 14 people, whilst the Minster Suite can accommodate as many as 120. Numerous attractions are within easy reach, such as Sherwood Forest Country Park, Hardwick Hall, Newstead Abbey and Clumber Park.

Our inspector loved: The perfectly preserved Elizabethan wall painting in the King Charles Room.

THE LAMB INN

SHEEP STREET, BURFORD, OXFORDSHIRE OX18 4LR

The Lamb Inn, set in the small Cotswold town of Burford, is everyone's idea of the archetypal English inn, where it is easy to imagine that time has slipped back to some gentler age. The inn is set in a quiet location within a pretty walled garden. To step inside is to recapture something of the spirit of the 14th century: flagged floors, gleaming copper, brass and silver reflect the flicker of log fires and the well-chosen antiques all enhance the sense of history. New owners, Bruno and Rachel Cappuccini have renovated the restaurant, whilst maintaining its traditional character, and added many personal touches throughout this wonderful inn. Imaginative modern British cuisine is complemented by superb wines from an extensive list. The bedrooms offer comfortable accommodation, with oak beams, chintz curtains, antique furniture and luxurious toiletries. The inn is located near the heart of the town, where guests can browse through antiques shops or laze by the waters of the river Windrush. Burford is within easy reach of Oxford, Cheltenham, Stow-on-the-Wold and the many attractive Cotswold villages.

Our inspector loved: *The tasteful simplicity of the renovated bedrooms and new super bathrooms.*

Directions: Sheep Street is off the main street in Burford. Burford is 20 miles west of Oxford.

Web: www.johansens.com/lambinnburford
E-mail: info@lambinn-burford.co.uk
Tel: 0870 381 8674
International: +44 (0)1993 823155
Fax: +44 (0)1993 822228

Price Guide:
single from £80
double from £125

THE PLOUGH AT CLANFIELD

BOURTON ROAD, CLANFIELD, OXFORDSHIRE OX18 2RB

Directions: The hotel is located on the edge of the village of Clanfield, at the junction of the A4095 and B4020, between the towns of Witney and Faringdon, some 15 miles to the west of the city of Oxford.

Web: www.johansens.com/ploughatclanfield
Tel: 0870 381 8826
International: +44 (0)1367 810222
Fax: 01367 810596

Price Guide:
single £90
double £120–£130

The Plough at Clanfield is an idyllic hideaway for the romantic at heart. Set on the edge of the village of Clanfield, typical of the Oxfordshire Cotswolds, The Plough dates from 1560 and is a fine example of well-preserved Elizabethan architecture. The hotel is owned and personally run by John and Rosemary Hodges, who have taken great care to preserve the charm and character of this historic building. As there are only 12 bedrooms, guests can enjoy an intimate atmosphere and attentive, personal service. All the bedrooms are beautifully appointed to the highest standard and all have en suite bathrooms. At the heart of the hotel is the Shires Restaurant, regarded as one of the finest in the area. The cuisine is superbly prepared and impeccably served, with an interesting selection of wines. 2 additional dining rooms are available for private entertaining. The hotel is an ideal base from which to explore the Cotswolds or the Thames Valley. There are many historic houses and gardens in the area, as well as racing at Newbury and Cheltenham. Hotel closed 24th December to 7th January

Our inspector loved: *The beautifully manicured gardens.*

THE GEORGE HOTEL

HIGH STREET, DORCHESTER-ON-THAMES, OXFORD OX10 7HH

In the heart of the Thames Valley lies The George. Dating from the 15th century, it is one of the oldest inns in the country. In the days of the stage coach, it provided a welcome haven for many an aristocrat including the first Duchess of Marlborough, Sarah Churchill. However, more recent times have seen famous guests of a different hue such as author D H Lawrence. The buildings of the George Hotel have changed little since their heyday as a coaching inn. It retains all the beauty and charm of those days, whilst offering every modern amenity. All rooms are en suite and furnished with fine antiques; the décor suits the requirements of modern times whilst maintaining the spirit of the past. Only the freshest and finest produce is used for the daily changing menu. The imaginative cuisine, awarded AA Rosettes, is beautifully presented and delicious. The beamed dining room provides a delightful setting in which to enjoy an excellent meal, served by friendly, professional staff. Dorchester-on-Thames provides easy access to the Cotswolds, Blenheim Palace and Oxford, Stratford-upon-Avon, Henley, Windsor. Guests can go for beautiful walks and enjoy cultural and sporting activities. Excellent meeting facilities for up to 36 in the Stable Suite and 2 smaller rooms each for up to 8 people.

Our inspector loved: *The intimate restaurant with its water feature garden.*

Directions: On A4074, 9 miles south of Oxford.

Web: www.johansens.com/georgedorchester
Tel: 0870 381 8539
International: +44 (0)1865 340404
Fax: 01865 341620

Price Guide:
single £75
double £95
four poster £120

NEW

THE WHITE HART HOTEL

NETTLEBED, HENLEY-ON-THAMES, OXFORDSHIRE RG9 5DD

Directions: Between Wallingford and Henley-on-Thames on the A4130.

Web: www.johansens.com/whitehartnettlebed
E-mail: info@whitehartnettlebed.com
Tel: 0870 381 9292
International: +44 (0)1491 641245
Fax: 01491 649018

Price Guide:
double/twin £105-£145

Within easy reach of London, Birmingham and Bristol via the M4 and M40, The White Hart Hotel is just a 5-minute drive from Henley-on-Thames, 15 minutes from Reading and ½ hour from Oxford. The site of a coaching inn since 1456, today, guests enter through the 17th-century façade into a surprisingly contemporary, minimalist interior where modern luxury combines perfectly with Old World charm. The soothing colour scheme of grey, beige, taupe and aubergine lends a relaxing atmosphere throughout the hotel where 12 individually styled en suite guest rooms feature Internet connection and CD player as standard. Pre-dinner drinks may be taken in the cosy bar before entering The Nettlebed restaurant, which is renowned for its simple, seasonal and contemporary food. Alternatively, guests may dine in the more informal White Hart Bistro where an affordable, upmarket and classic English pub menu is on offer. Al fresco dining on the Terrace is available during the summer months. Conferences and small parties for up to 34 can be accommodated in The Veuve Clicquot room. Places of interest nearby include Blenheim Palace, Stonor Park and Grey's Court. Golf at nearby Huntercombe Golf Club.

Our inspector loved: The imaginative modern British food and warmth of service.

THE KINGS HEAD INN & RESTAURANT

THE GREEN, BLEDINGTON, NR KINGHAM, OXFORDSHIRE OX7 6XQ

The award-winning Kings Head Inn and Restaurant is peacefully located beside a traditional village green, complete with a bubbling brook inhabited by friendly ducks. During the summer months Morris dancers and musicians can regularly be seen in action on the green performing the Bledington Dances. The building has always served as a hostelry and much of its medieval character remains. With its exposed stone walls, original beams, inglenook fireplace and old settles, the Kings Head fulfils everyone's anticipations of a traditional English inn. The attractive timbered bedrooms are all furnished to complement the full facilities. The carefully compiled menu is changed regularly and is backed up by a selection of fine wines. Excellent inventive bar food is served at lunchtime and in the evenings together with a changing selection of real ales. The Kings Head Inn is situated in the heart of the Cotswolds, within easy reach of Oxford, Stratford-upon-Avon, Cheltenham and Blenheim.

Our inspector loved: This inn sitting on the green with a lovely welcome and log fires in winter.

Directions: Take the A44 Oxford–Woodstock road to Chipping Norton, then the B4450 to Bledington; or take the Oxford–Burford road to Stow-on-the-Wold and join the B4450. Nearest motorway M40 junction 11.

Web: www.johansens.com/kingshead
E-mail: kingshead@orr-ewing.com
Tel: 0870 381 8654
International: +44 (0)1608 658365
Fax: 01608 658902

Price Guide:
single £50
double £70–£95
four-poster £100

DUKE OF MARLBOROUGH COUNTRY INN

WOODLEYS, WOODSTOCK, OXFORD OX20 1HT

Directions: The inn is mid-way between Oxford and Chipping Norton, and is situated on the main A44 road, north of Woodstock.

Web: www.johansens.com/dukeofmarlborough
E-mail: sales@dukeofmarlborough.co.uk
Tel: 0870 381 9219
International: +44 (0)1993 811460
Fax: 01993 810165

Price Guide:
single £60
double/twin £80
suite £100

Banbury

Oxford

Henley-on-Thames

This delightful, traditional British inn is just a few minutes from the bustling town of Woodstock, and a drive away from the university city of Oxford. Its new hotel accommodation has been created in a separate rustic building, designed in keeping with the rural setting. The 13 en-suite rooms are comfortably furnished and warmly lit, with colour televisions, tea and coffee making facilities, telephones and modem points. Priding itself on its levels of service and hospitality, the Duke of Marlborough serves thoughtfully prepared seasonal dishes in its 2 restaurants. Guests can choose between the Modern Restaurant with its contrasting pastel shades, imposing prints and vaulted ceilings and the Traditional Restaurant, which boasts oak-clad and exposed Cotswold walls, soft lighting and a log fire. The standard of cuisine is consistently high throughout, and menus make good use of locally sourced produce. Visitors are also warmly welcomed into the bar, and can enjoy an extensive wine list and collection of real ales. The beer garden provides a safe and secure area for youngsters when the weather is fine. Further afield, Blenheim Palace, the birthplace of Winston Churchill, is well worth a visit, as are Woodstock itself, Oxford and the glorious Cotswolds.

Our inspector loved: *The spacious new bedrooms as an addition to this gem of an inn.*

BARNSDALE LODGE

THE AVENUE, RUTLAND WATER, NR OAKHAM, RUTLAND, LEICESTERSHIRE LE15 8AH

Situated in the ancient county of Rutland, amid unspoilt countryside, Barnsdale Lodge overlooks the rippling expanse of Rutland Water. After 13 years, the expansion is finally complete and guests are invited to enjoy the hospitality offered by the friendly and efficient staff. A restored 17th-century farmhouse, the atmosphere and style are distinctively Edwardian. This theme pervades throughout, from the courteous service to the furnishings and gardens. The 45 en-suite bedrooms, mostly on the ground floor, including 2 superb rooms specifically designed for disabled guests, evoke a mood of relaxing comfort. Traditional English cooking and fine wines are served. A bistro style menu using locally sourced produce can be enjoyed in the garden, conservatory, courtyard and dining rooms. There are 5 conference rooms and facilities for wedding receptions and parties. Interconnecting bedrooms are available for families. Belvoir and Rockingham Castles are nearby. Rutland Water, a haven for nature lovers, offering several water sports as well as birdwatching and cycling.

Our inspector loved: The black cast iron kitchen range and bread oven from the original farmhouse.

Directions: The Lodge is on A606 Oakham–Stamford road.

Web: www.johansens.com/barnsdalelodge
E-mail: enquiries@barnsdalelodge.co.uk
Tel: 0870 381 8342
International: +44 (0)1572 724678
Fax: 01572 724961

Price Guide:
single £75
double/twin £99.50
lake view/family room £120

THE OLD VICARAGE HOTEL

WORFIELD, BRIDGNORTH, SHROPSHIRE WV15 5JZ

Directions: 8 miles west of Wolverhampton, 1 mile from A454, 2 miles from A442, 8 miles south of M54, junction 4.

Web: www.johansens.com/oldvicaragewolverhampton
E-mail: admin@the-old-vicarage.demon.co.uk
Tel: 0870 381 8790
International: +44 (0)1746 716497
Fax: 01746 716552

Price Guide:
single £80–£110
double/twin £120–£175
suites £155–£175

Enthusiastic and welcoming husband and wife owners, David and Sarah Blakstad, believe and succeed in placing guests above everything and providing a relaxed and homely atmosphere that immediately makes them feel at ease. The hotel's location is also a help. A former Edwardian parsonage it stands serenely on the crest of a hill overlooking the timeless, conservation village of Worfield and is reached by a rambling leafy lane. Around the hotel's red brick exterior, topped by delightful, decorative chimneys, are 2 acres of lawned grounds and colourful gardens that offer peace, tranquillity and escapism - an idyllic scene that guests can also enjoy from their rooms or The Old Vicarage's spacious conservatory. Elegance and tasteful décor are the hallmarks of the interior with rooms liberally highlighted with period furniture, antique clocks, Moorcroft pottery and fine paintings. Bedrooms are charming and individually furnished in Edwardian and Victorian styles to complement the features of the house. 2 Coach House rooms have French windows leading into a private garden. Award-winning cuisine can be enjoyed in an intimate restaurant. The Ironbridge Gorge Museum complex, the Severn Valley Railway, stately homes, castles and National Trust gardens are among easily reached attractions.

Our inspector loved: *This refreshing retreat and delightful dining.*

OVERTON GRANGE HOTEL

OVERTON, NR LUDLOW, SHROPSHIRE SY8 4AD

Set in the beautiful South Shropshire countryside, Overton Grange is an ideal base from which to discover the hidden delights of the Welsh Marches. This privately owned Edwardian country house, within delightful grounds, overlooking the Shropshire hills, was built in 1905 and still retains its homely charm with blazing log fires in the winter and pleasant lawns to stroll around in the summer sunshine. The 14 comfortable en-suite bedrooms offer excellent views. With an atmosphere of tranquillity, tradition, indulgence and a reputation for friendly hospitality, fine food and efficient service, an enjoyable stay is guaranteed. Highly acclaimed head chef, Olivier Bossut, is passionate about food and serves dishes of exceptional flavour rooted in classical French cuisine in the 3 AA Rosette awarded restaurant. Overton Grange is the perfect setting for private gatherings, celebrations and house parties. Private facilities are available ensuring total peace and quiet for conducting business in a concentrated atmosphere with colleagues and clients.

Our inspector loved: The dining experience.

Directions: From the A49, exit 2 miles south of Ludlow. Take the B4361 Ludlow - Richard Castle Road. The hotel is about ¼ of a mile along this road.

Chester

Oswestry

Shrewsbury   Wolverhampton

● Bridgnorth

Web: www.johansens.com/overton
E-mail: info@overtongrangehotel.com
Tel: 0870 381 9135
International: +44 (0)1584 873500
Fax: 01584 873524

Price Guide:
single £75–£130
double £130–£160

Pen-Y-Dyffryn Hall Hotel

RHYDYCROESAU, NR OSWESTRY, SHROPSHIRE SY10 7JD

Directions: From A5 and Oswestry town centre take B4580 west towards Llansiln for approximately 3 miles. After a sharp bend turn left in village.

Web: www.johansens.com/penydyffryn
E-mail: stay@peny.co.uk
Tel: 0870 381 8809
International: +44 (0)1691 653700
Fax: 01691 650066

Price Guide:
single £79
double £98–£150

From the moment you drive up to this picturesque, silver-stone rural retreat you realise that you're somewhere special. Pen-Y-Dyffryn Hall is a gem in a spectacular setting with lush green pastures, gently sloping hillsides and dramatically rising mountains. It's a region of unspoilt natural beauty where falcons and buzzards rule the skies and badgers and foxes roam below. Built in 1845 as a rectory for an eccentric Celtic scholar, the listed Hall stands 1,000 feet up the last hill in Shropshire between Chester and Shrewsbury. It combines tranquility, superb comfort, unobtrusive hospitality and good food with an unpretentious atmosphere and enchanting charm. The best feature, however is the glorious views over the garden to the nearby Welsh mountains. For guests preferring an extra touch of seclusion there are 4 bedrooms in an adjacent Coach House with their own stone-walled private patios. Some bedrooms have spa baths. During cooler months log fires burn in the lounge and restaurant where superb, adventurous cuisine has earned the Hotel a prestigious AA 2 Rosettes food award, also the Good Hotel guide Cesar award for Country Hotel of the Year 2003, Independent on Sunday award for the best view and Which? Hotel Guide Rural Retreat award 2004. 4 National Trust properties and 6 golf courses are within easy reach.

Our inspector loved: Walking in the wonderful countryside surrounding the hotel then returning to this true oasis. Wonderful homemade cakes too!

SHROPSHIRE - TELFORD (NORTON)

THE HUNDRED HOUSE HOTEL, NORTON

BRIDGNORTH ROAD, NORTON, NR SHIFNAL, TELFORD, SHROPSHIRE TF11 9EE

Run by the charming Phillips family, this hotel is best described as an intriguing blend of hospitality, eccentricity, warmth and wit. Its name comes from medieval times when England was divided into Hundreds. Beyond stained-glass doors with the words "Temperance Hall", there are lavishly decorated bars and dining rooms with old quarry tiled floors, exposed brickwork, beamed ceilings and oak panelling. All bedrooms are en suite and offer every modern facility, whilst the superior rooms are sumptuously furnished with period furniture and half-tester or four-poster beds. They also come with a very special feature: each has got its own velvet-covered swing! Designed by the owners, Sylvia and Henry, a charming garden filled with unusual roses, trees and a large working herb garden enhances the delightful atmosphere of the house. The Hundred House has received 2 AA Rosettes for food for the seventh consecutive year and was awarded "Top Dining Pub of the Year" in the Good Pub Guide 2003. Stuart, the younger son, is a Michelin-trained chef and his brother, David, selects traditional beers, milds and stouts, as well as Old and New World wines for the extensive wine list. The newly converted Tithe Barn, with its own reception and bar area and mezzanine level, is the ideal venue for corporate events, conferences or receptions, accommodating parties of up to 100 persons.

Directions: Norton is on the A442 Bridgnorth-Telford road.

Web: www.johansens.com/hundredhousetelford
E-mail: reservations@hundredhouse.co.uk
Tel: 0870 381 8629
International: +44 (0)1952 730353
Fax: 01952 730355/0845 6446 040

Price Guide:
single £69–£85
double £99–£125

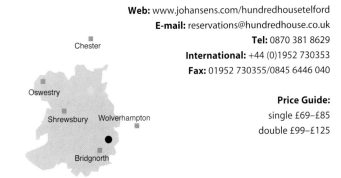

Our inspector loved: It, so charismatic. a very special garden too.

SOULTON HALL

NR WEM, SHROPSHIRE SY4 5RS

Directions: M54 to end, then take A5 to junction with A49. Go north on A49, then join B5065 west to Wem.

Web: www.johansens.com/soultonhall
E-mail: j.ashton@soultonhall.fsbusiness.co.uk
Tel: 0870 381 8899
International: +44 (0)1939 232786
Fax: 01939 234097

Price Guide:
single £40–£55
double £76–£110

Historic and imposing Soulton Hall stands in 550 acres of beautiful Shropshire parkland 2 miles east of the ancient market town of Wem. Dating from the 15th and 17th centuries, this Tudor brick built manor, with a magnificent pillared courtyard and beautiful walled garden, retains much of the grandeur and character of those bygone days, enhanced with all modern facilities. Ann and John Ashton, descendants of the Protestant Lord Mayor of London who bought Soulton in 1556, have created a hotel of warmth whilst retaining many of the unique features in the 4 spacious bedrooms in the house. 2 more modern bedrooms in the coach house are equally comfortably and provide total privacy. Ann Ashton presides in the kitchen where her skills in traditional English cooking are enhanced by imagination and flair. Specialities might include hand-raised game pie or butter baked salmon served with saffron oil. The restaurant is open to non-residents for dinner. There is a congenial bar and ample parking space. Hawkstone Country Park, Hodnet Hall and Gardens, Grinshill, Nescliffe Hill, Ironbridge, Shrewsbury, Chester, Stoke and Worcester are within easy reach. Soulton Hall is ideal for exclusive use for family parties and coporate meetings.

Our inspector loved: *This totaly unspoilt ancient hall, with a traditional welcome to match.*

COMPTON HOUSE
TOWNSEND, AXBRIDGE, SOMERSET BS26 2AJ

With a wealth of charm and atmosphere dating back to a less hectic era, this impressive 17th-century, Grade II listed manor house is a real gem. Beautifully and peacefully situated in historic Axbridge, at the foot of the southern slopes of scenic Mendip Hills, it commands spectacular views over the Somerset Levels to Glastonbury Tor. Delightfully designed and surrounded by an expansive and secluded lawned garden, Compton House is steeped in history. Parts of the hotel date back to Elizabethan times and there is an abundance of oak panelling, elegant mouldings and wonderful fireplaces throughout. Enthusiastic owners, Patricia and Robert Tallack, whose interest is routing local walks, have created a homely, relaxing ambience and their continual pursuit of excellence has earned the hotel a reputation for comfort, hospitality and service. Meeting facilities are available and intimate weddings can be arranged. The generous en-suite bedrooms boast many original features, and Patricia uses the freshest of West Country produce for the superb dishes served in the attractive dining room, following apèritifs, if desired, on the sun-catching garden terrace. Cheddar, with its fascinating gorge, is just 2 miles away, Wells and its magnificent cathedral 10 miles, Bath and Bristol, with its airport, are both within easy reach.

Our inspector loved: All the wonderful surprises that greets guests when walking through the front door.

Directions: From the M5 take junction 22 then the A38 towards Bristol. After 6 miles turn right onto the A371 to Cheddar/Wells. Compton House is ½ mile on the right, west of Axbridge.

Web: www.johansens.com/comptonhouse
E-mail: info@comptonhse.com
Tel: 0870 381 8441
International: +44 (0)1934 733944
Fax: 01934 733945

Price Guide:
single from £65
double/twin from £100

ASHWICK COUNTRY HOUSE HOTEL

DULVERTON, SOMERSET TA22 9QD

Directions: From the M5, exit at junction 27 onto the A361 to Tiverton. Take the A396 north until joining the B3222 to Dulverton and then the B3223 signposted Lynton and Exford. After a steep climb drive over a second cattle grid and turn left to Ashwick House.

Web: www.johansens.com/ashwickcountryhouse
E-mail: ashwickhouse@talk21.co.uk
Tel: 0870 381 8327
International: +44 (0)1398 323868
Fax: 01398 323868

Price Guide: (including dinner)
single £86–£90
double £146–£160

This small, charming AA Red Star Edwardian Country House stands in 6 acres of beautiful grounds above the picturesque valley of the River Barle within Exmoor National Park. Sweeping lawns lead to woods and water gardens where guests can relax in summer shade and breathe in sweet scents of wild flowers. Ashwick House offers Old World hospitality. Its atmosphere is sunny with flowers in summer and elegantly cosy with candlelight and log fires in winter. The baronial-style hall with its long, broad gallery and cheerful log fire, the restaurant opening onto a terrace where breakfast is served and the comfortably furnished lounge offer a peaceful sanctuary not easily found in today's busy world. All bedrooms are spacious and pleasantly decorated, finished with many thoughtful personal touches. Chef-patron Richard Sherwood presents quality cuisine using fresh local produce. Shooting and riding facilities are close by. Magnificent walks on Exmoor from the hotel. Dunster's Norman Castle and 17th- century Yarm Market, Exmoor Forest, many National Trust houses and gardens are nearby.

Our inspector loved: *As always the idyllic location and warm welcome.*

THREE ACRES COUNTRY HOUSE

THREE ACRES, BRUSHFORD, DULVERTON, SOMERSET TA22 9AR

Hidden by trees in large secluded grounds on the edge of Exmoor, the peaceful Three Acres Country House is an ideal oasis in which to escape the pressures of modern day living. The spacious rooms have been decorated with relaxation and comfort in mind, with generous sofas, log fires, and a licensed bar with a sun terrace. There is no morning rush for a delicious breakfast, which includes daily specials using fresh local produce. Excellent restaurants, cafés and pubs full of character can be found in the area and the owners are very helpful with making recommendations and booking tables. Each of the luxury bedrooms has been individually decorated and styled, featuring comfortable beds, crisp white linen, superb facilities and delightful views. Bathrooms, some with free-standing baths, have fluffy white towels and delicately scented toiletries. The hotel is ideally situated for visiting the dramatic coast, local treasures and beauty spots, which are too numerous to list. The unspoilt charm of Dulverton is nearby with shops, art galleries and antiques. Exmoor National Park is a haven of wildlife including red deer, bird life and trout filled rivers. A plethora of outdoor pursuits can be arranged including cycling, horse riding, fishing and shooting.

Our inspector loved: *The peaceful and tranquil ambience throughout the hotel.*

Directions: From Exmoor Visitors Centre follow the main Tiverton Road (B3222) out of Dulverton. Follow this road until you reach Brushford. Turn right at the Carnarvon Arms garage. After 300 yards turn right at a small crossroads. The hotel is just ahead.

Web: www.johansens.com/threeacres
E-mail: enquiries@threeacrescountryhouse.co.uk
Tel: 0870 381 9229
International: +44 (0)1398 323730

Bath

Taunton   Yeovil

Price Guide:
single £50–£65
double/twin £70–£100

THE OLD RECTORY

CRICKET MALHERBIE, ILMINSTER, SOMERSET TA19 0PW

Directions: The nearest motorway is M5. Exit at junction 25, join A358 towards Chard at A303 roundabout take the Chard exit again onto A358. Drive through the village of Donyatt, turn left for Ilminster and then right for Cricket Malherbie.

Web: www.johansens.com/oldrectoryilminster
E-mail: info@malherbie.co.uk
Tel: 0870 381 8785
International: +44 (0)1460 54364
Fax: 01460 57374

Price Guide:
single £55–£65
double £85–£95

The Old Rectory is an enchanting thatched house with weathered hamstone walls and Strawberry Hill gothic windows. This beautiful retreat, renowned for its large traditional English gardens, orchards and huge trees, was recently voted "Best Bed and Breakfast in the South West by the Taste of the West " and "Top 30" by *Which? Hotel Guide*. The interior is equally as stunning with a flagstone hall, beautiful carved oak beams and décor with emphasis on simplicity inkeeping with the period of the house. Up to 10 people can be accommodated in the 5 immaculate bedrooms, which are elegantly decorated and extremely comfortable with sweeping views over the pretty gardens and surrounding farmlands. The patio around an old well, which catches the last of the evening sun, is the perfect spot for pre-dinner drinks before dining in the deep blue dining room, ideal for dinner parties and weekends with friends. Highly acclaimed, locally sourced food is served in 4 courses and is suitably accompanied by linen napkins, silver cutlery and bone china. Each morning there is a scrumptious breakfast laid out with plenty of choice ranging from fresh fruit to a traditional English breakfast. The Old Rectory is a great base for exploring the historical towns of Bath, Wells and Glastonbury as well as the World Heritage Jurassic Coast and Stonehenge.

Our inspector loved: *The welcome, the superb presentation and the totally relaxing atmosphere.*

PORLOCK VALE HOUSE

PORLOCK WEIR, SOMERSET TA24 8NY

This former hunting lodge positioned in a truly spectacular setting pinioned by the sea and lush forest, offers a welcome friendly, informal and comforting atmosphere to visitors tired of the formality of traditional hotel accommodation. Porlock Vale's extensive gardens are a sight to behold, visitors always cherish fond memories of the lazy summer afternoons spent there in quiet repose. Winter season also sticks in the mind, with the coast and the Bristol channel viewed from the tranquillity of the lounge with its crackling log fire. Visitors dine in a beautiful dining room, where delicious local fare is served within mouth-watering menus. The delightful bedrooms are all individually styled, commanding views of the ocean, the tastefully laid out gardens or the wooded combe that flanks the hotel. Situated at the heart of the Exmoor National Park, the Porlock Vale House is the ideal base for a walking tour around this region of dramatic beauty. The area is literally awash with quaint traditional villages dotted along the awe-inspiring coast. Famous landmarks, such as the Dunkery Beacon and the Doone Valley, are also close at hand. Midweek special breaks are available.

Our inspector loved: The location within acres of woodland and grounds leading down to the sea.

Directions: Join the A39 and follow the signs to Minehead. When in Porlock Village, pick up the signs for Porlock Weir.

Web: www.johansens.com/porlockvale
E-mail: info@porlockvale.co.uk
Tel: 0870 381 8830
International: +44 (0)1643 862338
Fax: 01643 863338

Price Guide:
single £55–£70
double £95–£135

157

FARTHINGS HOTEL & RESTAURANT

HATCH BEAUCHAMP, SOMERSET TA3 6SG

Directions: Exit M5 Junction 25, join A358. Go through Henlade and carry on for approximately a mile, then turn left signed Hatch Beauchamp.

Web: www.johansens.com/farthings
E-mail: farthing1@aol.com
Tel: 0870 381 8515
International: +44 (0)1823 480664
Fax: 01823 481118

Price Guide:
single £75–£90
double/twin £105–£125
suites £135

Situated in the delightful village of Hatch Beauchamp, Farthings overlooks a cricket pitch and is surrounded by 3 acres of beautiful grounds. With a wonderfully relaxing and informal atmosphere it is a place to unwind in a pleasant, totally non-smoking environment. Owners Stephen and Hilary Murphy have over 20 years experience in welcoming guests, and as chef Stephen creates superb menus, cooked and presented to your choice in the 2 AA Rosette awarded restaurant. Each of the 10 spacious en-suite rooms is extremely comfortable with excellent facilities, whilst the self-contained Maple Suite comprises a well-appointed bedroom, Regency-style sitting room and modern conservatory with access to the main gardens. Elsewhere in the hotel, the tasteful lounge and bar with open fires provide a sociable ambience for an evening drink, and in winter an escape from the cold outside. The hotel has its own fascinating 250-year-old history but there are numerous places to visit nearby including Barrington Court, Forde Abbey and Gardens, Hestercombe Gardens, Wells Cathedral and the city of Bath. Cheddar Gorge and both the north and south Devon coasts can also be explored from here. Farthings is open over the Christmas period; prices are available on request.

Our inspector loved: This tucked away country house hotel offering total relaxation, yet so near the busy world.

BERYL

WELLS, SOMERSET BA5 3JP

This 19th-century Gothic mansion is a true little gem, set in 13 acres of parkland and gardens, which have been lovingly restored with great skill. Tastefully furnished with antiques, it also offers hospitality of the highest order. Holly Nowell and her daughter Mary-Ellen are charming hostesses, and take pride in the great attention to detail evident throughout the house. Guests are invited to use the honesty bar in the Green Room or enjoy drinks and wines on the lawn in summer. Overnight guests and house parties are a speciality, whilst there are a host of highly recommended pubs and restaurants within easy reach. The en-suite bedrooms have interesting views and offer all modern comforts. Places of interest nearby include Wells Cathedral (1 mile), Wookey Hole Caves, Cheddar Gorge, Glastonbury Abbey, Longleat House, Stourhead, Farleigh Castle, The Roman Baths at Bath, and many more fascinating places. For more active guests, there is Beryl's outdoor pool, marvellous golf, fishing, riding, excellent walking and a nearby leisure centre.

Our inspector loved: *The warm feel of wanting to return to this enchanting country house.*

Directions: Leave Wells on Radstock Road B3139. Follow the signs to "The Horringtons" and the "H" sign for hospital. After the hospital turn left into Hawkers Lane, Beryl is signed at the top with a leafy 500-yard drive to the main gate.

Web: www.johansens.com/beryl
E-mail: stay@beryl-wells.co.uk
Tel: 0870 381 8358
International: +44 (0)1749 678738
Fax: 01749 670508

Price Guide:
single £55–£75
double £75–£120

GLENCOT HOUSE

GLENCOT LANE, WOOKEY HOLE, NR WELLS, SOMERSET BA5 1BH

Directions: From the M4, exit at junction 18. Take the A46 to Bath and then follow the signs to Wells and Wookey Hole. From the M5, exit at junction 22. Join the A38 and then the A371 towards Wells and Wookey Hole.

Web: www.johansens.com/glencothouse
E-mail: relax@glencothouse.co.uk
Tel: 0870 381 8552
International: +44 (0)1749 677160
Fax: 01749 670210

Price Guide:
single £72–£85
double £96–£130

Idyllically situated in 18 acres of sheltered gardens and parkland with river frontage, Glencot House is an imposing Grade II listed Victorian mansion built in grand Jacobean style. It has been sensitively renovated to its former glory to provide comfortable country house accommodation and a homely atmosphere. This elegantly furnished hotel has countless beautiful features: carved ceilings, walnut panelling, mullioned windows, massive fireplaces, antiques and sumptuous chandeliers. The bedrooms are decorated and furnished with period pieces, full en-suite facilities, good views and all have four poster beds. Guests can enjoy pleasant walks in the garden, trout fishing in the river, snooker, table tennis, a sauna or a dip in the jet-stream pool. The dining room overlooks the grounds and diverse and delicious fare is served in the restaurant, enriched by beautiful glassware, silver and china. Places of interest include the caves at Wookey Hole, the cathedral city of Wells. The houses and gardens of Longleat, Stourhead and Montacute are all nearby as are Glastonbury, Bath, the Mendip Hills and Cheddar Gorge.

Our inspector loved: The beautiful house, features and magnificent grounds.

KARSLAKE HOUSE HOTEL & RESTAURANT

HALSE LANE, WINSFORD, EXMOOR NATIONAL PARK, SOMERSET TA24 7JE

Originally a 15th-century malthouse, Karslake House was subsequently named after Sir John Burgess Karslake, a prominent lawyer and member of Parliament during the 1860s. Nestling in the wooded hills of Exmoor, Karslake stands in an ideal location for exploring the North and South of Devon's coast. Views of the Exe valley and hotel's garden can be enjoyed from 3 of the 6 en-suite bedrooms and the four-poster guest room offers total luxury. Karslake's AA Rosette awarded restaurant prepares fresh cuisine created from seasonal, local produce and all the bread, jams and marmalades served with breakfast are homemade. A comprehensive wine list accompanies the menu together with a well-stocked bar. The welcoming and cosy sitting room enables guests to relax in the deep-seated sofas by the wood burner but for the more active guest there are many activities on offer to occupy the time. Shooting on the Exmoor hills and valleys, pony trekking along the rolling moorland and walking expeditions, complete with special packed-lunch provided by the hotel, can all be arranged. Fly-fishing, salmon or trout fishing tuition can also be organised nearby during a 1, 2 or 3-day course. Day-tickets are available for experienced fishermen.

Our inspector loved: *The idyllic moorland village location and overall feeling of warmth and welcome.*

Directions: Exit the M5, junction 27. Follow the A361 for approximately 3 miles to the roundabout. Take the first exit signed Dulverton (A396) then follow signs to Minehead and turn left at the first Winsford sign.

Web: www.johansens.com/karslake
E-mail: enquiries@karslakehouse.co.uk
Tel: 0870 381 9134
International: +44 (0)1643 851242
Fax: 01643 851242

Price Guide:
single £55-£70
double £75-£110

SOMERFORD HALL

BREWOOD, STAFFORDSHIRE ST19 9DQ

A Palladian-style hall, built in 1730, Somerford is a grand venue featuring original plasterwork and a galleried oak staircase. Architectural delights feature throughout the Hall and the ballroom ceiling is a beautiful example of period plasterwork, which has been carefully restored. With over 30 acres of extensive gardens, parkland woods and lakes, guests have no choice but to relax and unwind in this secluded location whilst only being 2 miles from the M6 and M54 motorway networks. Somerford Hall prides itself on its high standard of professional and considerate service. Advice and help for events such as wedding ceremonies are available and with the surrounding parkland and attractive gazebo within the grounds the perfect location for photographs. The 20 individually designed suites and rooms, as well as charming sitting rooms provide tranquil, relaxing environments with beautiful views. There is also a variety of conference rooms available accommodating up to 120 persons. The extensive restaurant serves a variety of menus and the Hall's bar is a delightful sanctuary.

Directions: 2 miles from junction 12/M6. 3 miles from the new M6 Toll Road. 2 miles from junction 2/M54. From the M6 northbound take junction 10A to the M54 then exit at junction 2 to Stafford and continue straight ahead then take the left turning.

Web: www.johansens.com/somerford
E-mail: info@somerfordhall.co.uk
Tel: 0870 381 9120
International: +44 (0)1902 850108
Fax: 01902 850163

Price Guide:
single from £85
double from £110
suite from £150

Our inspector loved: *Its delightful Georgian plaster-work which is in total keeping with its comfortable atmosphere. A true balance of Georgian tradition with 21st-century modernisation.*

CLARICE HOUSE

HORRINGER COURT, HORRINGER ROAD, BURY ST EDMUNDS SUFFOLK IP29 5PH

Clarice House is a residential spa housed within a beautifully refurbished neo-Jacobean mansion. Set within 20 acres of Suffolk countryside its grounds include ancient woodland and a protected site of scientific interest. Inside, an air of calm relaxation pervades. Guests are welcomed in the large lounge with lovely panelling and carved wood whilst informal meals are served in the bar. The excellent restaurant is open to residents and non-residents alike. For those choosing to stay for bed and breakfast, bedrooms are comfortable and well-appointed with luxurious en-suite bathrooms. A variety of Spa Break packages are available which also include dinner and of course full use of the spa facilities, prices start from £135 per person. The gym comprises hi-tech equipment with computerised personal programme management. There is a team of dedicated instructors and a full programme of classes run daily. A beautiful 20-metre indoor swimming pool leads into a spa bath, steam room and sauna. The suite of beauty salons offers a huge range of indulgent treatments from the more traditional facials, manicures and pedicures to holistic treatments such as reflexology, reiki and Indian head massage. The hotel is within easy reach of the racing at Newmarket, the university city of Cambridge and glorious Constable country. Fly fishing and clay pigeon shooting can also arranged.

Our inspector loved: *The combination of modern comfort within the period surroundings.*

Directions: About 1 mile outside Bury St Edmunds, situated on the A143 towards Haverhill.

Web: www.johansens.com/clarice
E-mail: enquire@clarice–bury.fsnet.co.uk
Tel: 0870 381 8431
International: +44 (0)1284 705550
Fax: 01284 716120

Price Guide:
single £55-£75
double/twin £85-£100

NEW

THE BROME GRANGE HOTEL

BROME, EYE, SUFFOLK IP23 8AP

Directions: From the A14, east of Bury St Edmunds, take the A140 towards Norwich.

Web: www.johansens.com/bromegrange
E-mail: bromegrange@fastnet.co.uk
Tel: 0870 381 9299
International: +44 (0)1379 870456
Fax: 01379 870921

Price Guide:
single from £65
double from £85

Originally founded in the 16th century, The Brome Grange Hotel has recently returned to the loving care of private ownership and is enjoying a wonderful transformation. Set in lush countryside, the property is surrounded by delightful gardens and screened from the convenient A140. The characteristic interior offers every comfort and visitors are greeted by a warm welcome from owners and staff. Each of the courtyard bedrooms enjoys a view over the hotel gardens and the individual style of the rooms, with their distinctive beds, is a key feature of the hotel. The en-suite bathrooms are light, bright, airy and of ample size. Within the grounds the fully equipped Tithe Barn is an ideal venue for weddings, conferences and other functions. The restaurant serves English and international cuisine of the highest standard and specializes in fish dishes, caught directly from nearby Lowestoft. Other locally grown produce is used to create a mouthwatering and memorable dining experience. The Brome Grange Hotel is only a 45-minute drive from Norwich, Bury St Edmunds and Ipswich. Nearby attractions include Bressingham Steam Museum, Bressingham Plant Centre, Banham Zoo, Earsham Otter Trust and the Bruis Vineyard.

Our inspector loved: *The romantically inviting "Snailmaker" restaurant and its quirky namesake.*

WORLINGTON HALL COUNTRY HOUSE HOTEL

WORLINGTON, SUFFOLK IP28 8RX

Set in 5 acres of secluded gardens, encompassing a tranquil ornamental lake, this former manor house offers visitors impeccable hospitality in a relaxing atmosphere. The original building dates back to 1570, and recent refurbishments reflect the charm and elegance of that period. Comfort is a priority at Worlington Hall, and in all of the 8 individually designed bedrooms guests are welcomed with a complimentary decanter of sherry, fresh fruit and flowers. All rooms have every modern amenity guests expect from a distinguished country house hotel; the unique Coachhouse Suite boasts a four-poster bed. Dining is a memorable experience at Worlington Hall. Guests can enjoy pre-dinner drinks in the lounge bar before eating in the restaurant, which is complete with carved wood panelling and traditional log fire. The Bistro perpetuates the relaxed ambience of the rest of the hotel. Breakfast may be taken in the Alcove room, which also serves as an excellent venue for business lunches and small private parties, whilst the spacious Garden Suite is ideal for weddings and conferences. The attractive village location is within easy reach from main road networks as well as Stansted and Luton Airports. Newmarket, Cambridge, Ely and Bury St Edmunds are all close by.

Our inspector loved: The original panelling and open fire in the comfortable lounge/bar.

Directions: M11 jct 9 A11 (A14) - Worlington is signed just before the roundabout at Barton Mills.

Web: www.johansens.com/worlington
E-mail: info@worlingtonhall-hotel.co.uk
Tel: 0870 381 9161
International: +44 (0)1638 712237
Fax: 01638 712631

Price Guide:
single £60
double/twin £75–£80
coachhouse £150

STANHILL COURT HOTEL

STAN HILL ROAD, CHARLWOOD, NR HORLEY, SURREY RH6 0EP

Built in 1881 in the Scottish Baronial style, Stanhill Court Hotel is set in 35 acres of ancient wooded countryside and offers total peace and tranquillity. It boasts an original Victorian walled garden and amphitheatre available for concerts or corporate presentations and events. These facilities are enhanced by the rebuilding of the Orangery, offering further accommodation for events/conferences and banqueting. The hotel is traditionally furnished to provide an intimate, warm and comfortable atmosphere, with pitch pine panelling throughout the hall, minstrels gallery and barrel roof. There is a wide choice of bedrooms, all decorated and furnished to the same high standards and offering a full selection of facilities. Restaurant 1881 serves a superb à la carte menu which is international in flavour and complemented by an excellent range of regional and vintage wines. A choice of vegetarian dishes is always included and old-style, personal service is guaranteed. Versatile conference facilities include meeting rooms and 6 function rooms. Stanhill Court Hotel has a renowned reputation for wedding receptions, family celebrations and social gatherings. Voted Most Romantic Hotel by the AA, awarded 3 RAC Blue Ribbons and Michelin listed.

Directions: Charlwood is north-west of the airport off the M23/A23 via Hookwood or Lowfield Heath. Go through Charlwood and follow signs towards Newdigate.

Web: www.johansens.com/stanhillcourt
E-mail: enquiries@stanhillcourthotel.co.uk
Tel: 0870 381 8908
International: +44 (0)1293 862166
Fax: 01293 862773

Egham
Kingston upon Thames
Epsom
Guildford
Gatwick

Price Guide:
single from £95
double from £120

Our inspector loved: *The sparkling new bathrooms, and the stunning staircase.*

CHASE LODGE

10 PARK ROAD, HAMPTON WICK, KINGSTON-UPON-THAMES, SURREY KT1 4AS

Chase Lodge is situated in a quiet conservation area of architectural merit adjacent to Bushy Park. Originally built in 1870 as an artisan's house, the Lodge is now a very successful, bustling small hotel run by its owner, Denise Dove and her young staff. The interiors have been designed to a high standard, with particular regard to the bijou nature of the building and with well chosen items of furniture complementing bold décor and fabrics. The bedrooms are cosy and the most recently refurbished bathrooms all feature either a Jacuzzi bath or a steam shower. The conservatory-style restaurant, with its cane furniture and marble topped tables, looks onto the tiny courtyard garden. Its proximity to many major events in the English social season makes Chase Lodge an outstanding choice for value: Wimbledon tennis; the Oxford and Cambridge Boat Race; horse racing at Kempton Park, Epsom Downs, Sandown Park and Royal Ascot; rugby at Twickenham; and now the annual flower show at Hampton Court. Central London with its shops and theatres is a short train ride away. Other places of interest nearby are Richmond and Syon Park, Windsor Castle, Ham House and Kew Gardens.

Our inspector loved: *Its individual character and the imaginative use of space within a tiny town house setting.*

Directions: From the M3 (junction 1) or Kingston take the A308. At western end of Kingston Bridge is the Hampton Wick roundabout, take the White Hart exit into High Street (A310), then left at The Forresters into Park Road.

Egham

Kingston upon Thames

Epsom

Guildford

Gatwick

Web: www.johansens.com/chaselodge
E-mail: info@chaselodgehotel.com
Tel: 0870 381 8419
International: +44 (0)20 8943 1862
Fax: 020 8943 9363

Price Guide:
single from £65
double from £71

THE HOPE ANCHOR HOTEL

WATCHBELL STREET, RYE, EAST SUSSEX TN31 7HA

Directions: From the A268 circumnavigate Rye clockwise via the A259. Turn right by the Heritage Centre and straight up Mermaid Street. Turn right into West Street, right into Church Square and right again into Watchbell Street. The Hope Anchor is at the end of the street.

Web: www.johansens.com/hopeanchor
E-mail: info@thehopeanchor.co.uk
Tel: 0870 381 8607
International: +44 (0)1797 222216
Fax: 01797 223796

Price Guide:
double/twin £95–£150

Dating back to the mid-18th century, The Hope Anchor was featured in Malcolm Saville's children's books and with its beautiful old timbers, nooks and crannies and secret passages it possesses immense character and charm. An enviable position in one of Rye's most enchanting and interesting cobbled streets means it boasts stunning views across Romney Marsh, Camber Castle and the rivers Brede and Tillingham. Individually furnished bedrooms offer a range of double and family accommodation and all are en suite with tea and coffee making facilities and direct dial telephones. The hotel comprises a bar, lounge and an excellent restaurant that welcomes residents and non-residents alike. Menus portray an imaginative use of fresh, seasonally available local ingredients. Rye itself was described as, "about as perfect as a small town can get," by the Daily Telegraph and landmarks such as Mermaid Street, Church Square, St Mary's Church, Lamb House and the 13th-century Ypres Tower are all within a few minutes' stroll.

Our inspector loved: *The space and style in the Admiral's Apartment - just across the cobbled way with a view to the sea and its own tiny terrace garden.*

THE MILL HOUSE HOTEL

MILL LANE, ASHINGTON, WEST SUSSEX RH20 3BX

This charming Grade II listed building exudes warmth and character. Vestiges of the past are evident throughout the country house, and the original paintings adorning the walls and the antiques in the public rooms form a lasting testament to its 17th-century origins. Following extensive renovation, the house combines the charm and attentive service associated with bygone days with the modern facilities of the present. The enthusiastic owners, Simon and Maria Hudson, and their friendly staff provide a helpful yet unobtrusive service. The bedrooms are simple yet stylish. Gastronomes will be impressed with the excellent cuisine, which is complemented by a good selection of wines, liqueurs and Cognacs. The menu includes the ever popular griddled fillet steak with a rustique camembert and mixed peppercorn crust, served with a rich port sauce presented on wild mushrooms. Accommodating up to 30 people, the meeting room is ideal for small conferences and for private dining. Heritage enthusiasts will be delighted with the situation of this property, as Parham House and Arundel Castle and Cathedral are within easy reach. Petworth, Chichester and Brighton offer good shopping and antique hunting.

Our inspector loved: Its delightful seclusion and quiteness.

Directions: Ashington is west of the A24 and north of the junction with the A283. If travelling from the north, follow the large brown sign.

Web: www.johansens.com/millhousehotelashington
E-mail: ashingtonmill@aol.com
Tel: 0870 381 8735
International: +44 (0)1903 892426
Fax: 01903 892855

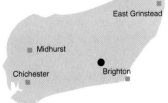

Price Guide:
single from £52
double £82–£92

THE OLD TOLLGATE RESTAURANT AND HOTEL

THE STREET, BRAMBER, STEYNING, WEST SUSSEX BN44 3WE

Directions: Bramber is off the A283 between Brighton and Worthing, easily accessed from the A24 or A27.

Web: www.johansens.com/oldtollgatebrighton
E-mail: info@oldtollgatehotel.com
Tel: 0870 381 8789
International: +44 (0)1903 879494
Fax: 01903 813399

Price Guide: (room only)
single from £78
double £78–£128
suite from £128

An original Tollhouse centuries ago, travellers now look forward to stopping here and paying their dues for wonderful hospitality. Part of the old building is still in evidence with newer additions attractively blending. There are some splendid suites and four-posters, which are excellent value, and delightful bedrooms, some of which are reached across the courtyard. The hotel is a popular meeting place for visitors and locals alike, with friendly staff adding to the welcoming ambience. The restaurant has built up a fine reputation, extending far beyond Sussex. It has a magnificent award-winning carvery and sumptuous cold table. Breakfast, lunch and dinner are all catered for at various price structures according to the number of courses consumed. Soups and broths, fresh and smoked fish, roasts and casseroles, pies and puddings and vegetarian dishes are in abundance. A secluded garden suntrap has been newly created. Bramber is famous for its Norman Castle and spectacular views over the South Downs. Brighton, with its shops, beach and Pavilion is an easy drive away, as is Worthing. Sporting activities nearby include riding, golf and fishing.

Our inspector loved: What everybody loves - the finest twice a day buffet in the south.

CROUCHERS COUNTRY HOTEL & RESTAURANT

BIRDHAM ROAD, APULDRAM, NEAR CHICHESTER, WEST SUSSEX PO20 7EH

This former farmhouse, set just ½ a mile from the Yacht Basin and 2 miles from the centre of Chichester, has been re-styled into a fine country hotel and awarded 3 AA stars for its 18 bedrooms, good food and most attentive service. The new, spacious open-plan ground floor impresses guests the moment they arrive at reception and the bedrooms, most of which are located in the converted coach house and barn, do not disappoint. However, it is the newly designed public areas which will excite approval: the bar and lounge areas and the fine new 60 seat restaurant have transformed Crouchers. Dishes, freshly prepared from the very finest ingredients and the inspiration of chef Gavin Wilson, have already won the first Rosette recognition. Meals are complemented by a carefully constructed and interesting wine list, reflecting the family's connections with South Africa. Crouchers Country Hotel will delight those wishing merely to relax and escape the pressures of a hectic lifestyle. In the summer months a tranquil ambience envelopes the courtyard as guests sip chilled drinks and laze in the sun.

Our inspector loved: The light, bright and spacious dining room with wonderful fish and shellfish choices and other good things from local suppliers.

Directions: From the M27, junction 12, take the A27 to Chichester and then the A286 south towards The Witterings. Crouchers Country Hotel is on the left.

Web: www.johansens.com/crouchersbottom
Tel: 0870 381 8462
International: +44 (0)1243 784995
Fax: 01243 539797

Price Guide:
single from £65
double from £95

THE ROYAL OAK INN

POOK LANE, EAST LAVANT, NR GOODWOOD, CHICHESTER, WEST SUSSEX PO18 0AX

The Royal Oak combines Georgian elegance, the warmth of a traditional inn and up-to-date facilities, with each of its 5 bedrooms coming complete with Internet access, direct dial telephones and state-of-the-art plasma television and audio systems. The rooms are accessed from a courtyard at the rear of the inn, which affords guests beautiful views of the open countryside. Furnishings are comfortable, and extend into the smart en-suite bathrooms. Renowned for its restaurant – booking is essential – the Royal Oak serves sumptuous menus, again fusing the modern with the more traditional. Dishes range from the exotic to classics such as premier Scottish fillet steak and roasted rump of lamb. The atmosphere is stylish but casual, with real ales drawn from a cask behind the "bar". Ideally situated for visitors to the region, the inn is close to the famous Goodwood Motor Circuit, Airfield and Racecourse, Chichester is nearby, and the South Downs provide excellent walking country.

Directions: From London take the A3 via the M25, and leave at the Milford Junction. Follow the A286 via Haslemere, Midhurst and on entering Lavant take a left turn signposted East Lavant. Go over a hump back bridge and the Royal Oak is on the left.

Web: www.johansens.com/royaloaksussex
E-mail: nickroyaloak@aol.com
Tel: 0870 381 9218
International: +44 (0)1243 527434

Price Guide:
single £60–£70
double/twin £90–£130

Our inspector loved: This dear little inn - worthy winner of the south east Pub of the Year Award.

WIDBROOK GRANGE

WIDBROOK, BRADFORD-ON-AVON, NR BATH, WILTSHIRE BA15 1UH

Widbrook Grange, home of resident owners Jane and Peter Wragg, is an elegant 250-year-old Georgian country house, peacefully located in 11 acres of grounds amidst rolling countryside yet only 17 minutes from the city of Bath. The hotel has an atmosphere of warmth and informality with cosy lounges and a log fire burning on cold winter nights. The service is attentive yet unobtrusive and for this, Widbrook Grange has been named RAC Little Gem Hotel of the Year for the last 6 years. The spacious, tastefully decorated bedrooms in the main house, courtyard and gardens include romantic four-posters, family rooms and facilities for the disabled. Families relax in the heated indoor swimming pool, as do delegates who use the hotel's conference suite. The intimate, AA Rosette award-winning Medlar Tree Restaurant serves fine British regional cuisine using fresh, home-grown produce, complemented by an interesting selection of New and Old World wines. Walks from the hotel lead to Kennet and Avon canal with its picturesque narrow boats, then on to the Saxon Tithe Barn and Church in the medieval town of Bradford-on-Avon. Longleat, Stonehenge and Lacock Abbey are all within easy driving distance, and for the more energetic, golf, horse riding and boat and cycle hire can be arranged.

Our inspector loved: The inviting indoor pool and pretty gardens.

Directions: From Bradford-on-Avon take the A363 Trowbridge Road. Widbrook Grange is 200 metres on the right after the Kennet and Avon canal.

Web: www.johansens.com/widbrookgrange
E-mail: stay@widbrookgrange.com
Tel: 0870 381 8996
International: +44 (0)1225 864750/863173
Fax International: +44 (0)1225 862890

Price Guide:
single £75–£105
double £90–£110
four poster £125
family rooms from £140

LUCKNAM PARK, BATH

COLERNE, CHIPPENHAM, WILTSHIRE SN14 8AZ

Directions: 15 minutes from M4, junctions 17 and 18, located between A420 and A4 near the village of Colerne.

Web: www.johansens.com/lucknampark
E-mail: reservations@lucknampark.co.uk
Tel: 0870 381 8707
International: +44 (0)1225 742777
Fax: 01225 743536

Price Guide: (room only)
single from £195
double/twin from £225
suite from £490

For over 250 years Lucknam Park has been a focus of fine society and aristocratic living, something guests will sense immediately upon their approach along the mile-long avenue lined with beech trees. Built in 1720, this magnificent Palladian mansion is situated just 6 miles from Bath on the southern edge of the Cotswolds. The delicate aura of historical context is reflected in fine art and antiques dating from the late Georgian and early Victorian periods. Award winning food can be savoured in the elegant restaurant, at tables laid with exquisite porcelain, silver and glassware, accompanied with wines from an extensive cellar. Set within the walled gardens of the hotel is the spa, comprising an indoor pool, sauna, solarium, steam room, whirlpool spa, gymnasium, beauty salon and snooker room. Numerous activities can be arranged on request, including hot-air ballooning, golf and archery. The Lucknam Park Equestrian Centre, which is situated on the estate, welcomes complete beginners and experienced riders and takes liveries. Bowood House, Corsham Court and Castle Combe are all nearby. Lucknam Park is a member of Relais & Châteaux.

Our inspector loved: *The mile long driveway, the grand suites and the inviting swimming pool and spa.*

HINTON GRANGE

NR HINTON, DRYHAM, WILTSHIRE SN14 8HG

Originally built in 1614 and extended in 1750, Hinton Grange nestles beneath a hill within the famous Anglo Saxon Battle of Dyrham site. Today, the hotel provides a hopelessly romantic, if somewhat slightly eccentric, retreat with its low doors and beams, old stone walls and frayed rugs. Converted barns house some of the best bedrooms and open fires are a feature throughout, providing the warmest welcome even on the coldest days. All of the rooms are individually decorated with four-poster beds and comfy Olde Worlde furnishings. Some have screened Victorian bathing alcoves with cast-iron baths, and dinner can also be served privately in a candle-lit, fireside setting. Cuisine at the hotel has an excellent reputation and daily changing menus are prepared using the finest and freshest ingredients. A choice of restaurants include: the Inglenook, the smaller Crofters Nookery, and the tropical Georgian Conservatory, while pre-dinner drinks can be enjoyed in the snug sitting rooms adorned with antiques. Hinton adjoins the National Trust estate and stately home of Dyrham Park and the renowned Cotswold Way Walk meanders close to the house. Other nearby places of interest include Castle Combe and Laycock and the hotel itself offers croquet, fishing and Pitch and Putt.

Our inspector loved: The quiet location and pretty gardens.

Directions: 15 to 20 minutes away from Bath and Bristol.

Web: www.johansens.com/hintongrange
E-mail: mail@hintongrange.co.uk
Tel: 0870 381 8596
International: +44 (0)117 937 2916
Fax: 0117 937 3285

Price Guide:
single £85
double/twin £120–£160
suite £170

175

THE OLD MANOR HOTEL

TROWLE, NR BRADFORD-ON-AVON, WILTSHIRE BA14 9BL

Directions: The Hotel is on the A363 towards Trowbridge, 1½ miles from Bradford-on-Avon.

Web: www.johansens.com/oldmanorbath
E-mail: romanticbeds@oldmanorhotel.com
Tel: 0870 381 8782
International: +44 (0)1225 777393
Fax: 01225 765443

Price Guide:
single £70–£90
double/twin £90–£110
suite £130

Set on Trowle Common, only 8 miles from the centre of Bath, a Doomsday Book site in the heart of Wiltshire, this magnificent Grade II listed farmhouse is of outstanding historic interest with a combination of medieval and Queen Anne architecture. Surrounded by 4½ acres of farmland and picture perfect gardens, The Old Manor exudes a sense of idyllic rural charm and peace. The main buildings, barns and stables have been lovingly converted into bedrooms and are built around an extremely pretty courtyard. Romantic, spacious bedrooms and heavily beamed suites have uninterrupted views over open fields and are decorated with stunning antiques, huge comfortable beds (some four-poster) and glorious furnishings. Open fires complement the cosy atmosphere of the public areas, where ease and comfort are sublime. Delicious home-cooked meals are served in the restaurant, which was converted from the original milking parlour and boasts a large stone fireplace. Bird lovers will be astonished by the abundance of kestrels, sparrowhawks, buzzards, herons and wild duck in the area. The hotel is also the perfect base for walking the lovely Kennet and Avon Canal path with its slow moving barges and picturesque views. Bradford-on-Avon is nearby with its Saxon church (900AD), tithe barn, period streets and buildings as well as Lacock Abbey where Harry Potter was filmed.

Our inspector loved: The lovely private dining room overlooking the garden.

STANTON MANOR HOTEL & GALLERY RESTAURANT

STANTON SAINT QUINTIN, NR CHIPPENHAM, WILTSHIRE SN14 6DQ

A wide, columned entranceway welcomes visitors to this attractive stone-built hotel standing in 7 acres of beautiful grounds in the delightful Wiltshire village of Stanton Saint Quintin. The house is listed in the Domesday Book. It was once owned by Lord Burghley, chief minister to Queen Elizabeth 1, and was rebuilt in 1840. Stanton Manor has been completely refurbished and the new owners Robert & Linda Davis are on hand to ensure that a friendly and attentive service is extended to guests. Modern facilities and comforts combine easily and unobtrusively with those of the past, which include magnificent Tudor fireplaces and stone flooring. The ensuite bedrooms are spacious and individually designed with toning fabrics and comfortable furniture. 4 have king-size four poster beds to compliment the stunning New Oriental or Provencal themed rooms. 4 rooms are interconnecting suitable for large families. Head Chef, Nigel Harding, and his team take pride in creating traditional British cuisine with flair and quality, which is immaculately served in the elegant and light Gallery Restaurant, overlooking the grounds, exhibiting an eclectic collection of art by prominent Oriental artists. All artwork is for sale to customers and guests. Light snacks are available all day in the cosy refurbished bar or lounge.

Our inspector loved: The lovely gardens and the restaurants excellent food.

Directions: Exit the M4 at junction 17 and join the A429 towards Cirencester. After approximately 200 yards, turn left to Stanton Saint Quintin. Stanton Manor is on the left in the village.

Swindon
Bath
Warminster
Salisbury

Web: www.johansens.com/stantonmanor
E-mail: reception@stantonmanor.co.uk
Tel: 0870 381 8910
International: +44 (0)1666 837552
Fax: 01666 837022

Price Guide:
single £95–£105
double executive £125
double deluxe £165

WHATLEY MANOR

EASTON GREY, MALMESBURY, WILTSHIRE SN16 0RB

Directions: The hotel is situated off the B4040, 8 miles from junction 17 of the M4 motorway. 2 hours from London.

Web: www.johansens.com/whatley
E-mail: reservations@whatleymanor.com
Tel: 0870 381 9197
International: +44 (0)1666 822888
Fax: 01666 826120

Price Guide:
single/double/twin from £275
suite from £650

After 2 1/2 years of ceaseless, meticulous restoration and building the result is exquisite. Guests staying at this breathtakingly stylish and sophisticated retreat, set amidst 12 acres of superb landscaped gardens, will find a relaxing yet luxurious atmosphere of understated elegance, reminiscent of a friendly, welcoming private home. Every detail has been thought of in the 15 bedrooms and 8 suites, which are all individually designed with Italian furniture and handmade French wallpaper, and equipped with state-of-the-art sound and vision systems. Renowned head chef Martin Burge creates innovative cuisine, which guests can enjoy in 2 restaurants: the elegant and luxuriously decorated Dining Room, which echoes the sumptuous décor of the hotel, and the less formal, brasserie-style Le Mazot, which evokes the ambience of a Swiss chalet with its roaring central fire. Designed to restore both the body and mind, the hotel's Aquarias Spa offers a wide range of luxurious facilities including one of the largest hydrotherapy pools in the country as well as a 5-star La Prairie beauty centre. The hotel also boasts a private cinema. The Georgian city of Bath, Cheltenham, Stonehenge and the beautiful Cotswold countryside are only a few of the attractions on the doorstep.

Our inspector loved: The most amazing spa.

THE GEORGE INN

LONGBRIDGE DEVERILL, WARMINSTER, WILTSHIRE BA12 7DG

A warm welcome awaits guests to this friendly inn. All rooms have been refurbished, and there is a public bar as well as a cosy residents lounge with a good selection of books and games to while away a lazy afternoon. The inn can cater for conferences, weddings and parties. The welcoming Kingston Restaurant and the Longbridge Bar, which is warmed by an open fire, serve an excellent à la carte menu and a good selection of mouth-watering home-cooked dishes that might include tender lamb shank braised in a rich red wine and redcurrant jus or oven-baked Dover sole with lemon and herb butter. Outside the Riverside Garden, which is set in 2 acres of gardens and has plenty of car parking, is a popular venue during the warmer months. Active guests can explore the surroundings on foot or by bicycle, whilst golf and fishing can also be arranged. The George Inn is the ideal base from which to explore nearby Longleat and Bath, Stourhead, Wookey Hole Caves, Stonehenge and Wardour Castle.

Our inspector loved: *The friendly welcome and good food.*

Directions: From the A303 take the A350 towards Warminster; the George is on the left. From the A36 take the A350 towards Shaftesbury; the George is on the right.

Web: www.johansens.com/georgewarminster
Tel: 0870 381 8542
International: +44 (0)1985 840396
Fax: 01985 841333

Price Guide:
single £45
double/twin £70–£95
family room £80–£85

BUCKLAND MANOR

NEAR BROADWAY, WORCESTERSHIRE WR12 7LY

Directions: From the M40, exit at junction 8. Take the A40 to Burford, the A424 to Broadway and then the B4632 signposted Winchcombe to Buckland.

Web: www.johansens.com/bucklandmanor
E-mail: enquire@bucklandmanor.com
Tel: 0870 381 9175
International: +44 (0)1386 852626
Fax: 01386 853557

Price Guide:
single £225-£360
double £235-£370

The warm glow of Buckland Manor's golden Cotswold stone exterior blends beautifully with the colourful flowers and green shades of the glorious grounds, serving as an appetiser to visitors of the tranquil luxury and history inside those weather-beaten walls. A manor house on the site was first mentioned in the records of Gloucester Abbey in 600AD when the Abbot received it as a gift from Kynred, ruler of Mercier and chief king of the 7 kingdoms of England. Managed by Nigel Power, Buckland retains gracious living and tradition, with the addition of all modern comforts and best service. Guests can relax before log fires in 2 delightfully decorated lounges, one with lovely panelling and a beamed ceiling. The 13 excellently decorated en-suite bedrooms are furnished with luxury fittings and accessories. Some have four-poster beds and fireplaces and all bathrooms use water drawn from the Manor's own spring. Views over the grounds with their small waterfalls, outdoor pool, tennis courts, putting green and croquet lawns are spectacular. The dining room is an oasis of calm, and chef Adrian Jarrad prepares delicious, award-winning cuisine. Broadway Golf Club, Cheltenham race course, Stratford, Stow-on-the-Wold, Warwick and Blenheim are nearby. Buckland Manor is a member of Relais & Châteaux hotels.

Our inspector loved: The magnificent gardens and attention to detail throughout the hotel.

NEW

RIVERSIDE RESTAURANT AND HOTEL

THE PARKS, OFFENHAM ROAD, NEAR EVESHAM, WORCESTERSHIRE WR11 8JP

The Riverside has great style and a superb position, perched high above the River Avon in the original Evesham Abbey's 15th-century deer park. 3 cleverly converted 17th-century cottages blend with the main house to create an elegant 1920's residence. There are 7 enchanting bedrooms, all thoughtfully appointed and interior designed in separate themes with views over the gardens and terrace to the river. The 2 AA Rosette awarded restaurant is under the personal direction of Deborah Sinclair and is a designated no-smoking area. The frequently changing menus are reasonably priced for their exceptional range and style of choices on offer. Interesting starters are followed by a selection of traditional and innovative dishes, including fresh monkfish and local pheasant and tempting desserts. The cellar holds 60 wines and is listed in the Atkins Fine Wine & Champagne Guide. The bar has deep sofas and armchairs with large windows overlooking the river; the ambience is that of a country house drawing room. Guests may fish in the Avon or visit the Royal Worcester Porcelain factory, go to Stratford-upon-Avon or relax watching county cricket at Worcester.

Our inspector loved: The intimate dining room with spectacular views of the River Avon.

Directions: Take the M5, junction 7 or the M40, junction 16 to Evesham and approach the hotel from the B4510 to Offenham down a private drive through market gardens.

Kidderminster

Worcester

Evesham

Web: www.johansens.com/riversiderestaurant
E-mail: info@theparksoffenham.freeserve.co.uk
Tel: 0870 381 9298
International: +44 (0)1386 446200
Fax: 01386 40021

Price Guide:
single £59–£79
double £98–£145

NEW

THE BOOT INN

RADFORD ROAD, FLYFORD FLAVELL, WORCESTERSHIRE WR7 4BS

Directions: Exit the M5 at junction 6 and follow A4538 to Evesham. Take the A422 to Flyford Flavell on Wychaven Way.

Web: www.johansens.com/thebootinn
E-mail: enquiries@thebootinn.com
Tel: 0870 381 9319
International: +44 (0)1386 462658
Fax: 01386 462547

Price Guide:
single £50
double/twin £60–£80

This attractive converted coach house dates back to the 13th century and present owners Sue and Norman Hughes extend the warmest of welcomes to their traditional, family-run property. The 5 en-suite bedrooms are extremely well appointed, and a wonderful feature of this inn is the abundance of personal touches and extra amenities. Guests enjoy the cordial hospitality of the staff and the fabulous cuisine on offer, in particular the acclaimed "specials" board. Whether choosing from the snack or à la carte menu only the best local produce is used and is tailored to incorporate the finest ingredients of the season. An extensive wine list complements the mouth-watering dishes and for those who prefer a good old fashioned pint, The Boot is a member of CAMRA, the Campaign for Real Ale. In the summer months visitors relax on the patio overlooking the delightful garden, and in winter, guests are kept warm in the cosy bar. The award-winning Boot Inn makes an ideal base to explore some of England's best-loved locations such as Stratford-upon-Avon, the Malverns and the Cotswolds. Also within easy reach are the Birmingham National Exhibition Centre and the National Indoor Arena.

Our inspector loved: The attractive accommodation.

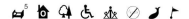

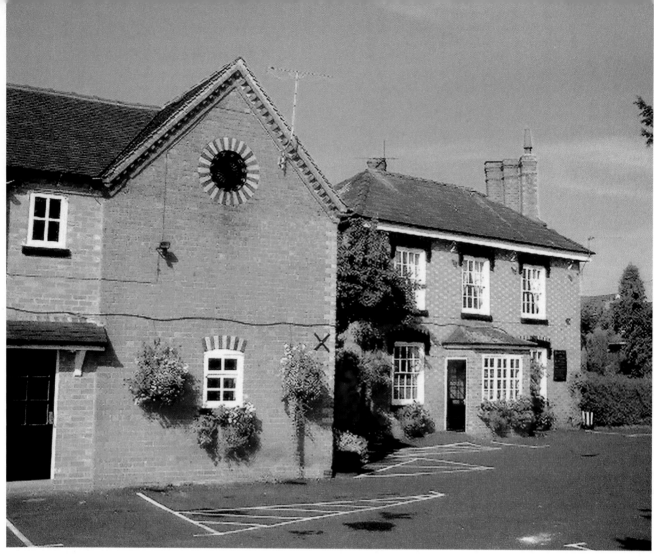

182

THE OLD RECTORY

IPSLEY LANE, IPSLEY, NEAR REDDITCH, WORCESTERSHIRE B98 0AP

The Old Rectory has stood for over 500 years, though it was "modernised" in 1812 by the great-grandson of Sir Christopher Wren, who lived in the house for 40 years. The site itself is steeped in history; the Domesday Book listed a building here, and along one boundary of the grounds runs the original Roman built Icknield Street. Today the emphasis is on hospitality and creating a relaxed, warm atmosphere and memorable stay for guests. All of the comfortable bedrooms – one of which is reputedly haunted – differ in shape, size and décor, with some featuring exposed beams, and one with a barrel ceiling. Dinner is served each night in the conservatory, and the restaurant prides itself on preparing everything possible on the premises from the freshest seasonal produce. Coffee and liqueurs may be enjoyed in the welcoming snug or lounge, whilst the beautiful gardens with their rhododendrons, Portugese laurel, old oak, cedar, silver birch and weeping ash trees beckon to be explored. In the heart of the beautiful Midlands, The Old Rectory is a 20-minute drive from Stratford-upon-Avon, Warwick and Birmingham, and within easy reach of the Cotswolds, Cheltenham and Oxford. The hotel is non-smoking throughout, but guests are welcome to make use of the grounds.

Our inspector loved: *The attractive conservatory restaurant overlooking the terrace and gardens with an array of unusual trees and shrubs.*

Directions: From the M42 take junction 3 and follow the A435 towards Redditch. Keep on this road until you reach the island at Mappleborough Green. Turn right, go straight over the next island and turn left into Icknield Street Drive. Take the first left into Ipsley Lane and the hotel is on the left.

Web: www.johansens.com/oldrecipsley
E-mail: ipsleyoldrectory@aol.com
Tel: 0870 381 9169
International: +44 (0)1527 523000
Fax: 01527 517003

Price Guide:
single from £95
double/twin from £120

COLWALL PARK

COLWALL, NEAR MALVERN, WORCESTERSHIRE WR13 6QG

Directions: Take the M5, junction 7, the A442 then the A449. Colwall village is on the B4218 between Malvern and Ledbury.

Web: www.johansens.com/colwallpark
E-mail: hotel@colwall.com
Tel: 0870 381 8437
International: +44 (0)1684 540000
Fax: 01684 540847

Price Guide:
single £70-£80
double/twin £110-£130
suite £150

This delightful country house style hotel is situated on the sunny western side of the breathtaking Malvern Hills, close to the centre of peaceful Colwall village where its famous water is bottled. Surrounded by beautiful gardens, there are footpaths from the hotel leading directly onto the Malvern Hills, where views over the surrounding countryside are spectacular. Efficient, knowledgeable and very friendly staff, winners of the prestigious AA Courtesy and Care Award, will show guests to one of the 22 bedrooms and suites. All are individually furnished and decorated to a very high standard and every room is en suite and features trouser press, satellite TV, direct dial telephone with data port, coffee and tea making facilities as well as home-made biscuits. The highly acclaimed, award-winning Seasons Restaurant (Michelin, Egon Ronay, Birmingham Restaurant of the Year, AA 2 Rosette) is a richly furnished oak-panelled room and serves delicious gourmet food. The popular Lantern Bar, a meeting place for locals and residents alike, features a crackling log fire during winter and offers real ales, superb house wines and an exciting menu of freshly made meals and snacks. Local attractions include Gloucester, Worcester, Hereford and Cheltenham and the historic market town of Ledbury.

Our inspector loved: The spacious and well appointed bedrooms and the wonderful views of the Malvern Hills from the hotels secluded gardens..

  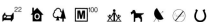

THE OLD WINDMILL

WITHYBED LANE, INKBERROW, WORCESTER WR7 4JL

Built circa 1840, this Grade II listed former working mill and quarry is set in an attractive 2-acre tree-lined garden with enchanting ponds. The 4-storey house has an original and intriguing layout, whilst its 3 en-suite bedrooms are exceptional and have been individually decorated with dramatic drapes, soft pastel hues and luxurious furnishings. An open fireplace dominates the comfortable drawing room and is particularly inviting during winter. The friendly service afforded by the charming owners, Sheila and Mike Dale, adds to the pleasant ambience of The Old Windmill. Dining can be organised by arrangement, and as the property is unlicensed, guests may bring their own wine. Visitors are also requested to arrive after 4 pm. Nature enthusiasts will be delighted with the gardens and surrounding countryside that are home to an abundance of wildlife, and the windmill is the ideal base from which to explore the Malvern Hills, the surrounding Worcestershire countryside, Stratford-upon-Avon, the Cotswolds and Warwick Castle. Fans of the popular "Archers" programme must visit The Old Bull pub in Inkberrow as it is claimed to be the "Bull in Ambridge". A spacious meeting room for 8 people has a wonderful ambience and the prospect of the unique quarry garden.

Our inspector loved: The peace and tranquillity coupled with the tasteful and luxurious furnishings - truly exceptional throughout.

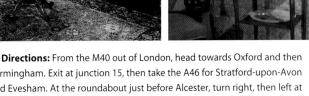

Directions: From the M40 out of London, head towards Oxford and then Birmingham. Exit at junction 15, then take the A46 for Stratford-upon-Avon and Evesham. At the roundabout just before Alcester, turn right, then left at the next roundabout. Follow the A422 and signs to Worcester and Inkberrow.

Web: www.johansens.com/oldwindmill
E-mail: sheila-dale@theoldwindmill.co.uk
Tel: 0870 381 9167
International: +44 (0)1386 792801
Fax: 01386 793762

Price Guide:
single £65
double £100

185

THE WHITE LION HOTEL

HIGH STREET, UPTON-UPON-SEVERN, NR MALVERN, WORCESTERSHIRE WR8 0HJ

Henry Fielding wrote part of his novel "The History of Tom Jones" way back in 1749 where he described the hotel as "the fairest Inn on the street" and "a house of exceedingly good repute". The owners Jon and Chris Lear have committed themselves to upholding this tradition with good old-fashioned hospitality along with examples of the finest cuisine in the area cooked for the popular Pepperpot Brasserie, which has been awarded an AA Rosette, RAC Dining Awards and the CAMRA Good Beer Award. Using only the finest ingredients Jon and his team produce an imaginative menu served with flair – and homemade treats – which have attracted the attention of a discriminating local clientele. A lunch time menu with lighter meals may be enjoyed in the lounge or in the congenial bar. All 13 bedrooms are from varying periods dating from 1510, the Rose Room and the Wild Goose Room at the White Lion are named in a Fielding book. The White Lion is central for visiting The Malvern Hills, The Three Counties Show Ground, the market town of Ledbury, Tewkesbury's Norman Abbey, Worcester, Cheltenham and Gloucester. The Cotswolds, Black Mountains and Stratford-upon-Avon are all within an easy drive.

Directions: From M5 Jct8 follow M50. Exit at Jct1 onto A38 north. After 3 miles turn left onto A4104. Go over the bridge, turn left, then right. Parking is at the rear.

Web: www.johansens.com/whitelionupton
E-mail: reservations@whitelionhotel.biz
Tel: 0870 381 8989
International: +44 (0)1684 592551
Fax: 01684 593333

Price Guide:
single £67.50–£90
double £92.50–£135
4-poster £115–£150
Multiple days negotiable

Kidderminster

Worcester

● Evesham

Our inspector loved: The intimate dining room and the old timbers dating back to the hotels 16th-century origins.

THE AUSTWICK TRADDOCK

AUSTWICK, VIA LANCASTER, NORTH YORKSHIRE LA2 8BY

Standing in 2 acres of peaceful, landscaped gardens in the heart of the Yorkshire Dales National Park is this fine Georgian country house hotel and restaurant, which oozes character, charm and the friendliest of hospitality. It is an ideal location for those wishing to enjoy dramatic scenery, spectacular walks, tranquillity and the freshest of country air. Surrounding the unspoilt village of Austwick is some of the most sensational limestone scenery in Europe, including the Ingleborough Cave with its dazzling stalagmites and stalagatites. Close by are the 3 famous peaks of Whernside, Pen-y-ghent and Ingleborough and within a short walk of the nearby market town of Settle are caves which have yielded finds from pre-history. Guests at The Traddock can relax after walking and sightseeing tours in a comfortable bar and lounge, warmed in winter by open log fires or enjoy a quiet nap in their bedroom. Each is individually designed, delightfully decorated and like the remainder of the building, beautifully furnished with English antiques. Chef, Peter Baillie, produces excellent Anglo-French cuisine in the award-winning restaurant complemented by an extensive wine list. Special breaks are available.

Our inspector loved: The warm and friendly welcome at this family-run hotel.

Directions: Austwick is a mile north west of Settle on the A65, midway between Skipton and junction 36 of the M6.

Web: www.johansens.com/austwick
E-mail: info@austwicktraddock.co.uk
Tel: 0870 381 8331
International: +44 (0)15242 51224
Fax: 015242 51796

Price Guide:
single £50–£80
double/twin £100–£140

STOW HOUSE HOTEL

AYSGARTH, LEYBURN, NORTH YORKSHIRE DL8 3SR

Directions: Stow House is situated on the A684 at the edge of the village of Aysgarth, which is midway between Leyburn and Hawes.

Web: www.johansens.com/stowhouse
E-mail: info@stowhouse.co.uk
Tel: 0870 381 8920
International: +44 (0)1969 663635

Price Guide:
single £44–£75
double/twin £72–£94

Tall, charming and attractive, this stone-built former Victorian Vicarage stands impressively in 2 acres of mature grounds. It is a 10-minute walk from famous Aysgarth Falls in the heart of beautiful Wensleydale, watered by the Ure, the most open and wooded of the Yorkshire Dales. Built in 1876 for Fenwick William Stow, Rural Dean of Wensleydale and over the years lovingly and sympathetically restored, it has 9 en-suite bedrooms, all individually decorated and furnished with every comfort. 2 luxury guest rooms, one with a four-poster, are slightly larger and offer panoramic views over the Dale, although all rooms have a lovely outlook. There is a cosy bar and a comfortable lounge which opens onto a garden that features an impressive selection of trees dating from the mid 19th century and a stunning view towards Bishopdale. Excellent meals can be enjoyed in the intimate dining room and chef, Michael Sullivan, uses the freshest of local produce. A croquet lawn and lawn tennis court are available during the summer months. Stow House specialises in house parties and shooting parties where guests are able to take over the whole hotel for their own special celebration. There are wonderful walks direct from the door and the area abounds in historic castles, abbeys and stately homes. There are 3 golf courses locally.

Our inspector loved: The panoramic views over Wensleydale from the four-poster bed.

THE RED LION

BY THE BRIDGE AT BURNSALL, NEAR SKIPTON, NORTH YORKSHIRE BD23 6BU

Beamed ceilings, creaky floors and log fires in winter greet you at this former 16th-century Ferryman's Inn on the banks of the River Wharfe in the picturesque Yorkshire Dales village of Burnsall. Owned and run by the Grayshon family, it is surrounded by glorious open countryside. Guests can step out for numerous walks straight from the front door. The hotel is actually on the "Dalesway". The bedrooms are all slightly different yet traditionally furnished, many with antiques and most have wonderful views over the village green, river and Burnsall Fell. The restaurant has been awarded an AA Rosette for serving food that is delicious and varied, imaginatively cooked and well-presented. Table d'hôte dishes such as local rabbit braised in ale and served with herb dumplings, or partridge with apricot seasoning and game chips, are complemented by international wines. Special half-board terms and winter warmer breaks are available. Bolton Abbey and Priory, the historic market town of Skipton with its medieval castle and the Settle to Carlisle Railway. The Red Lion has private fishing on the River Wharfe, 7 miles of trout and grayling fishing and offers partridge and pheasant shooting over 3000 acres on the nearby Grimwith Estate. Skipton and Ilkley golf courses are 11 miles away. 2 self-catering cottages are also available.

Directions: Burnsall is north of Skipton on B6160 between Grassington and Bolton Abbey. The inn is in the village centre by the bridge.

Web: www.johansens.com/redlionburnsall
E-mail: redlion@daelnet.co.uk
Tel: 0870 381 8850
International: +44 (0)1756 720204
Fax: 01756 720292

Price Guide:
single £60–£90
double £120–£145

Our inspector loved: The River Wharfe, which runs past the hotel.

HOB GREEN HOTEL AND RESTAURANT

MARKINGTON, HARROGATE, NORTH YORKSHIRE HG3 3PJ

Set in 870 acres of farm and woodland this charming country house hotel is only a short drive from the spa town of Harrogate and the ancient city of Ripon. The restaurant has an excellent reputation locally with only the finest fresh local produce being used, much of which is grown in the hotel's own garden. The interesting menus are complemented by an excellent choice of sensibly priced wines. All 12 bedrooms have been individually furnished and tastefully equipped to suit the most discerning guest. The drawing room and hall, warmed with log fires in cool weather, are comfortably furnished with the added attraction of fine antique furniture, porcelain and pictures. Situated in the heart of some of Yorkshire's most dramatic scenery, the hotel offers magnificent views of the valley beyond from all the main rooms. York is only 23 miles away. There is a wealth of cultural and historical interest nearby with Fountains Abbey and Studley Royal water garden and deer park a few minutes' drive. The Yorkshire Riding Centre is in Markington Village. Simply relax in this tranquil place where your every comfort is catered for. Special breaks available.

Directions: Turn left signposted Markington off the A61 Harrogate to Ripon road, the hotel is 1 mile after the village on the left.

Web: www.johansens.com/hobgreen
E-mail: info@hobgreen.com
Tel: 0870 381 8600
International: +44 (0)1423 770031
Fax: 01423 771589

Price Guide:
single £85–£115
double/twin £100–£145
suite £135–£155

Our inspector loved: *Strolling around the large lovingly tended Victorian walled herb, vegetable and cutting flower garden.*

THE BOAR'S HEAD HOTEL

THE RIPLEY CASTLE ESTATE, HARROGATE, NORTH YORKSHIRE HG3 3AY

Imagine relaxing in a luxury hotel at the centre of a historic, private country estate in England's incredibly beautiful North Country. The Ingilby family who have lived in Ripley Castle for 28 generations invite you to enjoy their hospitality at The Boar's Head Hotel. There are 25 luxury bedrooms, individually decorated and furnished, most with king-sized beds. The restaurant's menu is outstanding, presented by a creative and imaginative kitchen brigade and complemented by a wide selection of reasonably priced, good quality wines. There is a welcoming bar serving traditional ales straight from the wood and popular bar meal selections. When staying at The Boar's Head, guests can enjoy complimentary access to the delightful walled gardens and grounds of Ripley Castle, which include the lakes and a deer park. A conference at Ripley is a different experience – using the idyllic meeting facilities available in the Castle, organisers and delegates alike will appreciate the peace and tranquillity of the location, which also offers opportunities for all types of leisure activity in the Deer Park.

Our inspector loved: *The historic Ripley Castle and the pretty village of Ripley.*

Directions: Ripley is very accessible, just 10 minutes from the conference town of Harrogate, 20 minutes from the motorway network and Leeds/Bradford Airport, and 40 minutes from the City of York.

Web: www.johansens.com/boarsheadharrogate
E-mail: reservations@boarsheadripley.co.uk
Tel: 0870 381 8370
International: +44 (0)1423 771888
Fax: 01423 771509

Price Guide:
single £105–£125
double £125–£150

ROOKHURST COUNTRY HOUSE HOTEL

WEST END, GAYLE, HAWES, NORTH YORKSHIRE DL8 3RT

Nestling in the midst of Wensleydale, the front gate of this part-Georgian, part-Victorian country house opens onto the 250 mile-long Pennine Way. The cosy oak-beamed Georgian bedrooms are well appointed and the more spacious Victorian bedrooms are furnished with four-poster beds whilst the rustic attic is particularly ornate, featuring a half-tester bed. All the bedrooms are en suite. This is a non-smoking house. Judith specialises in traditional home-cooked English dishes, made with fresh, mostly locally produced, ingredients and bakes the bread for breakfast. An open fire creates a welcoming atmosphere in the sitting room, where guests can relax with a drink and enjoy the views over the landscaped garden and fields to the fells. Rookhurst is an ideal base for exploring Herriot country – the Yorkshire Dales are a delight for both serious walkers and strollers. Nearby is the Carlisle to Settle railway and you can be collected from Garsdale Station. Just round the corner is the Wensleydale Creamery, and in Hawes the Upper Dales folk museum. Special breaks are available.

Directions: Take the A684 Sedbergh–Bedale road. At Hawes take Gayle Lane to Gayle. At the top of the lane turn right and the hotel is 300 yards further on the right.

Web: www.johansens.com/rookhurst
E-mail: enquiries@rookhurst.co.uk
Tel: 0870 381 8865
International: +44 (0)1969 667454
Fax: 01969 667128

Price Guide:
single £55–£70
double £90–£130

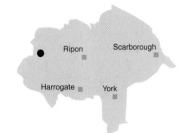

Our inspector loved: *Seeing the gardens evolve and mature in this secluded setting.*

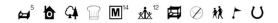

NEW

MIDDLEHAM GRANGE

MARKET PLACE, MIDDLEHAM, NORTH YORKSHIRE DL8 4NR

Nestling in the peaceful town of Middleham, renowned as the North's premier racehorse training centre and famed for its magnificent castle, this beautiful house is the ideal base from which to explore the stunning scenery of the Yorkshire Dales. Originally built in 1720 as a merchant's house, the impressive Georgian manor was later enlarged in the Regency period to incorporate the present gracious frontage. The house has undergone complete refurbishment, and whilst retaining all its period features it offers beautifully appointed en-suite bedrooms equipped with every modern comfort. The gold sitting room with its original fireplace and hob grate leads into the tented breakfast room, which overlooks the walled garden. Dinner is available by special arrangement at weekends for a minimum of 6 persons and is served in the crimson dinning room. Middleham is a very special place with a good selection of pubs and restaurants. The area has a wide variety of attractions to suit all tastes, including a colourful history, a thriving horseracing community and breathtaking surroundings dotted with stunning country houses, remote farms and heather covered grouse moors. Bolton and Richmond Castles, Aysgarth Falls, Ripon, York and Harrogate are all within easy reach.

Our inspector loved: *Relaxing in the walled garden, watching racehorses trotting by the front gates.*

Directions: To the centre of Middleham, on the A6108 between Masham and Leyburn.

Web: www.johansens.com/middlehamgrange
E-mail: tammi.t@tiscali.co.uk
Tel: 0870 381 9336
International: +44 (0)1969 622630
Fax: 01969 625437

Price Guide:
single £60
double £80

THE KINGS HEAD HOTEL

MARKET PLACE, RICHMOND, NORTH YORKSHIRE DL10 4HS

Directions: The Kings Head is in the centre of Richmond, overlooking the market square.

Web: www.johansens.com/kingsheadrichmond
E-mail: res@kingsheadrichmond.co.uk
Tel: 0870 381 9224
International: +44 (0)1748 850220
Fax: 01748 850635

Price Guide:
single £69-£95
double/twin £95-£130

Overlooking the largest cobbled square in England in the centre of historic Richmond, with views over the Norman Castle and stunning Church of the Holy Trinity, the 18th-century Kings Head is a charming and unique venue. Visitors are invited to enjoy the kind of welcoming Yorkshire hospitality that travellers have been receiving for nearly 300 years. Comfortable lounges with generous armchairs are perfect for relaxing and reading the morning papers. A large collection of working clocks can be admired in the Clock Lounge, the setting for mornings, lunchtime snacks or afternoon tea. Wholesome, traditional meals are delicious and are served either in the bar or in the hotel's award-winning Georgian restaurant upstairs along with an excellent choice of wines and beers. Beautiful, individually styled bedrooms have a romantic feel with antique beds, stylish fabrics, gleaming marble floored bathrooms (some with corner baths) and every facility expected of a hotel of this calibre. Easby Abbey, Richmond Castle and the Georgian Theatre Royal and Museum are all within a few minutes' walk whilst Richmond is a picturesque town to explore. Swaledale and Wensleydale are within minutes' drive from the town, perfect for walkers and nature lovers.

Our inspector loved: *The central location overlooking the cobbled market square of the historic town of Richmond.*

DUNSLEY HALL

DUNSLEY, WHITBY, NORTH YORKSHIRE YO21 3TL

Dunsley Hall hotel stands in 4 acres of magnificent landscaped gardens in the North Yorkshire Moors National Park and has remained virtually unaltered since being built at the turn of the 20th century. Most of the individually decorated bedrooms, some with four-poster beds, benefit from a fantastic view over the sea, which is only a few minutes walk away, and have rich, luxurious fabrics and fine furniture. All rooms are non-smoking. Mellow oak panelling, a handsome Inglenook carved fireplace and stained glass windows enhance the drawing room's relaxing and restful features. From the Oak Room, Terrace Suite or Pyman Bar, guests can savour the Rosette award-winning regional dishes and seafood specialities made from only the freshest of ingredients. There are up-to-date exercise and health facilities available with a fully equipped fitness room, sauna and large indoor pool. Outside are a hard-surface tennis court, a 9-hole putting green and a croquet lawn. Places of interest nearby include Castle Howard, Robin Hood's Bay, the North Yorkshire Moors Steam Railway and the birthplace of Captain Cook. Guests enjoy reduced green fees at Whitby Golf Course.

Our inspector loved: The stained glass windows in the drawing room.

Directions: From A171 Whitby–Teeside road, turn right at signpost for Newholme, 3 miles north of Whitby. Dunsley is the first turning on the left. Dunsley Hall is 1 mile further on the right

Web: www.johansens.com/dunsleyhall
E-mail: reception@dunsleyhall.com
Tel: 0870 381 8494
International: +44 (0)1947 893437
Fax: 01947 893505

Price Guide:
single £80–£120
double/twin £130–£176

HEY GREEN COUNTRY HOUSE HOTEL

WATERS ROAD, MARSDEN, WEST YORKSHIRE HD7 6NG

Directions: From Huddersfield, take A62 Oldham road to Marsden. Drive through the village and after approximately 1 mile the Hey Green is signed on the right.

Web: www.johansens.com/heygreen
E-mail: info@heygreen.com
Tel: 0870 381 8652
International: +44 (0)1484 844235
Fax: 01484 847605

Price Guide:
single £60-£80
double £109-£150

A solidly built, traditional West Yorkshire hotel with an imposing pillared entranceway, Hey Green Country House stands in superb landscaped grounds overlooking the spectacular countryside of the Colne Valley, midway between Huddersfield and Oldham. It is a peaceful, tranquil location just over 6 miles from the shops and entertainment of either town but with a multitude of historic and natural attractions within easy reach and a preponderance of green pastures, drystone walls and little grey farms in the surrounds. Style, good taste and a welcoming ambience personify the hotel with relaxation and attentiveness high on the list of staff priorities. Each en-suite bedroom has character and charm, every home comfort, little extra personal touches and most offer panoramic scenic views. An excellent á la carte menu featuring modern British cuisine is served in an attractive brasserie situated in the oldest part of the hotel, built about 1710. It has a superb flagstone floor and an open fire burning throughout winter months. A large, comfortable conservatory is popular for pre and after-dinner social chats. Corporate meeting and event facilities available.

Our inspector loved: *This peaceful retreat in The Last of the Summer Wine country.*

For further information on the Channel Islands, please contact:

Visit Guernsey
PO Box 23, St Peter Port, Guernsey GY1 3AN
Tel: +44 (0)1481 723552
Internet: www.visitguernsey.com

Jersey Tourism
Liberation Square, St Helier, Jersey JE1 1BB
Tel: +44 (0)1534 500777
Internet: www.jtourism.com

Sark Tourism
Harbour Hill, Sark, Channel Islands GY9 0SB
Tel: +44 (0)1481 832345
Internet: www.sark.info

Herm Tourist Office
The White House Hotel, Herm Island via Guernsey GY1 3HR
Tel: +44 (0)1481 722377
Internet: www.herm-island.com

or see pages 263-265 for details of
local attractions to visit during your stay.

Images from www.britainonview.com

THE WHITE HOUSE

HERM ISLAND, GUERNSEY, CHANNEL ISLANDS GY1 3HR

Directions: Herm is reached by boat from Guernsey.

Web: www.johansens.com/whitehouseherm
E-mail: hotel@herm-island.com
Tel: 0870 381 8988
International: +44 (0)1481 722159
Fax: 01481 710066

Price Guide: (including dinner)
double/twin £122–£170

As wards of Herm Island, Adrian and Pennie Heyworth assume responsibility for the wellbeing of all visitors to their island home which is for all to enjoy at leisure. For an island just 1½ miles long its diversity is remarkable and during a 2-hour stroll that takes in its cliff walks, white sandy coves and abundant wildlife no two moments are the same. The magic starts to work from the moment of arrival at the pretty harbour, for in the absence of cars on Herm a tractor laden with guests' luggage chugs up from the jetty to The White House. Here, relaxation is the key, and guests can enjoy afternoon tea or a drink in its succession of homely lounges, in the bar or on the poolside patio. In keeping with a cherished tradition there are no televisions, no clocks nor telephones in the hotel's 40 bedrooms, the best of which have balconies and sea views. Appointments are nonetheless faultless and all include spacious up-to-date private bathrooms. Families are made particularly welcome and high tea is a popular event with younger guests. Seafood plays a prominent part on the wonderful menus: Guernsey lobster, scallops and crab are landed regularly. Self-catering holiday cottages are also available.

Our inspector loved: *This delightful little island kingdom - total peace and superb beaches.*

EULAH COUNTRY HOUSE

MONT COCHON, ST HELIER, JERSEY, CHANNEL ISLANDS JE2 3JA

Set amongst beautiful gardens, this attractive and stylish Edwardian House enjoys a unique position overlooking St Helier and St Aubin's Bay. Formerly a vicarage, the house was refurbished and opened as a small luxury hotel 3 years ago taking care to maintain the ambience of a comfortable family country home. Most of the bedrooms, 3 of which are junior suites, have sea views. All are individually furnished with king-sized beds, antique furniture, wonderful fabrics and linens as well as satellite television, direct dial telephones, fax and modem points. Luxurious bathrooms include large baths and separate showers decorated with beautiful Spanish and Italian ceramic tiles. The owners of the hotel pride themselves on offering a homely, personalised service and in the elegant main lounge with its attractive paintings and décor there is an honesty bar where guests can serve themselves. Outside, the gardens, heated swimming pool and sun terrace provide the perfect atmosphere for relaxation. Breakfast, light snacks and refreshments are available and although there is no full restaurant facility staff are more than happy to advise visitors on local cuisine and make bookings at the many excellent nearby restaurants. The heart of St Helier is just a stone's throw away, as are the beach and beautiful surrounding countryside.

Our inspector loved: The splendid bedrooms with the crispest white linen and all the extras.

Directions: Immediately west of St Helier, at St Aubin's Bay, Le Mont Cochon (B27) runs due north from the A1/A2 coastal road.

Web: www.johansens.com/eulah
E-mail: eulah@jerseymail.co.uk
Tel: 0870 381 8509
International: +44 (0)1534 626626
Fax: 01534 626600

Price Guide:
single £125–£185
double/twin £160–£230

AVAL DU CREUX HOTEL

HARBOUR HILL, SARK, GUERNSEY, CHANNEL ISLANDS GY9 0SB

Directions: By air or sea to Guernsey and then by ferry from St Peter Port.

Web: www.johansens.com/avalducreux
E-mail: reception@avalducreux.co.uk
Tel: 0870 381 9173
International: +44 (0)1481 832036
Fax: 01481 832368

Price Guide: (including dinner)
double from £140

The tractor "bus" from the ferry will drop you at the top of Harbour Hill, 20 yards from this most conveniently located hotel. Handsome buildings of local stone and slate give a unique colonial style to the site, and set the mood for the relaxed and informal service. Rooms are accessed on different levels from smart timbered decks. There is a split-level heated swimming pool with a water feature and childrens' splash area. Families are well catered for with excellent value family rooms and High Tea offered for younger visitors. You may have dinner in the appropriately named Lobster Restaurant or outside on the sun terrace - local seafood features very strongly. The adventures of the day can begin nice and early with breakfast available from 8.00 a.m. No traffic is allowed on the island, which makes walking and cycling a joy. Guests can explore the stunning 40 miles of coastline, secluded bays and rocky outcrops of the island or have a fun day out in a horse-drawn carriage.

Our inspector loved: *The outstanding provision and dedication to the family market. Outside barbecues are a popular feature.*

LA SABLONNERIE

LITTLE SARK, SARK, CHANNEL ISLANDS GY9 0SD

Owner and manager Elizabeth Perrée considers La Sablonnerie an oasis of good living and courtesy rather than a luxury hotel. It is truly that – and more! It is an hotel of rare quality situated in a time warp of simplicity on a tiny, idyllic island where no motor cars are allowed and life ambles along at a peaceful, unhurried pace. A vintage horse-drawn carriage collects guests from Sark's tiny harbour to convey them in style to the islands' southernmost tip - Little Sark. Crossing la Coupée, a narrow isthmus, guests can enjoy breathtaking views of the coast. Tranquil cosiness, friendliness and sophistication characterise this hotel with its low ceilings and 400-year-old oak beams. Opened in 1948 and retaining many of the characteristics of the old farmhouse, La Sablonnerie has been extended and discreetly modernised to provide 22 bedrooms which are charmingly individual in style and offer every amenity. The granite-walled bar, with its open fire, is a comfortable extra lounge where pre-dinner drinks can be enjoyed before sampling the delights of the candle-lit restaurant. The hotel has a reputation for superb cuisine. Many of the dishes are prepared from produce grown on its own farm and gardens and enhanced by locally caught lobster and oysters.

Our inspector loved: The welcome - hospitality and your pleasure in this keyhole home.

Directions: By air or sea to Guernsey and then by ferry from St Peter Port.

Web: www.johansens.com/lasablonnerie
Tel: 0870 381 8666
International: +44 (0)1481 832061
Fax: 01481 832408

Grandes Rocques
Herm
St Peter Port
Sark
Airport

Price Guide: (including dinner)
single from £78

Recommendations in Ireland appear on pages 204-212

For further information on Ireland, please contact:

The Irish Tourist Board
(Bord Fáilte Éireann)
Baggot Street
Dublin 2
Tel: +353 (0)1 602 4000
Internet: www.ireland.ie

Northern Ireland Tourist Information
Belfast Welcome Centre
47 Donegall Place
Belfast, BT1 5AD
Tel: +44 (0)28 9024 6609
Internet: www.gotobelfast.com

or see pages 263-265 for details of
local attractions to visit during your stay.

Images from Fáilte Ireland

GREGANS CASTLE

BALLYVAUGHAN, CO CLARE, IRELAND

Directions: From Shannon airport take the N18 to Ennis, then N85 to "Fountain Cross" then R476 and R480 to Gregan's. From Galway take N18, then N67 to Ballyvaughan. Follow the N67 out of the village and Gregans Castle can be found on the left approx 3 miles away.

Web: www.johansens.com/gregans
E-mail: stay@gregans.ie
Tel: 00 353 65 7077005
Fax: 00 353 65 7077111

Price Guide:
single €178–€270
double/twin €240–€290
suite €350–€420

This wonderful, family-run hotel dates back to the 1600s, and today owners Simon and Frederieke Haden welcome guests into its warm, comfortable atmosphere. Careful attention to detail is very much in evidence, from the blazing turf fires to the antique furniture, and the collection of Raymond Piper paintings of local flora. Each of the bedrooms and suites is individually decorated in a relaxing country house style, and public rooms such as the Corkscrew Room and Drawing Room offer conducive areas for enjoying a book, board game or apéritif before dinner. The bay views from the dining room are stunning, and in summer a beautiful light is created by the rays of the setting sun travelling across Galway Bay and striking the limestone mountains. Burren lamb and fresh fish regularly appear on the menu, and where possible organic and local produce is used. The Burren is a unique terrain, and provides a home to many rare and rich Alpine and Arctic flowers. Nearby country roads are ideal for cycling and horse riding, whilst beaches and hills are simply waiting to be walked upon. Many golf courses including Lahinch and Doonbeg GC are within easy reach. Only 1 hour from Shannon Airport.

Our inspector loved: *The view to Ballyvaughan Bay.*

BALLYLICKEY MANOR HOUSE

BALLYLICKEY, BANTRY, CO CORK

Home of the Franco-Irish Graves family for four generations, this secluded manor house nestles among the rugged inlets of stunning Bantry Bay. The atmosphere is very much that of a private family home, displaying numerous personal touches and great attention to detail. Ballylickey Manor was originally built over 300 years ago as a shooting lodge by Lord Kenmare, and has since been carefully restored by its present owner managers, who came here in the 1940s. Robert Graves, an uncle of the present owners, paid numerous visits to the manor over the years, and Ballylickey soon became a haven for writers, artists and musicians. The accommodation ranges from sumptuous Manor House Suites to pretty Garden Cottages dotted around the beautiful swimming pool. Guests can enjoy gourmet cuisine in the Red Dining Room, or choose the Blue Dining Room with wonderful views over Bantry Bay. All meals are complemented by fine wines from the Graves' vineyards in Bordeaux. The manor is ideally suited to hold conferences and corporate events, with the Georgian library accommodating up to 12 people. Private dining can be arranged. For a minimum stay of one week, Ballylickey Manor House is available for private lettings, with full staffing and services on hand.

Our inspector loved: The view over Bantry Bay.

Directions: On main road N71 between Bantry and Glengariff/Kenmare Road.

Web: www.johansens.com/ballylickey
E-mail: ballymh@eircom.net
Tel: 00 353 27 50071
Fax: 00 353 27 50124

Price Guide:
single €80–€170

MERRION HALL HOTEL

54-56 MERRION ROAD, BALLSBRIDGE, DUBLIN 4

Directions: From the city centre take Merrion Road; the hotel is on the left hand side overlooking the RDS Convention Centre.

Web: www.johansens.com/merrionhall
E-mail: merrionhall@iol.ie
Tel: 00 353 1 668 1426
Fax: 00 353 1 668 4280

Price Guide:
single €106–€139
double/twin €139–€189
deluxe €169–€249
garden suites €239–€319

Balbriggan

Dublin

Dun Laoghaire

This exclusive Edwardian property is located close to the RDS Convention centre just minutes from downtown Dublin. Merrion Hall shares its neighbourhood with the world's embassies in the fashionable Ballsbridge area of Dublin City. Executive bedrooms, some with four-poster suites, offer air conditioning, whirlpool spas and all the modern comforts expected by the discerning traveller. The hotel's library stocks a fine selection of Irish and international literature, whilst afternoon teas and fine wines are served in the main drawing room. A feature of this Edwardian town house is a very special breakfast, which can be enjoyed in the conservatory, overlooking mature secluded gardens. There are also numerous restaurants within a short stroll of the hotel, leaving guests utterly spoilt for choice. Near to Lansdowne Road, it is linked to major tourist sites and the business district by the DART electric train. There is a direct luxury coach link to and from Dublin airport. For the corporate guests there is a boardroom, meeting rooms, business facilities and wireless internet access. Residents have complimentary parking on the grounds. The hotel can arrange golfing packages and scenic tours.

Our inspector loved: The convenient location of this Edwardian house.

ZETLAND COUNTRY HOUSE HOTEL

CASHEL BAY, CONNEMARA, CO GALWAY, IRELAND

Standing on the edge of Cashel Bay, amongst the outstanding natural beauty of the Connemara landscape, the house was originally built as a sporting lodge in the early 1800s and takes its name from the Earl of Zetland. Today it is owned and managed by Ruaidhri Prendergast. Its flickering turf fires, elegant antique furniture and abundance of fresh flowers create a cosy, timeless atmosphere, and all of the bedrooms and suites are stylishly furnished and enjoy spectacular sea views. The hotel has an outstanding reputation for its food, with fresh local fish and seafood and Connemara lamb regular features. Delicious home-baked goods are served with afternoon tea, and Mona cultivates many of the herbs and vegetables are cultivated in the kitchen garden. Ruaidhri, is always delighted to advise on wines from the extensive cellar. Tennis, croquet and billiards can be played within the hotel's grounds, and fishing is available on its privately owned fishery. Golfers have a choice of 2 18-hole championship courses nearby, and horse riding and pony-trekking can be arranged. The hotel is an excellent base for exploring the mountains, lakes and beaches of Connemara.

Our inspector loved: A gracious and peaceful house.

Directions: From Galway take the N59 in the direction of Clifden via Oughterard. 1½ miles after recess take a left turn, and the hotel is signposted.

Web: www.johansens.com/zetland
E-mail: zetland@iol.ie
Tel: 00 353 95 31111
Fax: 00 353 95 31117

Price Guide: (per person)
single €115–€170
double/twin €85–€135

ROSS LAKE HOUSE HOTEL

ROSSCAHILL, OUGHTERARD, CO GALWAY, IRELAND

Ross Lake House is a wonderful Georgian house nestling amidst 7 acres of rambling woods and rolling lawns at the gateway to magnificent Connemara, famous for its rugged landscape, mountains and lakes. Peace and tranquility are the hallmarks of this country house unspoilt by the advance of time. Henry and Elaine Reid have carefully and tastefully restored the house combining modern day comforts with oldworld charm. Comfort and good taste are also reflected in the hotel's 13 bedrooms, 2 of which are suites. Quality Irish food is served with dishes enhanced by fresh produce from the Connemara hills, streams and lakes. For the active there is tennis in the grounds, game fishing on Lough Corrib and course fishing on Ross Lake, 5 superb golf courses including the Oughterard 18-hole parkland course are close by. Places of interest include Aughnanure Castle, Kylemore Abbey, Connemara National Park, the Aran Islands, Cliffs of Moher and the Burren.

Directions: Ross Lake House is off N59, 14 miles north west of Galway.

Web: www.johansens.com/rosslake
E-mail: rosslake@iol.ie
Tel: 00 353 91 550109
Fax: 00 353 91 550184

Price Guide:
single €105–€115
double €150–€200
suite: €260–€300

Our inspector loved: How close this wonderful country house hotel is to so many great golf courses.

CARAGH LODGE

CARAGH LAKE, CO KERRY, IRELAND

The breathtaking slopes of Ireland's highest mountain range, McGillycuddy Reeks, rise majestically above this elegant Victorian hotel whose award-winning gardens run gently down to Caragh Lake. Less than a mile from the spectacular Ring of Kerry, Caragh Lodge offers an unsurpassed blend of luxury, heritage, tranquillity, hospitality and service. A member of Ireland's Blue Book, it has won an RAC Blue Ribbon in 1999 and Gold Ribbon in 2000, 2001,2002, 2003 and the Johansens Country House Award in 1999. All bedrooms are en suite and decorated with period furnishings and antiques, with the converted garden rooms looking over magnificent displays of magnolias, camellias, rhododendrons, azaleas and rare subtropical shrubs. The dining room overlooks the lake and Mary Gaunt prepares menus of the finest Irish food, including fresh salmon, succulent Kerry lamb, garden-grown vegetables and home-baked breads. Open end-April to mid-October. Salmon and trout swim in the lake and 2 boats are available for angling guests. Ghillies or permits for fishing in the 2 local rivers can be arranged. There are local golf courses, Dooks, Beaufort, Killarney and Waterville, where tee off times can be organised.

Our inspector loved: *The award winning gardens that sweep down to the lake.*

Directions: From Killorglin travel on N70 towards Glenbeigh and take second road signposted for Caragh Lake. At lake turn left, Caragh Lodge is on your right.

Web: www.johansens.com/caraghlodge
E-mail: caraghl@iol.ie
Tel: 00 353 66 9769115
Fax: 00 353 66 9769316

Price Guide:
single €140
double €195–€250
suite €350

EMLAGH HOUSE

DINGLE, CO KERRY, IRELAND

Beautifully located on the picturesque Dingle Peninsula, Emlagh House is a quiet Georgian-style country house hotel set within lovely landscaped gardens. Purpose-built to create luxury with outstanding quality and standards the house, displays a fine, original Irish art collection. Exceeding the needs of every discerning traveller, attentive staff create a friendly, informal atmosphere with a personal touch. The private drawing room with views over the garden and harbour has an intimate serenity enhanced by an open fireplace, books and games. Individually decorated bedrooms feature the delightful theme of native Irish wild flowers with luxurious en-suite bathrooms and all modern conveniences; some have patios and harbour views. Drinks are available in the friendly Honour Bar whilst the bright conservatory breakfast and dining room serves freshly prepared dishes using only the best local produce. Famous for its sandy beaches, stunning scenery and numerous archaeological sites, the Dingle Peninsula is the perfect getaway. Guests may enjoy breathtaking walks, eco tours, bird watching and fishing, whilst horse riding, golf and water sports, are all nearby. Dingle has an abundance of boutique shops, arts and crafts, galleries and excellent restaurants. Rental of the entire house is available.

Directions: Dingle is situated on the N86, 32 miles from Tralee and 40 miles from Killarney. Emlagh House is a 5-minute walk from Dingle town centre and harbour.

Web: www.johansens.com/emlagh
E-mail: info@emlaghhouse.com
Tel: 00 353 66 915 2345
Fax: 00 353 66 915 2369

Price Guide:
single from €120–€170
double/twin from €160–€260

Our inspector loved: The banana & walnut cake for tea.

GORMAN'S CLIFFTOP HOUSE & RESTAURANT

GLAISE BHEAG, BALLYDAVID, DINGLE PENINSULA – TRALEE, CO KERRY, IRELAND

Surrounded by dramatic mountains, cliffs, coves and sandy beaches, the serenity of the Dingle Peninsula is breathtaking. Probably the most westerly establishment in Europe, the quiet Gorman's Clifftop House is a peaceful getaway from the hustle and bustle of daily life with an extremely welcoming atmosphere. Gorman's Restaurant features large picture windows with stunning views over Ballydavid Head, Three Sisters and the Atlantic Ocean – the perfect place to watch the sunset on a summer evening. A successful combination of hospitality, comfort and friendly service enhances the excellent cuisine, which includes homemade brown bread, fresh wild salmon chowder and an extensive international wine list. Well-appointed, spacious bedrooms with tasteful décor and handmade pine furniture have views of the ocean and mountains. Ideal for hiking, the hotel is situated on the Dingle Way long distance walking route. Other activities are golf on Dingle championship course, horse riding, fishing and cycling. Guests can explore the Gallarus Oratory, the oldest place of Christian worship in Western Europe, and there are plenty of archaeological sites in the area.

Our inspector loved: The vibrant interior design and the location.

Directions: Drive through Dingle with harbour on left to the roundabout west of town. Go straight across the road signposted "An Fheothanach"; 8 miles from roundabout keep left but do not turn left.

Web: www.johansens.com/gormans
E-mail: info@gormans-clifftophouse.com
Tel: 00 353 66 9155162
Fax: 00 353 66 9155003

Price Guide:
single €85–€125
double/twin €130–€160
suite €185

COOPERSHILL HOUSE

RIVERSTOWN, CO SLIGO, IRELAND

Directions: Leave N4 Sligo–Dublin road at Drumfin follow signs for Coopershill. 1 mile on, turn left.

Web: www.johansens.com/coopershillhouse
E-mail: ohara@coopershill.com
Tel: 00 353 71 9165108
Fax: 00 353 71 9165466

Price Guide:
single €123–€135
double €202–€228

Winner of Johansens 1995 Country House Award, Coopershill is a fine example of a Georgian family mansion. Home to 7 generations of the O'Hara family since 1774, it combines the spaciousness and elegance of an earlier age with modern comforts. Public rooms are furnished in period style with gilt-framed portraits, hunting trophies and antiques. 6 of the bedrooms have four-poster or canopy beds and all have private bathrooms. Dinner is served by candlelight in the elegant dining room, where good cooking is complemented by a wide choice of wines. Open log fires and personal attention from owners Brian and Lindy O'Hara help to create the warm atmosphere and hospitality that typify Coopershill. Out of season the house is open to parties of 12 to 16 people at a special rate. Tariffs are reduced if guests stay for 3 consecutive nights or more. The River Arrow winds through the 500-acre estate; trout and coarse fishing are available. Shooting is not permitted, leaving the abundant wildlife undisturbed. There is an excellent hard tennis court and also a croquet lawn. There are marvellous mountain and lakeside walks to enjoy in the area. Closed 1st November to 1st April.

Our inspector loved: *"Penny" the parrot who lives in the drinks cabinet.*

For further information on Scotland, please contact:

Visit Scotland
23 Ravelston Terrace, Edinburgh EH4 3TP
Tel: +44 (0)131 332 2433
Internet: www.visitscotland.com

or see pages 263-265 for details of
local attractions to visit during your stay.

Images from www.britainonview.com

BALGONIE COUNTRY HOUSE

BRAEMAR PLACE, BALLATER, ROYAL DEESIDE, ABERDEENSHIRE AB35 5NQ

Directions: Upon entering Ballater from Braemar on the A93, Balgonie House is signposted on the right.

Web: www.johansens.com/balgoniecountry
E-mail: balgoniech@aol.com
Tel: 0870 381 8335
International: +44 (0)13397 55482
Fax: 013397 55497

Price Guide:
single £75
double £130

In the heart of one of Scotland's most unspoilt areas, on the outskirts of the village of Ballater, lies Balgonie House. Winner of the 1997 Johansens Country House Award for Excellence. This Edwardian-style building is set within 4 acres of mature gardens and commands wonderful views over the local golf course towards the hills of Glen Muick beyond. Balgonie's 9 bedrooms are each named after a fishing pool on the River Dee. They are individually decorated and furnished and most offer lovely outlooks from their windows. Amenities include private bathrooms, colour television and direct-dial telephones. At the heart of the hotel is the dining room, offering superb Scottish menus, including fresh salmon from the Dee, succulent local game, high-quality Aberdeen Angus beef, seafood from the coastal fishing ports and vintage wine chosen from an excellent list. Balgonie has won the coveted Taste of Scotland Prestige Award for its cuisine, also 2 AA Red Stars and 2 Rosettes. The village of Ballater, a 5-minute walk away, is a thriving community. As suppliers to the Queen, many of its shops sport Royal Warrant shields. This is an ideal centre for golf, hillwalking, sightseeing and touring. Balmoral Castle is within easy reach, as are both the Malt Whisky Trail and Castle Trail.

Our inspector loved: *A relaxed retreat with a highly personal style. Oh that all hotels do not have such immaculate upkeep!*

CASTLETON HOUSE HOTEL

GLAMIS, BY FORFAR, ANGUS DD8 1SJ

This elegant 2 AA Rosette Edwardian hotel lies in the beautiful vale of Strathmore, a lush enclave beneath the Angus glens. Built in 1902, it stands on the site of a 12th-century fortification, the surrounding ditch being presumed to be a former defensive moat. Recently completely refurbished by its new owners, it now has an ambience of relaxed elegance where attention to detail and personal service are paramount. Each of the 6 bedrooms has been individually furnished, whilst the Regency four-poster suite has an additional dressing room housed in the turret. Guests may dine in the beautiful period dining room or the more informal conservatory; in either location a carefully planned menu of local ingredients with a winning combination of traditional and contemporary dishes is served. Glamis Castle is just 3 miles away and a must for every visitor. The family home of the late Queen Mother, it is surprisingly free of rope restricted areas and has a number of family photographs as well as 2 resident ghosts! Dundee and Perth are within easy driving distance and Blairgowrie lies just 15 minutes away. Beyond Rosemount lies the route to the Highlands for true historians and the more adventurous. One the AA's top 200 hotels in the UK

Our inspector loved: *The top class, personal service and wonderful innovative cooking in this miniture grand hotel.*

Directions: From Edinburgh, take M90 Juntion 11; take A90 through Dundee, then A928 to Glamis, left on to A94. 3 miles on right.

Web: www.johansens.com/castletonhouse
E-mail: hotel@castletonglamis.co.uk
Tel: 0870 381 8411
International: +44 (0)1307 840340
Fax: 01307 840506

Price Guide:
single £90
double/twin £120
four-poster £165

BALLACHULISH HOUSE

BALLACHULISH, ARGYLL PH49 4JX

Directions: A82 to Ballachulish and then A828 under Ballachulish Bridge and first left.

Web: www.johansens.com/ballachulish
E-mail: mclaughlins@btconnect.com
Tel: 0870 381 8336
International: +44 (0)1855 811266
Fax: 01855 811498

Price Guide:
double/twin £60–£140
suites £125–£188

Steeped in Scottish history and proud of its origins, Ballachulish House has recently undergone an extensive refurbishment programme. No expense has been spared to ensure the ambience is one of total comfort and luxury, whilst retaining every scrap of the character of this 17th-century laird's house. Once home to the Stewarts of Ballachulish, this is the scene of the famous Red Fox murder, and later the subject of Robert Louis Stevenson's "Kidnapped", and fans of Scottish history will love to visit this significant landmark. The welcome here is one of the warmest to be found and a reassuring indicator of what is to follow. A traditional piper heralds the start of dinner, and the chef, winner of the Scottish chef of the year, carefully prepares an innovative fusion of classic French cooking teamed with some wonderful local fayre, awarded 2 AA Rosettes and a Michelin sta. All of the 7 en-suite bedrooms have been carefully designed to afford views of the garden, loch or hill; and with elegant furnishings and plenty of space this is a place of total tranquillity and relaxation. Mull and Skye are accessible for day trips, while Glencoe, Ben Nevis and Fort William are all nearby. A ghillie is provided for salmon fishing, or a guide for intrepid hill walkers, perhaps followed by a trip to the nearby Nevis distillery for a wee dram.

Our inspector loved: *The ever attentive service and great food.*

THE FROG AT DUNSTAFFNAGE BAY

DUNSTAFFNAGE MARINA, CONNEL, BY OBAN, ARGYLL PA37 1PX

Located on the Dunstaffnage Marina and overlooking the bay and castle, The Frog is an ideal stop-over for weekend travellers or budding sailors, as many local yachtsmen live nearby. Stuart and Linda Byron concentrate on creating a casual, relaxed atmosphere for their guests as well as those who enjoy the bars and restaurant on a regular basis. Made up of converted old farm buildings, the hotel acts as a jolly meeting place and on its ground floor is where the eating happens. An all-day food service provides breakfast through to dinner and a good selection of bar snacks and novelty children's dishes. Menus combine the best quality of local produce and as expected, feature a wide variety of fresh seafood. The bars serve an impressive range of draught, bottled beers, malt whiskies, wines and spirits. 10 non-smoking en-suite bedrooms have been added to The Frog , each equipped with colour television, direct dial telephones, bath and power shower. Rooms, though not huge, are full of character with quirky crooked ceilings and all new furnishings. Accommodation is comfortable but fairly basic, as reflected in the excellent price. Nearby attractions include Dunstaffnage Castle, diving, angling, scenic trips and the Oban Distillery.

Our inspector loved: *The relaxed and informal feeling in the heart of the marina.*

Directions: The Frog is 2 ½ miles north of Oban on the A85.

Web: www.johansens.com/thefrog
E-mail: frogenqs@aol.com
Tel: 0870 381 8533
International: +44 (0)1631 567005
Fax: 01631 571044

Price Guide: (room only)
double/twin £45–£65

HIGHLAND COTTAGE

BREADALBANE STREET, TOBERMORY, ISLE OF MULL PA75 6PD

Directions: There are frequent crossings from the mainland each day. When entering Tobermory on the main Salen road, go straight across at the mini roundabout, over the narrow stone bridge and immediately turn right. This is Breadalbane Street and the hotel is on the right opposite the Fire Station.

Web: www.johansens.com/highlandcottage
E-mail: davidandjo@highlandcottage.co.uk
Tel: 0870 381 9184
International: +44 (0)1688 302030

Price Guide:
single from £95
double from £120

Highland Cottage is a delightful, intimate hotel that sits above Tobermory, a picturesque town on the Isle of Mull. Set in a quiet conservation area of the town, it evokes feelings of restful tranquillity yet is only a 5-minute walk from the town's main streets and Fisherman's Pier. Comfortable chairs in the sunny public rooms are perfect to relax and read the paper in. The cottage also has a large selection of books. Themed bedrooms, which are decorated in an island style, are cheerful and uplifting with homely touches and carefully chosen furniture for a truly comfortable stay. The hotel's restaurant is recognised for its high quality and has been awarded with 2 highly acclaimed AA Rosettes as well as the prestigious RAC Gold Ribbon award and AA Red Star Top 200 status. Perhaps its greatest accolade however is Hotel of the Year in the Scottish Thistle Awards. Exceptionally delicious and imaginative dishes are prepared using top quality, locally produced ingredients. Seafood often comes direct from the Tobermory boats, caught by local divers and fishermen and the meat is of West Highland stock. The beautiful Isle of Mull has lots to offer and is completely different from any other Scottish island, with a fascinating character and picturesque landscape. A car is essential as public transport on the island is not good and there are many scenic drives to enjoy.

Our inspector loved: The amazing attention to detail.

PTARMIGAN HOUSE

THE FAIRWAYS, TOBERMORY PA75 6PS

Ptarmigan is idyllically set within an acre of landscaped grounds overlooking the enchanting Bay of Tobermory and the Sound of Mull. Michael and Sue Fink have welcomed guests from around the world to the Isle of Mull for many years, having sold their hotel, are now continuing the tradition in this beautiful newly built house where they promise a comfortable and relaxing stay. 4 superb modern en-suite rooms have been decorated with exquisite furnishings and carefully chosen fabrics. All rooms benefit from stunning views and are extremely spacious. A most delicious Scottish breakfast is served in the conservatory-style breakfast room where only the best local produce is used to complement the free range eggs produced on the property. Although dinner is not served at the house, The Anchorage restaurant is only a short drive away in picture-postcard Tobermory, a brightly coloured fishing village. Guests will feast on sumptuous local fish dishes and seafood whilst admiring its seafront location and lively harbour views. Ptarmigan is an excellent base for exploring the many delights of Mull and Iona, and to enjoy Scotland's untouched island scenery and wildlife. No visit is complete without a visit to the Tobermory Distillery established in 1823, which produces 1 million litres of fine whisky every year.

Our inspector loved: This is a unique luxury bed and breakfast built to the highest standard and offers the best views for miles.

Directions: There are frequent ferry crossings from the mainland each day. When entering Tobermory on the Main Road go straight across the mini roundabout over Narrow Stone Bridge and turn immediately right. Drive along Breadalbane Street. At the end turn left and follow the signs to the golf course. The house is on the left.

Isle of Mull   Oban

Dunoon

Glasgow

Campbelltown

Web: www.johansens.com/ptarmigan
E-mail: sue.fink@btopenworld.com
Tel: 0870 381 9343
International: +44 (0)1688 302863
Fax: 01688 302913

Price Guide:
double £70–£90

CULZEAN CASTLE – THE EISENHOWER APARTMENT

MAYBOLE, AYRSHIRE KA19 8LE

Directions: From Glasgow, take the A77 towards Ayr. Culzean Castle is 12 miles south of Ayr on the A719.

Web: www.johansens.com/culzeancastle
E-mail: culzean@nts.org.uk
Tel: 0870 381 8469
International: +44 (0)1655 884455
Fax: 01655 884503

Price Guide:
single £140–£250
double £250–£375

Troon

Ayr

Girvan

Situated in the heart of one of Scotland's most magnificent country parks and dramatically perched on a cliff top with breathtaking views, Culzean Castle is the ideal base for a golfing trip in an area that boasts some of Scotland's finest links courses. The Eisenhower Apartment is a presidential retreat for guests bored with 5-star hotels. The 6-bedroom upper floor of Culzean was retained for General Eisenhower when the Castle was handed over to The National Trust for Scotland in 1945. Now, guests can enjoy the style and comfort once reserved for the General and his family. Guests staying in the apartment can either enter the Castle through the impressive armoury at the front door or use the private lift at the side door. When you arrive on the top floor you feel like entering a rather splendid home and the friendly welcome from the staff simply amplifies this feeling. Whether you are travelling on your own, as a couple or maybe wishing to book all the rooms for that special party, the Castle will make you feel most welcome. Guests have access to the complete Castle during opening hours and can explore the 560-acre country park with its woodlands, deer park, newly recreated Victorian Vinery and exotic pagoda.

Our inspector loved: The completely different experience. The great hospitality from The National Trust for Scotland staff.

CASTLE CAMPBELL HOTEL

11 BRIDGE STREET, DOLLAR, CLACKMANNANSHIRE FK14 7DE

Overlooked in the distance by the impressive Castle Campbell and dating back to 1822, this comfortable Scottish hotel was once used as a coaching inn and staging post for travellers journeying between Stirling and St Andrews. It has a welcoming atmosphere, complemented by extremely friendly and hospitable staff. The comfortable lounge is tastefully decorated with leather sofas and has an open fire. All 8 of the bedrooms are en suite, simply decorated and have tea and coffee making facilities. Imaginative regional cuisine is lovingly prepared by the hotel's chefs using only the best quality produce available from local suppliers. Informal bar meals are popular with locals and visitors alike and guests have a choice of more than 70 fine malt whiskies and traditional beers. World-renowned St Andrews and Gleneagles golf courses are nearby and the hotel can arrange golf packages with Dollar Golf Club. The hotel is an ideal base from which to explore the whole of central Scotland, with Glasgow, Edinburgh, Perth, Stirling and St Andrews all less than 1 hour away. An exhilarating day out can be found in the Ochil Hills on one of many of the fantastic walks or stay closer to the hotel and walk up Dollar Glen, a National Trust site featuring breathtaking gorges and high waterfalls

Our inspector loved: *The welcoming style and traditional ambience of the hotel.*

Directions: From Stirling take the A91 to St Andrews until you reach Dollar

Web: www.johansens.com/castlecampbell
E-mail: bookings@castle-campbell.co.uk
Tel: 0870 381 9232
International: +44 (0)1259 742519
Fax: 01259 743742

Price Guide:
single from £52.50–£55
double/twin from £75–£80

FERNHILL HOTEL

HEUGH ROAD, PORTPATRICK DG9 8TD

Directions: From the A75 or A77 follow signs to Portpatrick. Just before the 30mph sign at the War Memorial turn right into Heugh Road. The hotel is 300 yards on the left.

Web: www.johansens.com/fernhill
E-mail: info@fernhillhotel.co.uk
Tel: 0870 381 8521
International: +44 (0)1776 810220
Fax: 01776 810596

Price Guide: (per person including dinner)
single/double/twin from £73
seaview from £85

Moffat
Stranraer
Dumfries

Set amidst beautiful, secluded gardens with views over the bustling yacht and fishing village of Portpatrick, Fernhill is a friendly, welcoming hotel. A huge picture window in the light and airy lounge displays the breathtaking scenery and, on a clear day, it is possible to see the coast of Ireland, some 21 miles away. Having just undergone major refurbishment, the hotel offers 28 elegant bedrooms decorated with warm colours and expertly chosen fabrics to create a sense of quiet luxury. Some have balconies and most have sea views. The new "Fernhill" bedroom has magnificent views and feature bathroom with slipper bath. The Stables House has a spacious four-poster suite and uninterrupted views over the gardens, village and sea. A mouth-watering choice of fresh, locally caught lobster as well as Scottish beef, game and poultry are on the menu, which is changed daily. The attractive cocktail bar and lounge are ideal for pre-dinner drinks or a relaxing get-together with friends. Guests can use the leisure facilities at North West Castle in Stranraer, and only a few minutes away, Portpatrick's craftshops and attractive harbourside are wonderful to explore. Walking enthusiasts will find great short walks as well as the start of the Southern Upland Way, whilst golf lovers can enjoy a superb golf course nearby.

Our inspector loved: *The superb clifftop views high above the fishing village of Portpatrick.*

GILLBANK GUEST HOUSE

8 EAST MORTON STREET, THORNHILL, DUMFRIESSHIRE DG3 5LZ

Situated on a quiet street in the centre of the picturesque town of Thornhill in Dumfries & Galloway, Scotland's "best kept secret", this traditional late Victorian guesthouse offers a homely, welcoming atmosphere with excellent service. Awarded AA 5 Diamond Status, the house has newly refurbished, tastefully decorated and comfortable bedrooms. All are en-suite, spacious, light and airy and offer every modern facility; one boasts an impressive four-poster bed. Breakfast is served in a stylish breakfast room with fireplace. Thornhill's shops, pubs and restaurants are only a 2-minutes walk or cycle away. Cyclists are very welcome and there is bicycle storage available as well as a private car park. Surrounded by beautiful Scottish countryside, Gillbank is the ideal base from which to explore this delightful area. Drumlanrig Castle, the home of the Duke of Buccleuch, is only 3½ miles away. The rural location is ideal for outdoor sports and activities, such as golf on Thornhill's 18-hole golf course, cycling, walking, and fishing for salmon and sea trout on the river Nith, ½ mile away.

Our inspector loved: *The thoughtfulness and style in the lovely bedrooms.*

Directions: From the North leave M74 at J14, take the A702 to Carronbridge, then A76 to Thornhill. At roundabout in centre of town turn left. From the South take A76 from Dumfries to Kilmarnoch. In Thornhill turn right at roundabout in town centre. Gillbank is on the left hand side.

Web: www.johansens.com/gillbank
E-mail: hanne@gillbank.co.uk
Tel: 0870 381 9355
International: +44 (0)1848 330597
Fax: 01848 330597

Price Guide:
single £30–£50
double £55–£75

TRIGONY HOUSE HOTEL

CLOSEBURN, THORNHILL, DUMFRIESSHIRE DG3 5EZ

Directions: Situated off the A76, 13 miles north of Dumfries and 1 mile south of Thornhill.

Web: www.johansens.com/trigony
E-mail: info@trigonyhotel.co.uk
Tel: 0870 381 9121
International: +44 (0)1848 331211

Price Guide: (including dinner)
double £115-£130

In the heart of Burns Country, within over 4 acres of secluded gardens and woodland, Trigony House Hotel stands in the magnificent Nithsdale Valley. Situated between Carlisle and Glasgow, this is the ideal hotel for a short break or stop-off on a journey north or south. This pink sandstone country house hotel was once a private home and a welcoming, homely ambience still remains. All 8 en-suite bedrooms boast spectacular views over the Lowther Hills to the east and the Nith Valley and Kier Hills to the west. The bar and lounge, with their open fires, offer tranquil havens in which to relax. Owners, Adam Moore and Jan Burgess, take great pride in creating sumptuous meals from as much organic produce as possible. Organic vegetables from the hotel's walled garden and free range or rare bred meat from local suppliers, together with locally caught game and fish, provide mouth-watering Scottish cuisine, accompanied by a carefully chosen wine list and fine selection of malt whiskies and Scottish beers. The grounds provide excellent areas for walking and cycling expeditions and several local golf courses can be enjoyed by guests; a day's membership can be arranged. Deer stalking, hare coarsing and salmon fishing on the Nith can all be organised.

Our inspector loved: *This old traditional Scottish home, which retains many of its original features, set in an ideal position for exploring Dumfries & Galloway.*

CORRIEGOUR LODGE HOTEL

LOCH LOCHY, BY SPEAN BRIDGE, INVERNESS-SHIRE PH34 4EB

Surrounded by 9 acres of woodland and gardens, with views over Loch Lochy, this former Victorian hunting lodge enjoys one of the finest settings in the "Great Glen", an area steeped in history. Recently refurbished, the hotel displays a warm and tasteful décor. Large comfy sofas and log fires create a welcoming atmosphere in the lounge and restaurant. The cosy bedrooms, which are currently being given a makeover, are adorned with hand-made furniture, imported lights, lovely silk drapes and designer carpets. Many having a state-of-the-art bathroom and have views of the loch. Service is friendly and relaxed and nothing is ever too much trouble. Winner of the coveted Taste of Scotland award. The Loch View Restaurant and conservatory offers exquisite cuisine, based on finest local produce such as venison, salmon and Highland lamb. The area is the gateway to the Highlands and west coast, and a true paradise for nature lovers, walkers and those simply wishing to recharge their batteries. Outdoor pursuits can be arranged, such as fishing, cycling, pony trekking and skiing. A small lochside beach with its own jetty is also available. Although Loch Ness is not far, guests need not venture any further, as Lizzie, Nessie's 3-humped cousin, has been sighted in Loch Lochy!

Our inspector loved: *The continual improvements, interesting food and lovely setting of this understated hotel.*

Directions: 17 miles north of Fort William on the A82, on the south side of Loch Lochy, between Spean Bridge and Invergarry on the way to Skye.

Web: www.johansens.com/corriegour
E-mail: info@corriegour-lodge-hotel.com
Tel: 0870 381 8447
International: +44 (0)1397 712685
Fax: 01397 712696

Price Guide:
single from £59.50
double/twin from£119
special seasonal breaks are available.

225

THE STEADINGS HOTEL

FLICHITY, FARR, SOUTH LOCH NESS, INVERNESS IV2 6XD

Directions: Leave Inverness southwards on the A9. After 5 miles turn right onto the B851 signposted Fort Augustus. The hotel is a further 7 ½ miles down this road.

Web: www.johansens.com/steadings
E-mail: stay@thesteadings.com
Tel: 0870 381 9138
International: +44 (0)1808 521314
Fax: 01808 521314

Price Guide:
single £39.50-£49.50
double £79-£99

Just 15-20 minutes south of Inverness, The Steadings Hotel stands amidst spectacular scenery of breathtaking Scottish lochs and heathered lands. The area originally belonged to the ancient MacGillivray Clan and it was from here that they set out to fight for Bonnie Prince Charlie at Culloden. Farm steadings, built in 1860, have been carefully and tastefully renovated to provide comfortable accommodation within this most relaxing environment. Within close proximity to Loch Ness, historical castles, landmarks and with uninterrupted, glorious views, this tranquil country hostelry offers a unique experience enhanced by the attentive staff. All of the bedrooms are en suite and the original stonework and timber beams together with many interesting artefacts are featured throughout the hotel. The Clach an' Airm restaurant serves delicious cuisine prepared from fresh Scottish and Highland produce, complemented by fine wine. Gameshooting, loch, river or sea fishing and golf can all be organised and arranged to specific requirements for groups' needs. Exclusive use of the hotel for private or corporate parties is available.

Our inspector loved: *The homely comforts and wonderful setting in the Strathnairn Valley.*

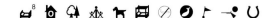

TORAVAIG HOUSE HOTEL

KNOCK BAY, SLEAT, ISLE OF SKYE IV44 8RE

Set amidst 2 acres of grounds in a secluded part of the island, with breathtaking views over the Sound of Sleat, Toravaig House has been completely and lovingly transformed by its owners, Anne Gracie and Kenneth Gunn, into a welcoming guesthouse. An extensive 4-month renovation and refurbishment programme has created one of the island's most exclusive and luxurious retreats, offering first-class service in peaceful surroundings and exceptional value for money. The tastefully furnished bedrooms have every amenity; 3 look out onto the sea, whilst the other 6 have views of the hills. Fresh local produce is used for the exquisite cuisine, accompanied by fine wines and malts and served in the elegant, traditionally decorated Iona restaurant. Small weddings and functions can be catered for, with a team of dedicated staff on hand to ensure that all needs are satisfied. Toravaig House Hotel is ideally situated for exploring the Isle of Skye, which is a paradise for nature lovers and walkers, with fantastic low level walking through the tiny villages, by the shores, through the forests or even climbing in the famous Cuillin mountains. Sleat is an area known for its unique highland culture; it has acquired an excellent reputation for its musical events throughout the season and a splendid Feis being held in mid July.

Our inspector loved: The bright airiness of this revitalised hotel under its enthusiastic new owners.

Directions: By the Skye Bridge take A87 to Broadford. Turn left to Armadale, Sleat (A851) on approach to Broadford. Continue towards Armadale for approx.10 miles. The hotel is less than 1 mile from the Tarskavaig junction on the main A851 and on the left hand side of the road.

Web: www.johansens.com/toravaig
E-mail: info@skyehotel.co.uk
Tel: 0870 381 9344
International: +44 (0)1471 833231
Fax: 01471 833231
Price Guide:
single £60–£85
double £110–£140

HOTEL EILEAN IARMAIN

SLEAT, ISLE OF SKYE IV43 8QR

Hotel Eilean Iarmain stands on the small bay of Isle Ornsay in the South of Skye with views over the Sound of Sleat. The hotel prides itself on its log fires, inventive cooking and friendly staff. 1997/8 accolades include the RAC Restaurant Award, RAC Merit Award for Hospitality, Comfort and Restaurant, AA Rosette for Restaurant, AA Romantic Hotel of Great Britain and Ireland Award, Les Routiers Corps d'Elite Wine Award and Macallan Taste of Scotland, runner-up Hotel of the Year Award. There are 12 indivdiually decorated bedrooms and 4 light and airy suites, each with a double bedroom and cosy sitting room with a sofa bed. Log fires warm the reception rooms and the wood-panelled dining room where candle-lit dinners can be enjoyed overlooking the bay and the island of Ornsay. The menu features game when in season and fresh seafood landed at the pier. Premier cru clarets feature on the extensive wine list, and a large selection of malt whiskies includes local Poit Dhubh and Talisker. Clan MacDonald Centre, Armadale Castle and Talisker Distillery are close by. Sports include sea-fishing, shooting and walking.

Directions: The hotel is in Sleat, between Broadford and Armadale on A851. 20 minutes from Skye Bridge; Linked by ferry to Mallaig Station and is 35 minutes by road from Lochalsh railway station over the Skye Bridge.

Web: www.johansens.com/eileanIarmain
E-mail: hotel@eilean–iarmain.co.uk
Tel: 0870 381 8619
International: +44 (0)1471 833332
Fax: 01471 833275

Price Guide:
single £90
double £125–£160
suites £190–£235

Our inspector loved: *This delightful, informal hostelry, quite magically situated, unpretentious food, charming staff and lovely fresh bright rooms.*

THE CROSS AT KINGUSSIE

TWEED MILL BRAE, ARDBROILACH ROAD, KINGUSSIE, INVERNESS-SHIRE PH21 1LB

Located in the pretty village of Kingussie, within the Cairngorm National Park and surrounded by mountains, rivers and lochs, the very atmospheric Cross at Kingussie is no ordinary restaurant with rooms. High-quality food and accommodation await guests in this welcoming, family-run establishment, which is set amidst 4 acres of riverside grounds. Converted from a 19th-century water-powered tweed mill, The Cross has maintained its unique character and some of the original features. Guests can relax in the spacious lounge on the first floor, filled with books, newspapers and magazines, or enjoy a wee dram in the comfortable lounge downstairs. On sunny days, champagne is served on the terrace, which runs alongside the restaurant overlooking the River Gynack. There are 8 bedrooms, individually decorated in a minimalist style, all with king, twin or canopied beds and spacious en-suite bathrooms; some have separate showers, and one room is suitable for a family. Fresh local produce is used for the exquisite food, including Highland beef, Shetland lamb and shellfish from Skye and Ullapool, served by an open fire in the spacious, stone walled and wood beamed restaurant. There is an abundance of wildlife, and walkers and climbers will enjoy the numerous walks in the surrounding area.

Our inspector loved: The tranquillity and personal attention with great emphasis on fine food and wine.

Directions: In the main street, turn uphill at the traffic lights onto Ardbroilach Road. The Cross is 300 yards up on the left.

Web: www.johansens.com/thecross
E-mail: relax@thecross.co.uk
Tel: 0870 381 9349
International: +44 (0)1540 661166
Fax: 01540 661080

Price Guide: (including dinner)
single £100–£150
double £140–£250

John O'Groats

Portree

Inverness

Fort William

Glasgow

229

Cairn Lodge Hotel

ORCHIL ROAD, AUCHTERARDER, PERTHSIRE PH3 1LX

Directions: On the western outskirts of town, the hotel is signposted off the main road on the link road to Crieff.

Web: www.johansens.com/cairnlodge
E-mail: info@cairnlodge.co.uk
Tel: 0870 381 9284
International: +44 (0)1764 662634
Fax: 01764 664866

Price Guide:
single £75–£140
double/twin £100–£210

The Cairn Lodge is a hotel of distinctive quality. Sitting in the heart of the splendid Perthshire countryside, it is easy to forget that Glasgow and Edinburgh are both only 1 hour away. Service at Cairn Lodge is second-to-none while ingredients gathered from the Scottish countryside contribute to the superb cuisine. Scottish hospitality is guaranteed to provide an unforgettable experience. The bedrooms are beautifully appointed, all are en suite and have tea and coffee making facilities, colour television and private telephone. Apart from the famous Gleneagles courses, golfers are within easy reach of St Andrews and Carnoustie, there are also a host of local courses. Alternative activities include fishing, horse riding, clay pigeon and game shooting, falconry and hill walking as well as a variety of water sports. Less energetic, but no less breathtaking is simply relaxing and taking in the beauty of the surrounding Perthshire countryside.

Our inspector loved: *The air of spaciousness and cheerful ambience.*

MONACHYLE MHOR

BALQUHIDDER, BY LOCHEARNHEAD, PERTHSHIRE FK19 8PQ

Monachyle Mhor is a beautiful award-winning hotel in the Braes of Balquhidder, surrounded by hills and with magnificent views over Loch Voil and Loch Doine. This romantic 18th-century farmhouse is a unique hotel offering unpretentious charm within 2000 acres of stunning surroundings. Open fires, warm traditional décor and elegant furnishings create a sense of wellbeing and comfort. The extremely talented and enthusiastic chef has a great following and prepares delicious food with a French twist using fish from the west coast and game from this and neighbouring estates as well as vegetables from the hotel's own organic garden. Bedrooms have a surprisingly modern feel and have been recently refurbished with elegant design and an uncluttered style to create a harmonious and restful ambience. Charming self-catering cottages with fully equipped kitchens and wood-burning stoves retain an individual character and are set within the hotel's courtyard. There are many outdoor pursuits on the estate including private salmon and trout fishing, Red Deer stalking and Grouse Moor (when in season). Monachyle Mhor is the perfect base for exploring the Trossachs and Scotland's first National Park and there are numerous prestigious golf courses nearby.

Our inspector loved: *The striking modernity and perfect wilderness location only 2 hours' drive from Glasgow or Edinburgh.*

Directions: Take the A9 then A84 past Callander. Leave the A84 at Kingshouse. The hotel is 6 miles up the glen through the hamlet of Balquhidder.

Web: www.johansens.com/monachylemhor
E-mail: info@monachylemhor.com
Tel: 0870 381 9231
International: +44 (0)1877 384622
Fax: 01877 384305

Price Guide:
single £65–£145
double/twin £95
suite £145–£220

THE FOUR SEASONS HOTEL

ST FILLANS, PERTHSHIRE PH6 2NF

Directions: Take the A85 west from Perth.

Web: www.johansens.com/fourseasons
E-mail: info@thefourseasonshotel.co.uk
Tel: 0870 381 8528
International: +44 (0)1764 685333
Fax: 01764 685444

Price Guide:
single £65–£80
double £82–£98

This rambling, white hotel is delightfully situated on the eastern edge of Loch Earn, which has been described as the jewel in the crown of Perthshire lochs. All around is unspoilt Southern Highland landscape, steep hillsides and towering, rugged mountains whose lower slopes are covered with deep green woodland. It is an area of scenic splendour, about 30 miles west of the historic city of Perth. The Four Seasons Hotel, under owner Andrew Low, is excellent in every way and superb value for money. The furnishings and décor throughout the hotel are in simple yet tasteful and open fires and several lounges add to the interior charm. The team of chefs create imaginative modern European cuisine featuring the best local produce. The bedrooms are beautifully proportioned and cosy. All are on the first floor and each has a private bathroom and home-from-home comforts. 6 fully equipped chalets on the hillside behind the hotel are suitable for families with one or two children or for those visitors seeking extra privacy. When not enjoying the magnificent views and changing colours from the hotel's south-facing terrace, guests can enjoy walking at Ben Vorlich or visiting the picturesque Southern Highlands villages. Closed in January and February.

Our inspector loved: *What a pleasant, friendly and relaxed hotel with excellent value for money cooking.*

KNOCKENDARROCH HOUSE

HIGHER OAKFIELD, PITLOCHRY, PERTHSHIRE PH16 5HT

Now a listed building, this elegant 19th-century Victorian mansion with its grand 3-storey high peaked tower stands imposingly on a plateau within the picturesque town of Pitlochry offering visitors superb views over the beautiful Tummel Valley. It is surrounded by landscaped gardens and framed by ancient oak trees which give Knockendarroch its name – from the Gaelic, meaning Hill of Oaks. Owned and run by Tony and Jane Ross, Knockendarroch House is a totally non-smoking property and has a reputation for its hospitality amid beautiful Highland scenery. Historic sights and castles abound and the battle-famed pass of Killiecrankie lies just a few miles to the north. Each of the 12 en-suite bedrooms is spacious and equipped with every comfort from television to electric blanket. First floor premier rooms have magnificent southerly or westerly views, 2 of the second-floor standard rooms have balconies. In the elegant restaurant, the finest local produce is the base of the expertly prepared menus and guests can enjoy a complimentary glass of sherry prior to dining. During the Pitlochry theatre season the restaurant opens from 6pm and the hotel runs a courtesy bus to and from the evening performances.

Our inspector loved: The panoramic position, a landmark overlooking Pitlochry and Tummel valley. This well run hotel gives great value.

Directions: On entering Pitlochry from the south via Atholl Road, pass Bells distillery on you right, then pass under the railway bridge; 100 yards turn right into East Moulin Road; after 200 yards take 2nd left into Higher Oakfield. Knockendarroch House is 300 yards on the left.

Pitlochry

Perth

Kinross

Web: www.johansens.com/knockendarrochhouse
E-mail: info@knockendarroch.co.uk
Tel: 0870 381 8662
International: +44 (0)1796 473473
Fax: 01796 474068

Price Guide: (including dinner)
single £63–£94
double £104–£146

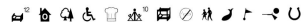

THE LAKE HOTEL

PORT OF MENTEITH, PERTHSHIRE FK8 3RA

Directions: Situated on the A81 road, south of Callander and east of Aberfoyle, on the northern banks of the Lake of Menteith.

Web: www.johansens.com/lakehotel
E-mail: enquiries@lake-of-menteith-hotel.com
Tel: 0870 381 8669
International: +44 (0)1877 385258
Fax: 01877 385671

Price Guide: (including dinner)
single £65–£112
double £110–£204

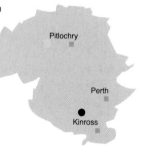

The Lake Hotel is set in a splendid sheltered position on the banks of the Lake of Menteith in the Trossachs. Its lawn runs down to the edge of the lake, which in winter months often freezes over. When this happens, it is not unusual for locals to bring out their skates for a skim over the ice. Guests are assured of all the amenities of an STB 3 Star Highly Commended hotel. All bedrooms have en-suite facilities and the details that will make your stay comfortable. There is an elegant lounge and a large conservatory from which the vista of lake and mountains is stunning. The table d'hôte menu presents a varied choice of imaginatively prepared dishes and are particularly good value: start with chicken & herb terrine with sun dried tomato dressing, followed by sorbet, then after a main course of grilled halibut with spinach, saffron potatoes and an orange & aniseed sauce, enjoy a Drambuie parfait with raspberry coulis before your coffee and homemade petits fours. Special rates are available for mini-breaks of 2 nights or more. Inchmahome Priory, Loch Lomond and Stirling Castle are nearby.

Our inspector loved: *The art deco style in the hotel and the superb views over Scotland's only lake.*

TRAQUAIR HOUSE

INNERLEITHEN, PEEBLESHIRE EH44 6PW

Originally owned by the kings of Scotland, Traquair House has been in the same family for generations and is Scotland's oldest continually inhabited house. The present owners are descendants of the original earls of Traquair and any guest staying at the house will instantly sense the feeling of staying amongst a family in their home and will enjoy a truly unique experience. The bedrooms are immaculately furnished with the most romantic and sumptuous antique canopied beds and elegant en suite bathrooms and is particularly suited to honeymoon couples seeking peace and solitude. Dinner can be served by prior arrangement, although many guests enjoy a glass of the house ale in the 18th century Lower Drawing Room before making their way down to the local pub to soak up the atmosphere. Beer drinkers will find a visit to the Traquair House Brewery essential – reopened in 1965, it now produces three rich dark ales, brewed in the traditional methods and winners of a five star accolade in the World Guide to Beer. Visitors will be delighted for hours by the immense history of Traquair, both Mary Queen of Scots and Bonnie Prince Charlie stayed here, the latter passing though Traquair's spectacular Bear Gates at the time of the 1745 rebellion.

Our inspector loved: This is not just an historical but a working house and it is great to stay and be part of it.

Directions: Take the A702 from Edinburgh bypass to Peebles, then the A72 towards Innerleithen. In Innerleithen take the B709 to Traquair House.

Web: www.johansens.com/traquair
E-mail: enquiries@traquair.co.uk
Tel: 0870 381 9104
International: +44 (0)1896 830323
Fax: 01896 830639

Price Guide:
single £90
double £150

For further information on Wales, please contact:

Wales Tourist Board
Brunel House, 2 Fitzalan Road, Cardiff CF24 0UY
Tel: +44 (0)29 2049 9909
Web: www.visitwales.com

North Wales Tourism
Tel: +44 (0)1492 531731
Web: www.nwt.co.uk

Mid Wales Tourism
Tel: (Freephone) 0800 273747
Web: www.visitmidwales.co.uk

South West Wales Tourism Partnership
Tel: +44 (0)1558 669091
Web: www.swwtp.co.uk

or see pages 263-265 for details of
local attractions to visit during your stay.

Images from www.britainonview.com

THE GREAT HOUSE

HIGH STREET, LALESTON, BRIDGEND, WALES CF32 0HP

Directions: From the M4 exit at junctions 35 or 37.

Web: www.johansens.com/greathouse
E-mail: enquiries@great-house-laleston.co.uk
Tel: 0870 381 8570
International: +44 (0)1656 657644
Fax: 01656 668892

Price Guide:
single £60–£90
double £85–£135

This is a superb example of charming Elizabethan architecture, delightfully situated overlooking an ancient church in the pretty conservation village of Laleston. Dating back to around 1550, the Grade II* listed Great House with its beautiful walled garden is said to have been a gift from Queen Elizabeth I to the Earl of Leicester and used by him as a hunting lodge. Owners, Stephen and Norma Bond, bought The Great House as a dilapidated shell in 1985 and have beautifully restored the building to its original condition, with modern comforts. Numerous interesting features include stone archways, mullioned windows, inglenook fireplaces, huge oak beams, a unique stone and wooden spiral staircase. The stone arch above the cocktail-bar fireplace is the single largest unbroken span of stone in Wales. Guest rooms are in the main house with 2 garden suites in converted stables, all with an individual personality reflecting the warmth and character throughout the house. Each is en suite and furnished with every modern comfort. Chef, Neil Hughes, produces imaginative, award-winning cuisine in the 2 AA Rosette restaurant, with its relaxed elegant ambience. Places of interest nearby include Margam Country Park, Sker House and St Fagans Welsh Folk Museum, Cardiff.

Our inspector loved: *The outstanding restoration of this magical Elizabethan building providing superb accommodation and comfort.*

THE INN AT THE ELM TREE

ST BRIDES, WENTLOOGE, NR NEWPORT NP10 8SQ

This is a warm, welcoming and extremely relaxing place. Situated in a little known coastal village just a 15-minutes drive from Cardiff and Newport, the Inn at the Elm Tree is described by owner Patricia Thomas as a 21st-century inn with traditional values. Surrounded by the flat river meadows of the Seven Estuary it is an ideal venue in which to escape from the noise and pressures of everyday life. Peace and tranquillity abound in an area of special scientific interest teeming with bird and wildlife, offering protection to rare and varied flora and fauna. The inn's bedrooms are excellent: designed to the highest standards of quality and comfort, homely and appealing whilst offering every facility, plus personal touches and little luxuries characteristic of a leading hotel. They have king-sized beds, iron and brass beds and four-posters, beamed ceilings, chunky pine furniture and rocking chairs. 2 ground-floor rooms can be booked as a family suite with its own entrance. The intimate, AA Rosette award-winning candle-lit restaurant with adjoining Café Bar, which opens onto a Tropical Courtyard, serves traditional favourites alongside the varied and seasonal European cuisine. Open fires burn during cooler months. Golf, horse riding, clay shooting, sea, trout and course fishing are all nearby.

Our inspector loved: The warm, welcoming atmosphere created by Patricia and her team with an abundance of extra personal touches throughout.

Directions: From Newport, exit M4 at junction 28 and take B4239 for approximately 3 miles.

Web: www.johansens.com/elmtree
E-mail: inn@the-elm-tree.co.uk
Tel: 0870 381 8637
International: +44 (0)1633 680225
Fax: 01633 681035

Price Guide:
single £80–£100
double/twin £90–£110

TY MAWR COUNTRY HOTEL

BRECHFA, CARMARTHENSHIRE SA32 7RA

Nestled in the glorious Welsh countryside in the beautiful Brechfa Forest, this charming 15th-century house is an ideal base for a country retreat. Literally meaning "big house" Ty Mawr is steeped in history and the property retains many original period features such as thick stone walls, low ceilings and old beams. The comfortable bedrooms are well appointed with antique pine furnishings, complimented by bathrooms with Italian tiled floors and claw foot baths. In the colder months crackling log fires create a cosy hideaway from the chilly outdoors. Guests can also warm up with a hearty dish from the mouthwatering supper menu. Welsh black beef might be the obvious choice, but the freshly caught seafood comes from nearby Cardigan Bay – definitely worth a try! In the summer visitors enjoy dining alfresco in the attractive lawned gardens with the River Marlais running through. This area of Wales is renowned for its spectacular castles and National Botanic Gardens. The historic town of Carmarthen is less than 20 minutes away, a little further afield is the Victorian seaside resort of Tenby. For recreation take a walk or bicycle ride through the breathtaking forest valleys.

Directions: Located 14 miles north east of Carmarthen on the B4310.

Web: www.johansens.com/tymawr
E-mail: info@wales-country-hotel.co.uk
Tel: 0870 381 9318
International: +44 (0)1267 202332/202437

Price Guide:
single £65-£85
double/twin £90–£110

Our inspector loved: The wealth of character of this 15th-century Welsh building with original timbers and exposed stone, and the River Marlais running at the end of the garden.

CONRAH COUNTRY HOUSE HOTEL

RHYDGALED, CHANCERY, ABERYSTWYTH, CEREDIGION SY23 4DF

One of Wales's much loved country house hotels, the Conrah is tucked away at the end of a rhododendron-lined drive, only minutes from the spectacular rocky cliffs and sandy bays of the Cardigan coast. Set in 22 acres of rolling grounds, the Conrah's magnificent position gives views as far north as the Cader Idris mountain range. Afternoon tea and Welsh cakes or pre-dinner drinks can be taken at leisure in the quiet writing room or one of the comfortable lounges, where antiques and fresh flowers add to the relaxed country style. The acclaimed restaurant uses fresh local produce, together with herbs and vegetables from the Conrah kitchen garden, to provide the best of both classic and modern dishes. The hotel is owned and run by the Heading family who extend a warm invitation to guests to come for a "real taste of Wales", combined with old-fashioned, high standards of service. For recreation, guests may enjoy a game of table tennis in the summer house, croquet on the lawn or a walk around the landscaped gardens. Those wishing to pay in euro's are welcome to do so. Golf, pony-trekking and sea fishing are all available locally, whilst the university town of Aberystwyth is only 3 miles away. Closed Christmas.

Our inspector loved: Its green relaxing lounges and calm restaurant complementing the peaceful open views. Quite Edwardian in a very nice way!

Directions: The Conrah lies 3 miles south of Aberystwyth on the A487.

Web: www.johansens.com/conrahcountryhouse
E-mail: enquiries@conrah.co.uk
Tel: 0870 381 8444
International: +44 (0)1970 617941
Fax: 01970 624546

Price Guide:
single £79–£100
double/twin £125–£160

241

YNYSHIR HALL

EGLWYSFACH, MACHYNLLETH, CEREDIGION SY20 8TA

Directions: Off main road between Aberystwyth and Machynlleth.

Web: www.johansens.com/ynyshirhall
E-mail: info@ynyshir-hall.co.uk
Tel: 0870 381 9020
International: +44 (0)1654 781209
Fax: 01654 781366

Price Guide:
single £110–£180
double/twin £125–£180
suite £210–£275

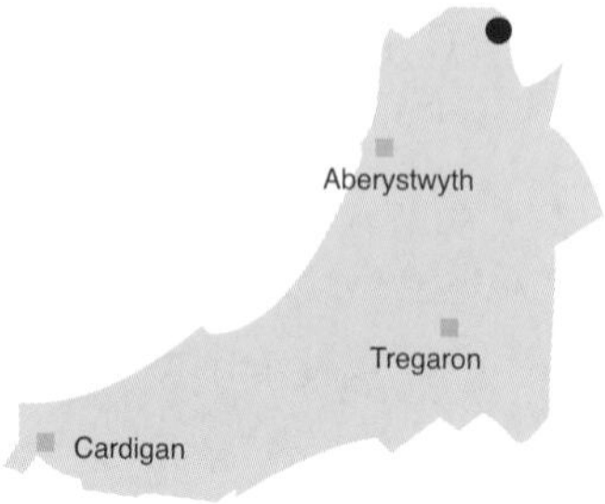

Once owned by Queen Victoria, Ynyshir Hall is a captivating Georgian manor house that perfectly blends modern comfort and Old World elegance. Its 12 acres of landscaped gardens are set alongside the Dovey Estuary, one of Wales's most outstanding areas of natural beauty. The hotel is surrounded by the Ynyshir Bird Reserve. Hosts Rob and Joan Reen offer guests a warm welcome and ensure a personal service, the hallmark of a good family-run hotel. Period furniture and opulent fabrics enhance the 9 charming bedrooms. The suites, including a four-poster room and ground floor room, are particularly luxurious. The interior features antiques, contemporary colour schemes, oriental rugs and original paintings, created by Rob, an acclaimed artist. With its calm, elegant atmosphere, the candle-lit restaurant provides the perfect backdrop for a sublime culinary experience. Chef Adam Simmonds, formerly of Le Manoir Aux Quat' Saisons, creates dishes prepared with superb local ingredients such as wild sea bass, Cardigan Bay lobster and tender Welsh mountain lamb, complemented by a fine wine list of over 300 bins from all over the world. Awarded The Catey's Independent Hotel of the Year 2002, Welsh Hotel of the Year 2001 by the AA. Winner of Johansens Most Excellent Restaurant Award 1999. Landmarks include Cader Idris, Wales's 2nd highest mountain. Closed in January.

***Our inspector loved:** This truly magical property very special in many ways.*

TAN-Y-FOEL

CAPEL GARMON, NR BETWS-Y-COED, CONWY LL26 0RE

This contemporary bijou-style house, built of magnificent Welsh stone has won many accolades as an outstanding small country house that blends finest country elegance with innovative interior design. The intimate reception rooms styled in earth tones offer a calming and tranquil atmosphere. Set in breathtaking surroundings, it commands views of the verdant Conwy Valley and the rugged peaks of Snowdonia. Once inside Tan-y-Foel a "no smoking" policy prevails. Each extremely comfortable bedroom has its own strikingly individual style, thoughtful small touches add to their charm and the bathrooms are delightfully appointed. Celebrated for her impeccable cuisine, Janet, a member of "The Master Chefs of Great Britain", sources the best local produce, fresh fish, Welsh black beef and organically grown vegetables for her creatively composed nightly menus, which have been recognised with 3 AA Rosettes. This, combined with an outstanding selection of wines, will ensure an experience to savour. The personal welcome, which perfectly complements the nature of the Pitmans' unique house, has resulted in the hotel receiving the award of 2 AA Red Stars for exemplary service and the prestigious accolade of 5 Star Country House with the Welsh Tourist Board.

Our inspector loved: No words can justify this special place and the views are superb..

Directions: From Chester, A55 to Llandudno, A470 towards Betws-y-Coed. 2 miles south from Llanrwst fork left towards Capel Garmon. Tan-y-Foel is just over a mile uphill on the left.

Web: www.johansens.com/tanyfoel
E-mail: enquiries@tyfhotel.co.uk
Tel: 0870 381 8938
International: +44 (0)1690 710507
Fax: 01690 710681

Price Guide:
single £99–£120
double £145–£170

THE OLD RECTORY COUNTRY HOUSE

LLANRWST ROAD, LLANSANFFRAID GLAN CONWY, CONWY LL28 5LF

Enjoy dramatic Snowdonian vistas, breathtaking sunsets and views of floodlit Conwy Castle from this idyllic country house set in large gardens overlooking Conwy Bird Reserve. An AOL Top Gourmet Hotel in the UK, chef, Wendy, is a Fellow of the World Master Chefs Society who creates gourmet 3-course dinners combining a lightness of touch and delicacy of flavour with artistic presentation. Prestigious red listing in Michelin, awarded 2 AA Red Stars for "outstanding levels of comfort, service and hospitality" and AA 3 Rosettes for food; Welsh mountain lamb, locally reared Welsh black beef and locally landed fish features on the menu complemented by an award-winning wine list. The restaurant is closed Sundays, except bank holidays. Antiques and Victorian watercolours decorate the interiors, and luxurious en-suite bedrooms have draped beds, bathrobes, ironing centres, fresh fruit and flowers. Michael is happy to share his knowledge of Welsh history and culture and will assist in planning touring routes. Three 18-hole golf courses are within 10 minute's drive. Relax in the garden, full of interesting plants, and watch the River Conwy ebb and flow and experience why this elegant Georgian home is "a beautiful haven of peace". An ideal venue for exclusive small conferences. Dogs are welcome in the Coach House with adjacent walks through the fields.

Directions: On the A470, ½ mile south of the A55 junction, 2 miles from Llandudno Junction Station. 3 hours from London Euston.

Web: www.johansens.com/oldrectorycountryhouse
E-mail: info@oldrectorycountryhouse.co.uk
Tel: 0870 381 8787
International: +44 (0)1492 580611
Fax: 01492 584555

Price Guide:
single £99–£129
double £129–£169

Llandudno
Conwy
Chester
Betws-y-Coed

Our inspector loved: *The consistency of wonderful dining year on year.*

PORTH TOCYN COUNTRY HOUSE HOTEL

ABERSOCH, PWLLHELI, GWYNEDD LL53 7BU

This is a rare country house seaside hotel – family-owned for 3 generations, the first of whom had the inspiration to transform a row of miners' cottages into an attractive, low white building, surrounded by enchanting gardens, with glorious views over Cardigan Bay and Snowdonia. The Fletcher-Brewer family have created a unique ambience that appeals to young and old alike. Children are welcome; the younger ones have their own sitting room and high tea menu. Nonetheless, Porth Tocyn's charm is appreciated by older guests, with its Welsh antiques and delightful, comfortable sitting rooms. Most of the pretty en-suite bedrooms have sea views, some are family-oriented and 3 on the ground floor are ideal for those with mobility problems. Enjoy cocktails in the intimate bar, anticipating a fabulous meal, for dining at Porth Tocyn is a memorable experience every day of the week. Scrumptious dishes and mellow wines are served in great style on antique tables. Lunch is informal, on the terrace or by the outdoor pool which is heated from May to September). There is a dining area for children and an excellent conservatory with Playstations, games, toys and outside an area for playing football. Glorious beaches, water sports, golf, tennis, riding and exploring the coast provide activities for all ages.

Our inspector loved: A year on and the same wonderful atmosphere, wonderful hosts, wonderful dining, just wonderful!

Directions: The hotel is 2 miles from Abersoch on the Sarn Bach road. Watch for bilingual signs – Gwesty/hotel – then the hotel name.

Web: www.johansens.com/porthtocyn
E-mail: bookings@porthtocyn.fsnet.co.uk
Tel: 0870 381 8832
International: +44 (0)1758 713303
Fax: 01758 713538

Price Guide: (incl. continental breakfast)
single from £63
double/twin from £83

BAE ABERMAW

PANORAMA HILL, BARMOUTH, GWYNEDD LL42 1DQ

Directions: From Dolgellau take the A496 to Barmouth. At Barmouth turn right, signposted Bae Abermaw.

Web: www.johansens.com/baeabermaw
E-mail: enquiries@baeabermaw.com
Tel: 0870 381 8332
International: +44 (0)1341 280550
Fax: 01341 280346

Price Guide:
single £86–£103
double/twin £126–£152

Situated high above the bay, Bae Abermaw is a truly delightful and surprising hotel. Its traditional Victorian and stone façade hides a stunning interior, which is elegant, progressive and relaxing. Cool neutral colours and streamlined sofas suggest a minimalist feel, yet retain a comfort and welcome that is rarely associated with such a modern style. Recently reopened by its new owners, the hotel really is one to watch in excitement over the next few years, as every care has been taken to ensure that the hotel offers the best of everything to all its guests and sets itself above the label of "seaside hotel". The cuisine is truly first class and again has some modern and exciting interpretations of classic dishes, which can be enjoyed in the elegant restaurant with its stunning views, accompanied by a balanced wine selection that caters excellently for all tastes and budgets. The bedrooms are carefully decorated in soft cream and honey tones, again promoting a sense of relaxation, which is enhanced by deep baths with masses of luxurious toiletries. There are some dramatic clifftop walks available right from the hotel's doorstep as well as some beautiful Welsh attractions nearby, such as Portmeirion Village and the Ffestiniog Railway.

Our inspector loved: *The exciting evolution of Bae Abermaw - so calming and quiet special.*

Llwyndu Farmhouse

LLANABER, NR BARMOUTH, GWYNEDD LL42 1RR

In Snowdonia's National Park, overlooking Cardigan Bay and the Lleyn Peninsula, Llwyndu Farmhouse offers relaxation and tranquillity in a house filled with character and history; this building has stood here for at least 400 years. This Grade II listed building features inglenook fireplaces, exposed stone walls and old beams creating a cosy atmosphere where guests are invited to treat the house as if it is their own home. All 3 bedrooms, including 2 four-poster beds within the Farmhouse and 4 more situated in the converted Granary next door, feature en-suite bath/shower rooms. Owners, Peter and Paula Thompson welcome guests to their home, which is surrounded by 4 acres of land. Peter is well-respected locally for his eclectic yet traditional menu influenced by Mediterranean cuisine. For explorers, Llwyndu is the ideal base to visit the Rhinog Mountains, and the nearby Panorama Walk offers some of the finest estuary views in Britain. There are mountains to climb, many castles, galleries and gardens to visit together with interesting walks leading to many narrow gauge railways through spectacular scenery. The old Welsh harbour town of Barmouth is also close by and the Italianate village of Portmeirion is only 20 minutes away.

Our inspector loved: Its charm – a little bit of ancient Wales.

Directions: Take the A496 towards Harlech for 2 miles until the street lighting and speed restrictions end. The entrance to the Farmhouse is 300 yards on the right.

Bangor

Pwllheli

Dolgellau

Web: www.johansens.com/llwyndu
E-mail: intouch@llwyndu-farmhouse.co.uk
Tel: 0870 381 9143
International: +44 (0)1341 280144
Fax: 01341 281236

Price Guide:
single £55
double/twin £74–£84

247

PLAS DOLMELYNLLYN

GANLLWYD, DOLGELLAU, GWYNEDD LL40 2HP

Directions: Plas Dolmelynllyn is off the main A470 Dolgellau– Llandudno road, 5 miles north of Dolgellau.

Web: www.johansens.com/plasdolmelynllyn
E-mail: info@dolly–hotel.co.uk
Tel: 0870 381 8825
International: +44 (0)1341 440273
Fax: 01341 440640

Price Guide:
single £75–£155
double £100–£180

Dating back at least to the reign of Elizabeth I and possibly to medieval times, this peaceful hotel oozes character and is a truly magical place. Its location amidst over 3 acres of gardens, high up above the Mawddach Valley in a clearing in the Coed y Brenin forest ensures wonderful views from all windows. New owners Janet Anderson-Kaye and her partner Barry have completely renovated the hotel, maintaining its original charm whilst adding a contemporary touch. Heavy oak beams and slate flooring adorn the Old Hall with its huge fireplace and deep red curtains. The 11 bedrooms are individually decorated and named after local Welsh rivers, whilst the Mawddach Suite boasts a magnificent four-poster bed. Named after the poet Percy Bysshe Shelley, who stayed here during his brief sojourn in Wales, the restaurant is housed in the oak-panelled dining room, the perfect setting for Janet's daily changing menus based on locally sourced ingredients. Located at upper terrace level is the conservatory and cocktail bar, where pre-dinner drinks, snack luncheons or afternoon tea can be taken. Guests can stroll to the waterfalls, ornamental lake and an ancient gold mine, and explore the awe-inspiring mountains, beautiful beaches and historic sites of Snowdonia. Activities include fishing, mountain biking, climbing, river rafting and golf.

Our inspector loved: "The country house dinner" very thoughtful menus for alternative dining. Very welcoming.

YE OLDE BULL'S HEAD INN

CASTLE STREET, BEAUMARIS, ISLE OF ANGLESEY LL58 8AP

Set in the south-east of the Isle of Anglesey in the picturesque town of Beaumaris, with breathtaking views of the Menai Strait and Snowdonia, this stylish 4-star inn offers a wonderful blend of traditional character, efficient service and 21st-century amenities. The Bull was built in 1472 as the original coaching house of the Borough and has been welcoming guests ever since. Each of the individually designed en-suite bedrooms and the suite offer a high standard of furnishings yet retain a unique character with antique furniture and fittings. Adorned with ancient artefacts including antique weapons, the traditional bar, unchanged since Charles Dickens enjoyed a glass of ale whilst staying here in 1859, is a convivial meeting place for locals and visitors alike. Guests can enjoy modern British cuisine in the informal brasserie, or opt for a fine dining experience in the elegant restaurant, set in the oldest part of the house. Winner of numerous culinary awards, its original beams and striking décor provide a stylish setting for the creative, modern European dishes, prepared with local ingredients including Welsh Black beef and a mouth-watering array of seafood. Beaumaris has an abundance of activities, sights and attractions including Edward I's 13th-century castle, and there are plenty of outdoor activities, such as birdwatching, fishing and cycling; a sailing centre is also close by.

Our inspector loved: This very special place and such wonderul contrasts.

Directions: Take from A55 expressway leave A55 on exit for, A545 to Beaumaris, which is 4 miles away. Less than 2 hours from Manchester airport and just 7 miles from Bangor railway station (main line London to Holyhead).

Web: www.johansens.com/yeoldebullshead
E-mail: info@bullsheadinn.co.uk
Tel: 0870 381 9017
International: +44 (0)1248 810329
Fax: 01248 811294

Price Guide:
single £70
double/twin £97
four-poster /suite £110/£145

THE BELL AT SKENFRITH

SKENFRITH, MONMOUTHSHIRE NP7 8UH

Directions: Leave the M4 (J24) take the A449 (A40) north. At the roundabout in Monmouth, turn left and then right at the traffic lights torwards Hereford. Travel 4 miles and turn left onto B4521 towards Abergavenny. The Bell is 3 miles on the left.

Web: www.johansens.com/bellskenfrith
E-mail: enquiries@skenfrith.co.uk
Tel: 0870 381 8354
International: +44 (0)1600 750235
Fax: 01600 750525

Price Guide:
single £70–£110
double/twin £95–£145
four-poster £170

Situated in a tiny picturesque village on the edge of the River Monnow and surrounded by unspoilt Monmouthshire countryside, The Bell, a carefully renovated 17th-century coaching inn and recently voted the Best Place to Stay in Wales by the tourist board, is an oasis for visitors. The inn looks out over the historic arched bridge as well as the old castle ruins and mill. Beautifully designed in a classical style, there are roaring log fires, flagstone floors and stunning oak beams complemented by antiques, sumptuous sofas and tasteful décor. Cosy bedrooms are homely and welcoming with beautiful Welsh blankets, crisp linen, all modern amenities and sweeping views over the rolling hills or river. Guests may enjoy sipping a glass of wine or real ale in the relaxed atmosphere of the bar with its open log fire, before enjoying the imaginative contemporary dishes created by the inn's 2 AA rosetted chef in the attractive restaurant overlooking the terrace and gardens. All meals are based on local, organic produce; a children's organic menu is also available. A private room can accommodate up to 40 persons for celebration meals and meetings. The Skenfrith area is rich in cultural and historical heritage and is an ideal base for many walks.

Our inspector loved: *The huge welcoming log fire, abundance of flowers and the outstanding quality of the décor throughout.*

PARVA FARMHOUSE AND RESTAURANT

TINTERN, CHEPSTOW, MONMOUTHSHIRE NP16 6SQ

Surrounded by the glorious, wooded hillsides of the beautiful lower Wye Valley and just a mile from 12th-century Tintern Abbey, one of the finest relics of Britain's monastic age, Parva Farmhouse is a homely haven where visitors can relax and forget the pressures of their daily world. This is an ideal spot for country lovers. The River Wye flows just 50 yards from the hotel's small, flower-filled garden, there is an abundance of wildlife and hundreds of tempting walks. Built during the 17th century, Parva today provides every comfort. The bedrooms are well-furnished and most have pretty views across the River Wye. The beamed lounge with its log-burning fireplace, "Honesty Bar" and deep Chesterfield sofas and chairs is the perfect place to relax and chat over the day's happenings. The crowning glory of Parva is the excellent food, home-cooked by chef-patron Dereck Stubbs and served in the AA Rosette Inglenook Restaurant before a 14-foot beamed fireplace. Golf, shooting and riding are close by and there is horse-racing at Chepstow. 2-night breaks inclusive of dinner are especially popular and good value for money. Places of interest nearby include Tintern Abbey, castles at Abergavenny and Chepstow, Offa's Dyke, the Royal Forest of Dean, many old ruins and ancient monuments.

Our inspector loved: *The spacious, well appointed and tastefully decorated bedrooms with views over the River Wye.*

Directions: Leave M48 at Jct2 and join A466 towards Monmouth. The hotel is on the north edge of Tintern Village.

Web: www.johansens.com/parvafarmhouse
E-mail: Parva_hoteltintern@hotmail.com
Tel: 0870 381 8803
International: +44 (0)1291 689411
Fax: 01291 689557

Abergavenny
Merthy Tydfil
Swansea
Newport
Cardiff

Price Guide:
single £55
double £76–£84

251

THE GOWER HOTEL & ORANGERY RESTAURANT

MILFORD TERRACE, SAUNDERSFOOT, PEMBROKESHIRE SA69 9EL

Ideally located in this picturesque corner of Wales, The Gower is a delightful hotel that prides itself on its warmth of welcome and high level of service. Set back from the charming harbour, it offers a winning combination of peace and tranquillity without being removed from the heart and soul of the resort. The hotel has 20 en-suite bedrooms and each has been carefully refurbished by the hotel's devoted new owners and provides comfortable accommodation in twin, double or family rooms. The Orangery Restaurant is refreshingly light and airy, and a pleasant setting to sample the excellently prepared meals of locally reared meat and fish, as well as some winning vegetarian selections. Staff share the desire of the owners to ensure that the atmosphere remains friendly and informal without sacrificing courtesy or discretion, and this ambience can also be found in the welcoming Arches bar, where guests can enjoy pre or post-dinner drinks. There are no less than 3 immaculate beaches within easy access of the hotel, as well as some superb gardens and Britain's first and only coastal national park, whilst Tenby is delightful and just a stone's throw away.

Our inspector loved: *The comfortable and welcoming atmosphere and the easy access to the beach front and Pembrokeshire countryside.*

Directions: From London take the M4 westbound and turn off for the A48. Take the A40 towards St Clears then the A477 towards Tenby. Take the A478 towards Saundersfoot then the B4316. Drive through the village and after the first turning (at the harbour) the hotel is in view.

Web: www.johansens.com/gower
E-mail: tim.rowe@rotels.com
Tel: 0870 381 9149
International: +44 (0)1834 813452
Fax: 01834 813452

Price Guide:
single £52–£62
double £84–£94
family £115–£130

WOLFSCASTLE COUNTRY HOTEL & RESTAURANT

WOLF'S CASTLE, HAVERFORDWEST, PEMBROKESHIRE SA62 5LZ

This former vicarage, situated in the glorious Pembrokeshire countryside, offers its guests a friendly and welcoming atmosphere. The owner/manager of 27 years, Andrew Stirling, is supported by a close network of staff, several of whom have been at Wolfscastle for many years. The charming non-smoking bedrooms, including 3 luxurious Executive Suites, have undergone recent refurbishment and now combine elegant period décor with modern conveniences; all have en-suite bathrooms, television and refreshment facilities. Wolfscastle prides itself on its exceptional cuisine based on fresh local produce. The restaurant provides an exemplary service, whilst maintaining the relaxed ambience of this country hotel, and the cosy bar is complete with blazing log fire. Both dining areas offer an à la carte and bar menu. These delightful premises are an ideal setting for conferences and social events. The main function room opens out onto a magnificent patio/garden area, and guests have use of a private bar. A popular venue for smaller parties is the Barclay Suite, named after the recently retired pianist of 25 years. The surrounding landscape is steeped in history, with Pembroke and Carew castles nearby. Visitors can explore the beautiful coastline on foot or take an exhilarating boat ride to see local wildlife.

Our inspector loved: *The warm and welcoming home from home atmosphere created by the owners and their staff.*

Directions: Located on the A40, in the village of Wolf's Castle, 7 miles from Haverfordwest. The hotel is on the left.

Web: www.johansens.com/wolfscastle
E-mail: enquiries@wolfscastle.com
Tel: 0870 381 9162
International: +44 (0)1437 741225
Fax: 01437 741383

Price Guide:
single £55–£75
double/twin £79–£109

FELIN FACH GRIFFIN

FELIN FACH, BRECON, POWYS LD3 0UB

Directions: Located on the edge of the Brecon Beacons National Park, 4 miles north east of Brecon and 8 miles from Hay on Wye.

Web: www.johansens.com/felinfach
E-mail: enquiries@eatdrinksleep.ltd.uk
Tel: 0870 381 9345
International: +44 (0)1874 620111
Fax: 01874 620120

Price Guide:
single £67.50
double £92.50
suite £115

Welshpool

Llandrindod Wells

Brecon

Abergavenny

Set amidst stunning scenery in a quiet Welsh valley on the edge of The Brecon Beacons National Park and with glorious views of the Black Mountains, the friendly Felin Fach Griffin is run by its owner, Charles Inkin, along the ethos of "simple things done well". This is reflected in the luxurious yet unfussy bedrooms and the deliciously simple cuisine, which was recognised in 2003 when the Griffin restaurant won AA Restaurant of the Year for Wales. The antithesis to large, impersonal hotel rooms, the 7 individually decorated bedrooms have no televisions and are completely chintz-free with luxuriously soft white bed linen and extremely comfortable, 2 of which have hand-carved four-poster beds. All rooms are en suite with large baths and power showers. Deep leather sofas, an open fire, and cheerful local staff ensure absolute relaxation. Guests can choose to dine in the brightly painted bar area or the red dining room. Head chef Ricardo van Ede uses only the best of seasonal ingredients for his utterly delicious cuisine. All have been sourced locally: vegetables come from the garden, beef from the surrounding area, lamb from Carmarthen, and trout from local rivers. Guests can explore some of the most breathtaking scenery in Britain directly on the doorstep, whilst the border towns of Hay on Wye and Brecon are only a few minutes away.

Our inspector loved: *This enchanting contemporary inn – so hospitable and run with such flair. Delicious dining. I loved breakfast too!*

NEW

FAIRYHILL

REYNOLDSTON, GOWER, NEAR SWANSEA SA3 1BS

Located on the stunning Gower peninsular, Britain's first Area of Outstanding Natural Beauty, Fairyhill is only a stone's throw from spectacular coastline where rolling landscape meets turquoise sea. The surrounding 24 acres of magnificent grounds encompass woodland, a lake and trout stream and this enchanting hotel offers guests outstanding hospitality, award-winning food and a relaxing ambience. The house itself dates back to the 18th century and provides accommodation of the highest standard. Each of the 8 stylish bedrooms has its own individual character and décor, with lighting and furnishings skillfully utilized to create a cosy, intimate setting. Every one of the rooms has a contemporary en-suite bathroom and modern conveniences one would expect from a high quality establishment. The restaurant is elegant yet informal with imaginative menus that incorporate the best seasonal local produce. Examples include cocktail of Gower lobster, fillet of Welsh black beef, filo tart of vine tomatoes and local goats cheese and vanilla poached pear with basil sorbet. Visitors to Fairyhill may cleanse mind, body and soul with a range of therapies from Reiki to Indian head massage. For outdoor pursuits why not enjoy a leisurely game of croquet on the lawn or a meander along the delightful garden paths.

Our inspector loved: *The fabulous breakfast followed by the magical stroll in the hotels woodlands. Simply enchanting.*

Directions: At the heart of the Gower Peninsula between reynildston and Llanrhidian.

Web: www.johansens.com/fairyhill
E-mail: admin@fairyhill.net
Tel: 0870 381 9321
International: +44 (0)1792 390139
Fax: 01792 391358

Price Guide:
double/twin £140–£245

Abergavenny
Merthy Tydfil
Swansea
Newport
Cardiff

EGERTON GREY

PORTHKERRY, NR CARDIFF, VALE OF GLAMORGAN CF62 3BZ

Directions: From the M4, junction 33, take the A4050. Follow airport signs for 10 miles then take the A4226 towards Porthkerry. After 400 yards turn into the lane between 2 thatched cottages, the hotel is at end of the lane.

Web: www.johansens.com/egertongrey
E-mail: info@egertongrey.co.uk
Tel: 0870 381 8501
International: +44 (0)1446 711666
Fax: 01446 711690

Price Guide:
single £92–£115
double/twin £100–£115
suite £130

A distinguished former rectory dating from the early 19th century, Egerton Grey was opened as a small luxury hotel in 1988. Tucked away in 7 acres of gardens in a secluded, wooded valley in the Vale of Glamorgan, no other houses or roads are visible; instead guests can savour glorious views towards Porthkerry Park and the sea. The house's historic character has been carefully preserved with interior design that complements its architectural features. An Edwardian drawing room has intricate plaster mouldings, chandeliers, an open fireplace and oil paintings, whilst a quiet library overlooks the garden. All 10 immaculately presented bedrooms are extremely comfortable and several have Victorian baths and brasswork. The main restaurant, once a billiard room, creates an air of intimacy with its original Cuban mahogany panelling and candle-lit tables. Owners Richard Morgan-Price and Huw Thomas take great pride in presenting high-quality cuisine and fine wines. Riding can be arranged and there is a pitch and putt course a short stroll away by the sea. The Welsh Folk Museum, Castle Coch and Cardiff Castle are nearby.

Our inspector loved: *Drawing back the curtains to see the seaview through the spectacular viaduct.*

Condé Nast Johansens are delighted to recommend over 380 properties across Great Britain and Ireland.

These properties can be found in *Recommended Hotels & Spas - GB & Ireland 2004*.

Call 0800 269 397 or see the order forms on page 303 to order Guides.

England

The Bath Priory Hotel And Restaurant	Bath & North East Somerset	0870 381 8345
The Bath Priory Hotel And Restaurant	Bath & North East Somerset	0870 381 8345
The Bath Spa Hotel	Bath & North East Somerset	0870 381 8346
Combe Grove Manor Hotel & Country Club	Bath & North East Somerset	0870 381 8438
The Francis Hotel	Bath & North East Somerset	0870 381 8728
Homewood Park	Bath & North East Somerset	0870 381 8605
Hunstrete House	Bath & North East Somerset	0870 381 8630
The Royal Crescent Hotel	Bath & North East Somerset	0870 381 8874
The Windsor Hotel	Bath & North East Somerset	0870 381 9003
Moore Place Hotel	Bedfordshire	0870 381 8745
Cliveden	Berkshire	0870 381 8432
Donnington Valley Hotel & Golf Club	Berkshire	0870 381 8484
Fredrick's – Hotel Restaurant Spa	Berkshire	0870 381 8531
The French Horn	Berkshire	0870 381 8532
Monkey Island Hotel	Berkshire	0870 381 8742

▼

Newbury Manor Hotel	**Berkshire**	**0870 381 9275**
The Regency Park Hotel	Berkshire	0870 381 8852
Sir Christopher Wren's House Hotel & Spa	Berkshire	0870 381 8896
Stirrups	Berkshire	0870 381 9238
The Swan At Streatley	Berkshire	0870 381 8928
The Vineyard At Stockcross	Berkshire	0870 381 8965
Hotel Du Vin & Bistro	Birmingham	0870 381 8618
New Hall	Birmingham	0870 381 8756
Hotel Du Vin & Bistro	Bristol	0870 381 8616
Danesfield House Hotel And Spa	Buckinghamshire	0870 381 8474
Hartwell House Hotel, Restaurant & Spa	Buckinghamshire	0870 381 8585
Stoke Park Club	Buckinghamshire	0870 381 8915
Taplow House Hotel	Buckinghamshire	0870 381 8939
The Cambridge Belfry	Cambridgeshire	0870 381 9312
The Haycock	Cambridgeshire	0870 381 8587
Hotel Felix	Cambridgeshire	0870 381 9056
The Alderley Edge Hotel	Cheshire	0870 381 8307
The Chester Crabwall Manor	Cheshire	0870 381 8423
The Chester Grosvenor and Grosvenor Spa	Cheshire	0870 381 9264
Crewe Hall	Cheshire	0870 381 8458
Green Bough Hotel	Cheshire	0870 381 8571
Hillbark Hotel	Cheshire	0870 381 9128
Mere Court Hotel	Cheshire	0870 381 8727
Nunsmere Hall	Cheshire	0870 381 8772
Rowton Hall Hotel	Cheshire	0870 381 8871

The Stanneylands Hotel	Cheshire	0870 381 8909
Alverton Manor	Cornwall	0870 381 9152
Budock Vean - The Hotel On The River	Cornwall	0870 381 8392
Fowey Hall Hotel & Restaurant	Cornwall	0870 381 8529
The Garrack Hotel & Restaurant	Cornwall	0870 381 8536
The Greenbank Hotel	Cornwall	0870 381 8573
Hell Bay	Cornwall	0870 381 8591
The Lugger Hotel	Cornwall	0870 381 8708
Meudon Hotel	Cornwall	0870 381 8730
The Nare Hotel	Cornwall	0870 381 8755
The Rosevine Hotel	Cornwall	0870 381 8867
Talland Bay Hotel	Cornwall	0870 381 8937
Treglos Hotel	Cornwall	0870 381 8951
Trenython Manor Hotel & Spa	Cornwall	0870 381 9139
The Well House	Cornwall	0870 381 8975
Armathwaite Hall Hotel	Cumbria	0870 381 8478
Gilpin Lodge	Cumbria	0870 381 8546
Holbeck Ghyll Country House Hotel	Cumbria	0870 381 8601
The Inn on the Lake	Cumbria	0870 381 8640
Lakeside Hotel On Lake Windermere	Cumbria	0870 381 8672
Linthwaite House Hotel	Cumbria	0870 381 8694
The Lodore Falls Hotel	Cumbria	0870 381 9314
Lovelady Shield Country House Hotel	Cumbria	0870 381 8705
Netherwood Hotel	Cumbria	0870 381 8729
Rampsbeck Country House Hotel	Cumbria	0870 381 8848
Rothay Manor	Cumbria	0870 381 8869
Sharrow Bay Country House Hotel	Cumbria	0870 381 8891
Storrs Hall	Cumbria	0870 381 8919
Tufton Arms Hotel	Cumbria	0870 381 8956
Callow Hall	Derbyshire	0870 381 8400
Cavendish Hotel	Derbyshire	0870 381 8412
East Lodge Country House Hotel	Derbyshire	0870 381 8496
Fischer's	Derbyshire	0870 381 8523
Hassop Hall	Derbyshire	0870 381 8586
The Izaak Walton Hotel	Derbyshire	0870 381 8642
The Lee Wood Hotel & Restaurant	Derbyshire	0870 381 8687
Riber Hall	Derbyshire	0870 381 8854
Ringwood Hall Hotel	Derbyshire	0870 381 8857
Riverside House	Derbyshire	0870 381 8860
The Arundell Arms	Devon	0870 381 8323
Bovey Castle	Devon	0870 381 9286
Buckland-Tout-Saints	Devon	0870 381 8391
Combe House Hotel & Restaurant	Devon	0870 381 8440
Fairwater Head Country House Hotel	Devon	0870 381 8511
Hotel Riviera	Devon	0870 381 8624
Ilsington Country House Hotel	Devon	0870 381 8635
Langdon Court Hotel & Restaurant	Devon	0870 381 9157
Lewtrenchard Manor	Devon	0870 381 9177
Mill End	Devon	0870 381 8734
Northcote Manor Country House Hotel	Devon	0870 381 8767
Orestone Manor Hotel & Restaurant	Devon	0870 381 8794
The Osborne Hotel & Langtry's Restaurant	Devon	0870 381 8795
The Palace Hotel	Devon	0870 381 8798
Percy's Country Hotel & Restaurant	Devon	0870 381 8817
Soar Mill Cove Hotel	Devon	0870 381 8897
The Tides Reach Hotel	Devon	0870 381 8947
Watersmeet Hotel	Devon	0870 381 8972
Woolacombe Bay Hotel	Devon	0870 381 9007
The Avonmouth Hotel and Restaurant	Dorset	0870 381 9333

MINI LISTINGS GREAT BRITAIN & IRELAND

Condé Nast Johansens are delighted to recommend over 380 properties across Great Britain and Ireland.
These properties can be found in *Recommended Hotels & Spas - GB & Ireland 2004*.
Call 0800 269 397 or see the order forms on page 303 to order Guides.

Langtry Manor	Dorset	0870 381 8681
Moonfleet Manor	Dorset	0870 381 8744
Plumber Manor	Dorset	0870 381 8829
The Priory Hotel	Dorset	0870 381 8841
Headlam Hall	Durham	0870 381 8590
Five Lakes Resort	Essex	0870 381 8524
Greenwoods Estate	Essex	0870 381 8575
Maison Talbooth	Essex	0870 381 8712
Barnsley House	Gloucestershire	0870 381 9327
The Bear Of Rodborough	Gloucestershire	0870 381 8348
Burleigh Court	Gloucestershire	0870 381 8664
Calcot Manor	Gloucestershire	0870 381 8398
Charingworth Manor	Gloucestershire	0870 381 8414
Corse Lawn House Hotel	Gloucestershire	0870 381 8448
Cotswold House Hotel	Gloucestershire	0870 381 8449
The Dial House	Gloucestershire	0870 381 9296
Fosse Manor	Gloucestershire	0870 381 9324
The Grapevine Hotel	Gloucestershire	0870 381 8564
The Greenway	Gloucestershire	0870 381 8574
Hatton Court	Gloucestershire	0870 381 8773
Hotel On The Park	Gloucestershire	0870 381 8623
Lords Of The Manor Hotel	Gloucestershire	0870 381 8704
Lower Slaughter Manor	Gloucestershire	0870 381 8706
The Manor House Hotel	Gloucestershire	0870 381 8717
The Noel Arms Hotel	Gloucestershire	0870 381 8763
The Painswick Hotel	Gloucestershire	0870 381 8797
The Swan Hotel At Bibury	Gloucestershire	0870 381 8931
The Unicorn Hotel	Gloucestershire	0870 381 8960
Washbourne Court Hotel	Gloucestershire	0870 381 8970
Thornbury Castle	South Gloucestershire	0870 381 8944
Careys Manor Hotel & Senspa	Hampshire	0870 381 8405
Chewton Glen	Hampshire	0870 381 8427
Chilworth Manor	Hampshire	0870 381 9057
Esseborne Manor	Hampshire	0870 381 8506
Hotel Du Vin & Bistro	Hampshire	0870 381 8615
Le Poussin at Whitley Ridge	Hampshire	0870 381 8994
The Montagu Arms Hotel	Hampshire	0870 381 8743
New Park Manor	Hampshire	0870 381 8761
Passford House Hotel	Hampshire	0870 381 8804
Tylney Hall	Hampshire	0870 381 8958
Down Hall Country House Hotel	Hertfordshire	0870 381 8489
The Grove Hotel	Hertfordshire	0870 381 8646
The Pendley Manor Hotel	Hertfordshire	0870 381 8812
Sopwell House	Hertfordshire	0870 381 8898
St Michael's Manor	Hertfordshire	0870 381 8906
The Priory Bay Hotel	Isle of Wight	0870 381 8839
Chilston Park	Kent	0870 381 8428
Eastwell Manor	Kent	0870 381 8498
Hotel Du Vin & Bistro	Kent	0870 381 8614
Rowhill Grange Hotel And Spa	Kent	0870 381 8870
The Spa Hotel	Kent	0870 381 8901
The Gibbon Bridge Hotel	Lancashire	0870 381 8544
Northcote Manor	Lancashire	0870 381 8766
The Pines Hotel	Lancashire	0870 381 9274
Quorn Country Hotel	Leicestershire	0870 381 8847
Stapleford Park Hotel, Spa, Golf & Sporting Estate	Leicestershire	0870 381 8912
The Angel and Royal Hotel	Lincolnshire	0870 381 9164
The George Of Stamford	Lincolnshire	0870 381 8543

The Lincoln Hotel	Lincolnshire	0870 381 9288
41	London	0870 381 8300
47 Park Street	London	0870 381 9282
51 Buckingham Gate	London	0870 381 8301
The Athenaeum Hotel & Apartments	London	0870 381 8329
Beaufort House	London	0870 381 8350
Cannizaro House	London	0870 381 8402
The Carlton Tower	London	0870 381 9326
The Cranley	London	0870 381 8456
Dolphin Square Hotel	London	0870 381 8483
The Dorchester	London	0870 381 8485
Dorset Square Hotel	London	0870 381 8488
Draycott House Apartments	London	0870 381 8490
The Goring	London	0870 381 9328
Kensington House Hotel	London	0870 381 8648
The Leonard	London	0870 381 8688
The Lowndes Hotel	London	0870 381 9285
The Mayflower Hotel	London	0870 381 9195
The Milestone Hotel & Apartments	London	0870 381 8732
Number Sixteen	London	0870 381 8771
Pembridge Court Hotel	London	0870 381 8808
The Richmond Gate Hotel And Restaurant	London	0870 381 8855
The Ritz	London	0870 381 9308
The Royal Park	London	0870 381 9289
Sofitel St James	London	0870 381 9185
Twenty Nevern Square	London	0870 381 8957
Warren House	London	0870 381 8969
West Lodge Park Country House Hotel	London	0870 381 8978
Didsbury House	Greater Manchester	0870 381 8481
Etrop Grange	Greater Manchester	0870 381 8507
Congham Hall	Norfolk	0870 381 8443
Park Farm Country Hotel & Leisure	Norfolk	0870 381 8800
Fawsley Hall	Northamptonshire	0870 381 8516
Whittlebury Hall	Northamptonshire	0870 381 8995
Marshall Meadows Country House Hotel	Northumberland	0870 381 8721

▼

Matfen Hall	Northumberland	0870 381 8724
Tillmouth Park	Northumberland	0870 381 8948
Hart's Hotel	Nottinghamshire	0870 381 9330
Lace Market Hotel	Nottinghamshire	0870 381 9325
Langar Hall	Nottinghamshire	0870 381 8676
The Bay Tree Hotel	Oxfordshire	0870 381 8347
Bignell Park Hotel & Restaurant	Oxfordshire	0870 381 8362
The Cotswold Lodge Hotel	Oxfordshire	0870 381 8450

Mini Listings Great Britain & Ireland

Condé Nast Johansens are delighted to recommend over 380 properties across Great Britain and Ireland.

These properties can be found in *Recommended Hotels & Spas - GB & Ireland 2004.*

Call 0800 269 397 or see the order forms on page 303 to order Guides.

Fallowfields	Oxfordshire	0870 381 8513
The Feathers Hotel	Oxfordshire	0870 381 8519
Hawkwell House	Oxfordshire	0870 381 8326
Phyllis Court Club	Oxfordshire	0870 381 8822
The Spread Eagle Hotel	Oxfordshire	0870 381 8902
The Springs Hotel & Golf Club	Oxfordshire	0870 381 8904
Weston Manor	Oxfordshire	0870 381 8981
Hambleton Hall	Rutland	0870 381 8582
The Lake Isle	Rutland	0870 381 8670
Dinham Hall	Shropshire	0870 381 8482
Madeley Court	Shropshire	0870 381 8711
Bindon Country House Hotel	Somerset	0870 381 8364
Daneswood House Hotel	Somerset	0870 381 8475
Holbrook House Hotel & Spa	Somerset	0870 381 9174
Mount Somerset Country House Hotel	Somerset	0870 381 8750
Ston Easton Park	Somerset	0870 381 8916
Hoar Cross Hall Spa Resort	Staffordshire	0870 381 8598
Angel Hotel	Suffolk	0870 381 8315
Black Lion Hotel & Restaurant	Suffolk	0870 381 8366
Brudenell Hotel	Suffolk	0870 381 9182
Hintlesham Hall	Suffolk	0870 381 8595
The Hotel Victoria	Suffolk	0870 381 9293
Ravenwood Hall Country Hotel & Restaurant	Suffolk	0870 381 8849
Salthouse Harbour Hotel	Suffolk	0870 381 9196
Seckford Hall	Suffolk	0870 381 8890
The Swan Hotel	Suffolk	0870 381 8929
The Swan Hotel	Suffolk	0870 381 9280
Swynford Paddocks Hotel And Restaurant	Suffolk	0870 381 8935
Foxhills	Surrey	0870 381 8530

Great Fosters	**Surrey**	**0870 381 8569**
Langshott Manor	Surrey	0870 381 8680
Lythe Hill Hotel & Spa	Surrey	0870 381 8709
Oatlands Park Hotel	Surrey	0870 381 8779
Pennyhill Park Hotel	Surrey	0870 381 8815
Ashdown Park Hotel And Country Club	East Sussex	0870 381 8325
Dale Hill	East Sussex	0870 381 8471
The Grand Hotel	East Sussex	0870 381 8560
Horsted Place Country House Hotel	East Sussex	0870 381 8609
Hotel Du Vin & Bistro	East Sussex	0870 381 8617
Newick Park	East Sussex	0870 381 8762
The PowderMills	East Sussex	0870 381 8835
White Lodge Country House Hotel	East Sussex	0870 381 8990
Alexander House Hotel	West Sussex	0870 381 8308
Amberley Castle	West Sussex	0870 381 8312

The Angel Hotel	West Sussex	0870 381 8314
Bailiffscourt Hotel & Health Spa	West Sussex	0870 381 8333
Ghyll Manor	West Sussex	0870 381 9331
The Millstream Hotel	West Sussex	0870 381 8739
Ockenden Manor	West Sussex	0870 381 8780
South Lodge Hotel	West Sussex	0870 381 8900
The Spread Eagle Hotel & Health Spa	West Sussex	0870 381 8903
The Vermont Hotel	Tyne & Wear	0870 381 8962
Alveston Manor	Warwickshire	0870 381 8310
Ardencote Manor Hotel, Country Club & Spa	Warwickshire	0870 381 8320
Billesley Manor	Warwickshire	0870 381 8363
Ettington Park	Warwickshire	0870 381 8508
The Glebe At Barford	Warwickshire	0870 381 8548
Mallory Court	Warwickshire	0870 381 8713
Nailcote Hall	Warwickshire	0870 381 8752
Nuthurst Grange	Warwickshire	0870 381 8776
Wroxall Abbey Estate	Warwickshire	0870 381 9013
Bishopstrow House	Wiltshire	0870 381 8365
Howard's House	Wiltshire	0870 381 8627
The Manor House Hotel & Golf Club	Wiltshire	0870 381 8718
The Old Bell	Wiltshire	0870 381 9209
The Pear Tree At Purton	Wiltshire	0870 381 8806
The Broadway Hotel	Worcestershire	0870 381 8381
Brockencote Hall	Worcestershire	0870 381 8382
The Cottage In The Wood	Worcestershire	0870 381 8452
Dormy House	Worcestershire	0870 381 8487
The Elms	Worcestershire	0870 381 8304
The Evesham Hotel	Worcestershire	0870 381 8510
The Lygon Arms	Worcestershire	0870 381 9190
Wood Norton Hall	Worcestershire	0870 381 9154
Willerby Manor Hotel	East Riding of Yorkshire	0870 381 8998
Aldwark Manor	North Yorkshire	0870 381 8491
The Boar's Head Hotel	North Yorkshire	0870 381 8370
The Devonshire Arms Country House Hotel	North Yorkshire	0870 381 8480
The Feversham Arms Hotel	North Yorkshire	0870 381 9283
The Grange Hotel	North Yorkshire	0870 381 8561
Grants Hotel	North Yorkshire	0870 381 8562
Hackness Grange	North Yorkshire	0870 381 8578
Hazlewood Castle Hotel	North Yorkshire	0870 381 8589
Hob Green Hotel And Restaurant	North Yorkshire	0870 381 8600
Hotel Du Vin & Bistro	North Yorkshire	0870 381 8493
Judges Country House Hotel	North Yorkshire	0870 381 9165
Middlethorpe Hall Hotel, Restaurant & Spa	North Yorkshire	0870 381 8731
Monk Fryston Hall Hotel	North Yorkshire	0870 381 8741
The Pheasant	North Yorkshire	0870 381 8821
The Royal Hotel	North Yorkshire	0870 381 9277
Rudding Park Hotel & Golf	North Yorkshire	0870 381 8879
Simonstone Hall	North Yorkshire	0870 381 8895
Swinton Park	North Yorkshire	0870 381 8934
The Worsley Arms Hotel	North Yorkshire	0870 381 9011
Wrea Head Country Hotel	North Yorkshire	0870 381 9012
Charnwood Hotel	South Yorkshire	0870 381 8417
Hellaby Hall Hotel	South Yorkshire	0870 381 8592
Whitley Hall Hotel	South Yorkshire	0870 381 8993
42 The Calls	West Yorkshire	0870 381 8737
Chevin Country Park Hotel	West Yorkshire	0870 381 8426
Haley's Hotel & Restaurant	West Yorkshire	0870 381 8579
Holdsworth House Hotel & Restaurant	West Yorkshire	0870 381 8603
Wood Hall	West Yorkshire	0870 381 9004

Condé Nast Johansens are delighted to recommend over 380 properties across Great Britain and Ireland.
These properties can be found in *Recommended Hotels & Spas - GB & Ireland 2004*.
Call 0800 269 397 or see the order forms on page 303 to order Guides.

Woodlands..................................West Yorkshire 0870 381 9356

Channel Islands

| The Atlantic Hotel | Jersey | 0870 381 8330 |
| Château La Chaire | Jersey | 0870 381 8420 |

Northern Ireland

| Bushmills Inn Hotel | Antrim | 0870 381 9315 |

Ireland

Dromoland Castle	Clare	00 353 61 368144
Harvey's Point	Donegal	00 353 74 972 2208
Rathmullan House	Donegal	00 353 74 915 8188
Renvyle House Hotel	Galway	00 353 95 43511
Cahernane House Hotel	Kerry	00 353 64 31895
Park Hotel Kenmare & Sámas	Kerry	00 353 64 41200
Parknasilla Hotel	Kerry	00 353 64 45122
Killashee House Hotel	Kildare	00 353 45 879277
Mount Juliet Conrad	Kilkenny	00 353 56 777 3000
Glin Castle	Limerick	00 353 68 34173
Ashford Castle	Mayo	00 353 94 95 46003
Knockranny House Hotel & Spa	Mayo	00 353 98 28600
Nuremore Hotel And Country Club	Monaghan	00 353 42 9661438
Dunbrody Country House & Cookery School	Wexford	00 353 51 389 600
Kelly's Resort Hotel	Wexford	00 353 53 32114
Marlfield House	Wexford	00 353 55 21124

Scotland

Darroch Learg	Aberdeenshire	0870 381 8477
Ardanaiseig	Argyll & Bute	0870 381 8319
Cameron House	Argyll & Bute	0870 381 8588
Loch Melfort Hotel & Restaurant	Argyll & Bute	0870 381 8699
Stonefield Castle	Argyll & Bute	0870 381 8918
Balcary Bay Hotel	Dumfries & Galloway	0870 381 8334
Cally Palace Hotel	Dumfries & Galloway	0870 381 8401
Kirroughtree House	Dumfries & Galloway	0870 381 8659
Knockinaam Lodge	Dumfries & Galloway	0870 381 9166
The Bonham	Edinburgh	0870 381 8373
Bruntsfield Hotel	Edinburgh	0870 381 8388
Channings	Edinburgh	0870 381 8413
The Chester Residence	Edinburgh	0870 381 9281
Christopher North House	Edinburgh	0870 381 9310
The Edinburgh Residence	Edinburgh	0870 381 8913
The Howard	Edinburgh	0870 381 8626
The Old Manor Country House Hotel	Fife	0870 381 9322
One Devonshire Gardens	Glasgow	0870 381 9146
Bunchrew House Hotel	Highland	0870 381 8393
Cuillin Hills Hotel	Highland	0870 381 8467
Culloden House	Highland	0870 381 9137
Glen Mhor Hotel	Highland	0870 381 8407
The Glenmoriston Town House Hotel & La Riviera Restaurant	Highland	0870 381 8555
The Golf View Hotel & Leisure Club	Highland	0870 381 8404

▼

Inverlochy Castle	Highland	0870 381 9278
Kincraig House Hotel	Highland	0870 381 9323
Loch Torridon Country House Hotel	Highland	0870 381 9136
Muckrach Lodge Hotel & Restaurant	Highland	0870 381 8751
The Royal Golf Hotel	Highland	0870 381 9199
Royal Marine Hotel	Highland	0870 381 9133
Skeabost Country House	Highland	0870 381 9294
Dalhousie Castle And Spa	Midlothian	0870 381 8472
Knockomie Hotel	Moray	0870 381 8663
Ballathie House Hotel	Perth & Kinross	0870 381 8337
Cromlix House	Perth & Kinross	0870 381 8460
Gleneagles	Perth & Kinross	0870 381 8553
Kinnaird	Perth & Kinross	0870 381 9124
The Royal Hotel	Perth & Kinross	0870 381 8875
Castle Venlaw	Scottish Borders	0870 381 8410
Cringletie House	Scottish Borders	0870 381 9279
Dryburgh Abbey Hotel	Scottish Borders	0870 381 9311
Ednam House Hotel	Scottish Borders	0870 381 8500
The Roxburghe Hotel & Golf Course	Scottish Borders	0870 381 8873
Enterkine Country House	South Ayrshire	0870 381 8505
Buchanan Arms Hotel & Leisure Club	Stirling	0870 381 9301

Wales

Llechwen Hall	Cardiff	0870 381 8698
Bodysgallen Hall & Spa	Conwy	0870 381 8372
St Tudno Hotel & Restaurant	Conwy	0870 381 8907
Wild Pheasant Hotel	Denbighshire	0870 381 8633
Hotel Maes-Y-Neuadd	Gwynedd	0870 381 9332
Palé Hall	Gwynedd	0870 381 8799
Penmaenuchaf Hall	Gwynedd	0870 381 8813
The Trearddur Bay Hotel	Isle of Anglesey	0870 381 8949
Allt-Yr-Ynys Hotel	Monmouthshire	0870 381 8309
Llansantffraed Court Hotel	Monmouthshire	0870 381 8697
Lamphey Court Hotel	Pembrokeshire	0870 381 8675
Penally Abbey	Pembrokeshire	0870 381 8810
Warpool Court Hotel	Pembrokeshire	0870 381 8968
Gliffaes Country House Hotel	Powys	0870 381 8557
The Lake Country House	Powys	0870 381 8668
Lake Vyrnwy Hotel	Powys	0870 381 8671
Llangoed Hall	Powys	0870 381 8696

HISTORIC HOUSES, CASTLES & GARDENS

Incorporating Museums & Galleries

We are pleased to feature over 150 places to visit during your stay at a Condé Nast Johansens recommended hotel.

England

Bedfordshire

Woburn Abbey - Woburn, Bedfordshire MK17 9WA.
Tel: 01525 290666

Berkshire

Anderton House - The Landmark Trust, Shottesbrooke,
Maidenhead, Berkshire SL6 3SW. Tel: 01628 825920

Dolbelydr - The Landmark Trust, Shottesbrooke,
Maidenhead, Berkshire SL6 3SW. Tel: 01628 825920

Old Campden House - The Landmark Trust, Shottesbrooke,
Maidenhead, Berkshire SL6 3SW. Tel: 01628 825920

Savill Garden - Windsor Great Park, Berkshire.
Tel: 01753 847518

Taplow Court - Berry Hill, Taplow, Nr Maidenhead,
Berkshire SL6 0ER. Tel: 01628 591209

Buckinghamshire

Hughenden Manor - High Wycombe, Buckinghamshire
HP14 4LA. Tel: 01494 755573

Stowe Landscape Gardens - Stowe, Buckingham,
Buckinghamshire MK18 5EH. Tel: 01280 818809

Waddesdon Manor - Waddesdon, Nr Aylesbury,
Buckinghamshire HP18 0JH. Tel: 01296 653211

Cambridgeshire

Ely Cathedral - The Chapter House, The College, Ely,
Cambridgeshire CB7 4DL. Tel: 01353 667735

The Manor of Green Knowe - Hemingford Grey,
Cambridgeshire PE28 9BN. Tel: 01480 463134

Cheshire

Dorfold Hall - Nantwich, Cheshire CW5 8LD.
Tel: 01270 625245

Gawsworth Hall - Gawsworth, Macclesfield,
Cheshire SK11 9RN. Tel: 01260 223456

Norton Priory Museum & Gardens - Tudor Road,
Manor Park, Cheshire WA7 1SX. Tel: 01928 569895

Tabley House Stately Home - Tabley House, Knutsford,
Cheshire WA16 0HB. Tel: 01565 750151

Co Durham

Raby Castle - Staindrop, Darlington, Co Durham DL2 3AH.
Tel: 01833 660207 / 660202

Cornwall

Mount Edgcumbe House & Park - Cremyll, Nr. Plymouth,
Cornwall PL10 1HZ. Tel: 01752 822236

Royal Cornwall Museum - River Street, Truro,
Cornwall TR1 2SJ. Tel: 01872 272205

Cumbria

Dove Cottage & The Wordsworth Museum - Grasmere,
Cumbria LA22 9SH. Tel: 015394 35544

Isel Hall - Cockermouth, Cumbria CA13 0QG.

Levens Hall & Gardens - Kendal, Cumbria LA8 0PD.
Tel: 01539 560321

Mirehouse & Keswick - Mirehouse, Keswick,
Cumbria CA12 4QE. Tel: 01768 772287

Windermere Steamboat Centre - Rayrigg Road,
Windermere, Cumbria LA23 1BN. Tel: 01539 445565

Derbyshire

Haddon Hall - Bakewell, Derbyshire DE45 1LA.
Tel: 01629 812855

Melbourne Hall & Gardens - Melbourne,
Derbyshire DE73 1EN. Tel: 01332 862502

Devon

▼

Bickleigh Castle - Bickleigh, Tiverton, Devon EX16 8RP.
Tel: 01884 855363

Downes Estate at Crediton - Crediton, Devon EX17 3PL.
Tel: 01392 439046

Ugbrooke Park - Ugbrooke, Chudleigh, Devon TQ13 0AD.
Tel: 01626 852179

Dorset

Chiffchaffs - Chaffeymoor, Bourton, Gillingham,
Dorset SP8 5BY. Tel: 01747 840841

Cranborne Manor Garden - Cranborne, Wimborne,
Dorset BH21 5PP. Tel: 01725 517248

Deans Court Garden - Deans Court, Wimborne,
Dorset BH21 1EE. Tel: 01202 886116

Lulworth Castle - The Lulworth Estate, East Lulworth,
Wareham, Dorset BH20 5QS. Tel: 01929 400352

Mapperton - Mapperton, Beaminster, Dorset DT8 3NR.
Tel: 01308 862645

Russell-Cotes Art Gallery & Museum - East Cliff,
Bournemouth, Dorset BH1 3AA. Tel: 01202 451800

Essex

Ingatestone Hall - Hall Lane, Ingatestone, Essex CM4 9NR.
Tel: 01277 353010

The Gardens of Easton Lodge - Warwick House, Easton
Lodge, Essex CM6 2BB. Tel: 01371 876979

Gloucestershire

Cheltenham Art Gallery & Museum - Clarence Street,
Cheltenham, Gloucestershire GL50 3JT.
Tel: 01242 237431

Hardwicke Court - Gloucester, Gloucestershire GL2 4RS.
Tel: 01452 720212

Hampshire

Beaulieu - John Montagu Building, Beaulieu,
Hampshire SO42 7ZN. Tel: 01590 612345

Beaulieu Vineyard and Gardens - Beaulieu Estate, John
Montagu Building, Beaulieu, Hampshire SO42 7ZN.
Tel: 01590 612345

Broadlands - Romsey, Hampshire SO51 9ZD.
Tel: 01794 505010

Gilbert White's House and The Oates Museum - Selborne,
Hampshire GU34 3JH. Tel: 01420 511275

Greywell Hill House - Greywell, Hook,
Hampshire RG29 1DG.

Pylewell House - South Baddesley, Lymington,
Hampshire SO41 5SJ. Tel: 01329 833130

Herefordshire

Eastnor Castle - Eastnor, Ledbury, Herefordshire HR8 1RL.
Tel: 01531 633160

Kentchurch Court - Kentchurch, Nr Pontrilas, Hereford,
HR2 0DB. Tel: 01981 240228

Hertfordshire

Ashridge - Ringshall, Berkhamsted, Hertfordshire HP4 1NS.
Tel: 01442 843491

Hatfield House, Park & Gardens - Hatfield,
Hertfordshire AL9 5NQ. Tel: 01707 287010

Isle of Wight

Deacons Nursery - Moor View, Godshill,
Isle of Wight PO38 3HW. Tel: 01983 840750

Kent

Cobham Hall - Cobham, Kent DA12 3BL.
Tel: 01474 823371

Graham Clarke Up the Garden Studio - Green Lane,
Boughton Monchelsea, Maidstone, Kent ME17 4LF.
Tel: 01622 743938

Groombridge Place Gardens & Enchanted Forest -
Groombridge, Tunbridge Wells, Kent TN3 9QG.
Tel: 01892 861444

Hever Castle & Gardens - Edenbridge, Kent TN8 7NG.
Tel: 01732 865224

Leeds Castle - Maidstone, Kent ME17 1PL.
Tel: 01622 765400

Marle Place Gardens - Marle Place Road, Brenchley,
Kent TN12 7HS. Tel: 01892 722304

Mount Ephraim Gardens - Hernhill, Nr Faversham,
Kent ME13 9TX. Tel: 01227 751496

Penshurst Place & Gardens - Penshurst, Nr Tonbridge,
Kent TN11 8DG. Tel: 01892 870307

HISTORIC HOUSES, CASTLES & GARDENS

Incorporating Museums & Galleries

www.historichouses.co.uk

Scotney Castle, Garden & Estate - Lamberhurst, Tunbridge Wells, Kent TN3 8JN. Tel: 01892 891081

The New College of Cobham - Cobhambury Road, Graves End, Kent DA12 3BG. Tel: 01474 814280

Lancashire

Townhead House - Slaidburn, Via Clitheroe, Lancashire BBY 3AG.

London

Pitzhanger Manor House - Walpole Park, Mattock Lane, Ealing, London W5 5EQ. Tel: 020 8567 1227

Sir John Soane's Museum - 13 Lincoln's Inn Fields, London WC2A 3BP. Tel: 020 7405 2107

Spencer House - 27 St. James's Place, London SW1A 1NR. Tel: 0207-514 1964

Merseyside

Knowsley Hall - Prescot, Merseyside L32 4AF. Tel: 0151 489 4437 / 0468 698640

Middlesex

Syon Park - London Road, Brentford, Middlesex TW8 8JF. Tel: 020 8560 0882

Norfolk

Walsingham Abbey Grounds - c/o The Estate Office, Little Walsingham, Norfolk NR22 6BP. Tel: 01328 820259 / 820510

Wolterton and Mannington Estate - Mannington Hall, Norwich, Norfolk NR11 7BB. Tel: 01263 584175

Northamptonshire

Althorp - Northampton, Northamptonshire NN7 4HQ. Tel: 01604 770107

Boughton House - Kettering, Northamptonshire NN14 1BJ. Tel: 01536 515731

Coton Manor Garden - Coton, Nr Guilsborough, Northamptonshire NN6 8RQ. Tel: 01604 740219

Cottesbrooke Hall and Gardens - Cottesbrooke, Northampton, Northamptonshire NN6 8PF. Tel: 01604 505808

Haddonstone Show Garden - The Forge House, Church Lane, East Haddon, Northamptonshire NN6 8DB. Tel: 01604 770711

Northumberland

Alnwick Castle - Alnwick, Northumberland NE66 1NQ. Tel: 01665 510777/ 511100

Chipchase Castle - Chipchase, Wark on Tyne, Hexham, Northumberland NE48 3NT. Tel: 01434 230203

Paxton House & Country Park - Berwick-upon-Tweed, Northumberland TD15 1SZ. Tel: 01289 386291

Seaton Delaval Hall - Seaton Sluice, Whitley Bay, Northumberland NE26 4QR. Tel: 0191 237 1493 / 0786

Oxfordshire

Kingston Bagpuize House - Kingston Bagpuize, Abingdon, Oxfordshire OX13 5AX. Tel: 01865 820259

Mapledurham House - Mapledurham, Nr Reading, Oxfordshire RG4 7TR. Tel: 01189 723350

River & Rowing Museum - Mill Meadows, Henley-on-Thames, Oxfordshire RG9 1BF. Tel: 01491 415600

Wallingford Castle Gardens - Castle Street, Wallingford, Oxfordshire. Tel: 01491 835373

Shropshire

Hawkstone Park & Follies - Weston-under-Redcastle, Shrewsbury, Shropshire SY4 5UY. Tel: 01939 200 611

Hodnet Hall Gardens - Hodnet, Market Drayton, Shropshire TF9 3NN. Tel: 01630 685786

The Dorothy Clive Garden - Willoughbridge, Market Drayton, Shropshire TF9 4EU. Tel: 01630 647237

Weston Park - Weston-under-Lizard, Nr Shifnal, Shropshire TF11 8LE. Tel: 01952 852100

Somerset

▼

Cothay Manor & Gardens - Cothay Manor, Greenham, Nr Wellington, Somerset TA21 0JR. Tel: 01823 672283

Great House Farm - Wells Road, Theale, Wedmore, Somerset BS28 4SJ. Tel: 01934 713133

Museum of Costume & Assembly Rooms - Bennett Street, Bath, Somerset BA1 2QH. Tel: 01225 477789 / 477785

Robin Hood's Hut - Halswell, Goathurst, Somerset. Tel: 01628 825920

Roman Baths & Pump Room - Abbey Church Yard, Bath, Somerset BA1 1LZ. Tel: 01225 477785

Staffordshire

Ancient High House - Greengate Street, Stafford, Staffordshire ST16 2JA. Tel: 01785 223181

Izaak Walton's Cottage - Shallowford, Nr Stafford, Staffordshire ST15 0PA. Tel: 01785 760 278

Stafford Castle - Newport Road, Stafford, Staffordshire ST16 1DJ. Tel: 01785 257 698

Whitmore Hall - Whitmore, Newcastle-under-Lyme, Staffordshire ST5 5HW. Tel: 01782 680478

Suffolk

Ancient House - Clare, Suffolk CO10 8NY. Tel: 01628 825920

Freston Tower - Nr Ipswich, Suffolk. Tel: 01628 825920

Newbourne Hall - Newbourne, Nr Woodbridge, Suffolk IP12 4NP. Tel: 01473 736764

Shrubland Park Gardens - Shrubland Estate, Coddenham, Ipswich, Suffolk IP6 9QQ. Tel: 01473 830221

Surrey

Claremont House - Claremont Drive, Esher, Surrey KT10 9LY. Tel: 01372 467841

Goddards - Abinger Common, Dorking, Surrey RH5 6TH. Tel: 01628 825920

Painshill Landscape Garden - Portsmouth Road, Cobham, Surrey KT11 1JE. Tel: 01932 868113

East Sussex

Merriments Gardens - Hurst Green, E Sussex TN19 7RA. Tel: 01580 860666

Firle Place - The Estate Office, Lewes, East Sussex BN8 6NS. Tel: 01273 858043

Garden and Grounds of Herstmonceux Castle - Herstmonceux Castle, Hailsham, East Sussex BN27 1RN. Tel: 01323 833816

Wilmington Priory - Wilmington, Nr Eastbourne, East Sussex BN26 5SW. Tel: 01628 825920

West Sussex

Borde Hill Garden - Balcombe Road, West Sussex RH16 1XP. Tel: 01444 450326

Denmans Garden - Clock House, Denmans, Fontwell, West Sussex BN18 0SU. Tel: 01243 542808

Goodwood House - Goodwood, Chichester, West Sussex PO18 0PX. Tel: 01243 755000

High Beeches Gardens - High Beeches, Handcross, West Sussex RH17 6HQ. Tel: 01444 400589

Weald and Downland Open Air Museum - Singleton, Chichester, West Sussex PO18 4JU. Tel: 01243 811363

West Dean Gardens - West Dean, Chichester, West Sussex PO18 0QZ. Tel: 01243 818210

Warwickshire

Arbury Hall - Nuneaton, Warwickshire CV10 7PT. Tel: 024 7638 2804

Shakespeare Houses - The Shakespeare Centre, Henley Street, Stratford-upon-Avon, Warwickshire CV37 6QW. Tel: 01789 204016

Barber Institute of Fine Arts - The University of Birmingham, Edgbaston, Birmingham, West Midlands B15 2TS. Tel: 0121 414 7333

Castle Bromwich Hall Gardens - Chester Road, Castle Bromwich, Birmingham, West Midlands B36 9BT. Tel: 0121 749 4100

Coventry Cathedral - 7 Priory Row, Coventry, West Midlands CV1 5ES. Tel: 0203 227597

The Birmingham Botanical Gardens and Glasshouses - Westbourne Road, Edgbaston, Birmingham, West Midlands B15 3TR. Tel: 0121 454 1860

North Yorkshire

Allerton Park - Knaresborough, North Yorkshire HG5 OSE.
Tel: 01423 330927

Duncombe Park - Helmsley, York,
North Yorkshire YO62 5EB. Tel: 01439 770213

Kiplin Hall - Nr Scorton, Richmond, North Yorkshire.
Tel: 01748 818178

Newby Hall & Gardens - Ripon, North Yorkshire HG4 5AE.
Tel: 01423 322583

Ripley Castle - Ripley Castle Estate, Harrogate,
North Yorkshire HG3 3AY. Tel: 01423 770152

Skipton Castle - Skipton, North Yorkshire BD23 1AQ.
Tel: 01756 792442

The Forbidden Corner - The Tupgill Park Estate, Coverham,
Middleham, North Yorkshire DL8 4TJ. Tel: 01969 640638

Thorp Perrow Arboretum & The Falcons of Thorp Perrow -
Bedale, North Yorkshire DL8 2PR. Tel: 01677 425323

West Yorkshire

Bramham Park - Estate Office, Bramham Park, Wetherby,
West Yorkshire LS23 6ND. Tel: 01937 846000

Harewood House - The Harewood House Trust,
Moorhouse, Harewood, Leeds, West Yorkshire LS17 9LQ.
Tel: 0113 218 1010

Ledston Hall - Hall Lane, Ledstone,
West Yorkshire WF10 3BB. Tel: 01423 523 423

Lotherton Estate & Garden - Aberford, Leeds,
West Yorkshire LS25 3EB. Tel: 0113 281 3259

Temple Newsam House & Estate - Leeds,
West Yorkshire LS15 0AE. Tel: 0113 264 7321

Wiltshire

Charlton Park House - Charlton, Malmesbury,
Wiltshire SN16 9DG. Tel: 01666 824389

Hamptworth Lodge - Landford, Salisbury,
Wiltshire SP5 2EA. Tel: 01794 390215

▼
Longleat - Warminster, Wiltshire BA12 7NW.
Tel: 01985 844400

Salisbury Cathedral - Visitor Services, 33 The Close,
Salisbury, Wiltshire SP1 2EJ. Tel: 01722 555120

Worcester

Harvington Hall - Harvington, Kidderminister,
Worcestershire DY10 4LR. Tel: 01562 777846

Spetchley Park Gardens - Spetchley Park, Worcester
Worcestershire WR5 1RS. Tel: 01453 810303

Little Malvern Court - Nr Malvern,
Worcestershire WR14 4JN. Tel: 01684 892988

N. Ireland

Co Down

Seaforde Gardens - Seaforde, Downpatrick,
Co Down BT30 8PG. Tel: 028 4481 1225

Ireland

Co Cork

Bantry House & Gardens - Bantry, Co Cork.
Tel: + 353 2 750 047

Co Offaly

Birr Castle Demesne & Ireland's Historic Science Centre -
Birr, Co Offaly. Tel: + 353 509 20336

Scotland

Aberdeenshire

Craigston Castle - Turriff, Aberdeenshire AB53 5PX.
Tel: 01888 551228

Ayrshire

Auchinleck House - Ochiltree, Ayrshire. Tel: 01628 825920

Blairquhan Castle and Gardens - Straiton, Maybole,
Ayrshire KA19 7LZ. Tel: 01655 770239

Maybole Castle - Maybole, Ayrshire KA19 7BX.
Tel: 01655 883765

Isle of Skye

Armadale Castle, Gardens & Museum of the Isles -
Armadale, Sleat, Isle of Skye IV45 8RS. Tel: 01471 844305

Kincardineshire

Arbuthnott House and Garden - Arbuthnott, Laurencekirk,
Kincardineshire AB30 1PA. Tel: 0561 361226

Orkney Islands

Balfour Castle - Shapinsay, Orkney Islands KW17 2DL.
Tel: 01856 711282

Peebles

▼
Traquair House - Innerleithen, Peebles EH44 6PW.
Tel: 01896 830323

Scottish Borders

Bowhill House & Country Park - Bowhill, Selkirk, Scottish
Borders TD7 5ET. Tel: 01750 22204

West Lothian

Newliston - Kirkliston, West Lothian EH29 9EB.
Tel: 0131 333 3231

Wales

Flintshire

Golden Grove - Llanasa, Nr. Holywell, Flintshire CH8 9NA.
Tel: 01745 854452

Gwynedd

Plas Brondanw Gardens - Menna Angharad, Plas
Brondanw, Llanfrothen, Gwynedd LL48 6SW.
Tel: 01766 770484

Pembrokeshire

St Davids Cathedral - The Deanery, The Close, St. David's,
Pembrokeshire SA62 6RH. Tel: 01437 720199

Powys

The Judge's Lodging - Broad Street, Presteigne,
Powys LD8 2AD. Tel: 01544 260650

Continental Europe

France

Château Royal D'Amboise - Chateau Royal, B.P. 271, 37403
Amboise, France. Tel: +33 2 47 57 00 98

The Netherlands

Palace Het Loo National Museum - Koninklijk Park 1, 7315
JA Apeldoorn, The Netherlands. Tel: +31 55 577 2400

Condé Nast Johansens are delighted to recommend over 360 properties across Europe and The Mediterranean.

These properties can be found in *Recommended Hotels & Spas - Europe & The Mediterranean*.

Call 0800 269 397 or see the order forms on page 303 to order guides.

Austria

Sporthotel Kristiania	Lech am Arlberg	+43 5583 25 610
Seeschlössl Velden	Velden	+43 4274 2824
Thurnhers Alpenhof	Zürs	+43 5583 2191

Belgium

Firean Hotel	Antwerp	+32 3 237 02 60
Hotel de Tuilerieën	Bruges	+32 50 34 36 91
Hotel Die Swaene	Bruges	+32 50 34 27 98
Hotel Prinsenhof	Bruges	+32 50 34 26 90
Hotel Damier	Kortrijk	+32 56 22 15 47
Hostellerie Trôs Marets	Malmédy	+32 80 33 79 17
Hotel Recour	Poperinge	+32 57 33 57 25
Manoir Ogygia	Poperinge	+32 57 33 88 38
Hostellerie Ter Driezen	Turnhout	+32 14 41 87 57

Croatia

Grand Hotel Villa Argentina	Dubrovnik	+385 20 440 555

Cyprus

Four Seasons Hotel	Limassol	+357 258 58000
Almyra	Paphos	+357 26 93 30 91
The Annabelle Hotel	Paphos	+357 26 938 333
Elysium	Paphos	+357 26 844 444
Anassa	Polis	+357 26 888 000

Czech Republic

Art Hotel Prague	Prague	+420 233 101 331
Bellagio Hotel Prague	Prague	+420 221 778 999
Hotel Hoffmeister	Prague	+420 251 017 111
Romantik Hotel U Raka	Prague	+420 2205 111 00

Denmark

Hindsgavl Slot	Middelfart	+45 64 41 88 00
Hotel Hesselet	Nyborg	+45 65 31 30 29

Estonia

Ammende Villa	Pärnu	+372 44 73888
Domina City Hotel	Tallinn	+372 681 3900
The Three Sisters Hotel	Tallinn	+372 630 6300

France

Le Pigonnet	Aix~en~Provence	+33 4 42 59 02 90
Hôtel Royal Picardie	Albert	+33 3 22 75 37 00
Château de Pray	Amboise	+33 2 47 57 23 67
Le Choiseul	Amboise	+33 2 47 30 45 45
Le Manoir Les Minimes	Amboise	+33 2 47 30 40 40

L'Hôtel Particulier	Arles	+33 4 90 52 51 40
Bastide du Calalou	Aups	+33 4 94 70 17 91
Château de Vault de Lugny	Avallon	+33 3 86 34 07 86
Ermitage de Corton	Beaune	+33 3 80 22 05 28
La Chartreuse du Val Saint Esprit	Bethune - Gosnay	+33 3 21 62 80 00
Hôtel du Palais	Biarritz	+33 5 59 41 64 00
Domaine de Rochevilaine	Billiers	+33 2 97 41 61 61
La Bastide de Capelongue	Bonnieux~en~Provence	+33 4 90 75 89 78
Château Hotel de Brélidy	Brélidy	+33 1 96 95 69 38
Château de Cocove	Calais - Recques~sur~Hem	+33 3 21 82 68 29
Château des Briottières	Champigné	+33 2 41 42 00 02
Château de L'Yeuse	Cognac – Châteaubernard	+33 5 45 36 82 60
Hostellerie Le Maréchal	Colmar	+33 3 89 41 60 32
Hôtel Les Têtes	Colmar	+33 3 89 24 43 43
Château d'Isenbourg	Colmar - Rouffach	+33 3 89 78 58 50
Le Beau Rivage	Condrieu	+33 4 74 56 82 82
Le Grand Ecuyer	Cordes~sur~Ciel	+33 5 63 53 79 50
La Sivolière	Courchevel 1850	+33 4 79 08 08 33
Château de Crazannes	Crazannes – Saintes	+33 6 80 65 40 96
Château de Divonne	Divonne~les~Bains	+33 4 50 20 00 32
Le Domaine de Divonne Casino, Golf & Spa Resort	Divonne~les~Bains	+33 4 50 40 34 34

▼

Château d'Etoges	Etoges	+33 3 26 59 30 08
Domaine Saint Clair, Le Donjon	Etretat	+33 2 35 27 08 23
Château Eza	Èze Village	+33 4 93 41 12 24
Château de Sassetot	Fecamp - Sassetot	+33 2 35 28 00 11
Château de Fère	Fère~en~Tardenois	+33 3 23 82 21 13
Château de Floure	Floure~Carcassonne	+33 4 68 79 11 29
Hostellerie Les Bas Rupts	Gérardmer – Vosges	+33 3 29 63 09 25
Bastide Saint Mathieu	Grasse	+33 4 97 01 10 00
Le Manoir de Gressy	Gressy~en~France– Chantilly	+33 1 60 26 68 00
Le Clair de la Plume	Grignan	+33 4 75 91 81 30
Manoir de la Roseraie	Grignan	+33 4 75 46 58 15
Manoir de la Poterie	Honfleur - Cricqueboeuf	+33 2 31 88 10 40
Hôtel Juana	Juan~les~Pins	+33 4 93 61 08 70
Les Violettes	Jungholtz	+33 3 89 76 91 19
Château de Bonaban	La Gouesnière - Saint~Malo	+33 2 99 58 24 50
Domaine de Bodeuc	La Roche~Bernard	+33 2 99 90 89 63
Château de Rochecotte	Langeais	+33 2 47 96 16 16
Le Bailli de Suffren	Le Rayol – Canadel~Sur~Mer	+33 4 98 04 47 00
Mas de l'Oulivié	Les~Baux~de~Provence	+33 4 90 54 35 78
Chalet Hôtel La Marmotte	Les Gêts	+ 33 4 50 75 80 33
Carlton Hotel	Lille	+33 3 20 13 33 13
Le Moulin de Lourmarin	Lourmarin	+33 4 90 68 06 69

Condé Nast Johansens are delighted to recommend over 360 properties across Europe and The Mediterranean.
These properties can be found in *Recommended Hotels & Spas - Europe & The Mediterranean*.
Call 0800 269 397 or see the order forms on page 303 to order guides.

La Tour Rose	Lyon	+33 4 78 92 69 10
Domaine des Etangs	Massignac	+33 5 45 61 85 00
Château de Mazan	Mazan	+33 4 90 69 62 61
Le Fer à Cheval	Megève	+33 4 50 21 30 39
Manoir de Kertalg	Moëlan~sur~Mer	+33 2 98 39 77 77
Moulin du Val de Seugne	Mosnac	+33 5 46 70 46 16
Les Muscadins	Mougins	+33 4 92 28 28 28
Hostellerie St Barnabé	Murbach – Buhl	+33 3 89 62 14 14
Hôtel La Pérouse	Nice	+33 4 93 62 34 63
Hotel à la Cour d'Alsace	Obernai	+33 3 88 95 07 00
Hôtel de L'Arcade	Paris	+33 1 53 30 60 00
Hôtel Le Lavoisier	Paris	+33 1 53 30 06 06
Hôtel Le Saint~Grégoire	Paris	33 1 45 48 23 23
Hôtel Le Tourville	Paris	+33 1 47 05 62 62
Hôtel Mayet	Paris	+33 1 47 83 21 35
Hôtel Opéra Richepanse	Paris	+33 1 42 60 36 00
Hôtel Plaza Athénée	Paris	+33 1 53 67 66 65
Hôtel San Régis	Paris	+33 1 44 95 16 16
L' Hôtel	Paris	+33 1 44 41 99 00
L'Hôtel Pergolèse	Paris	+33 1 53 64 04 04
La Trémoille	Paris	+33 1 56 52 14 00
La Villa Maillot	Paris	+33 1 53 64 52 52
Le Sainte~Beuve	Paris	+33 1 45 48 20 07
Pavillon de Paris	Paris	+33 1 55 31 60 00
Relais Médicis	Paris	+33 1 43 26 00 60
Victoria Palace Hôtel	Paris	+33 1 45 49 70 00
Le Logis Saint Martin	Poitiers – Saint~Maixent~L'Ecole	+33 549 0558 68
Hostellerie des Monts de Vaux	Poligny – Jura	+33 3 84 37 12 50
Le Spinaker	Port Camargue	+33 4 66 53 36 37
Château de la Commanderie	Saint~Amond Montrond	+33 2 48 61 04 19
Manoir du Vaumadeuc	Saint Malo - Pleven	+33 2 96 84 46 17
Le Mas d'Artigny	Saint~Paul~de~Vence	+33 4 93 32 84 54
Château des Alpilles	Saint~Rémy~de~Provence	+33 4 90 92 03 33
Château d'Esclimont	Saint Symphorien~Le~Château	+33 2 37 31 15 15
La Ferme d'Augustin	Saint~Tropez - Ramatuelle	+33 4 94 55 97 00
Hostellerie des Hauts de Sainte Maure	Sainte~Maure~de~Touraine	+33 2 47 65 51 18
Domaine du Château de Barive	Sainte Preuve	+33 3 23 22 15 15
Château de Sanse	Sainte~Radegonde – Saint~Emilion	+33 5 57 56 41 10
Le Prieuré	Saumur-Chênehutte~Les~Tuffeaux	+33 2 41 67 90 14
Domaine de Fontanelle	Savigneux	+33 4 74 08 12 15
Château de Coudrée	Sciez~sur~Léman	+33 4 50 72 62 33
L'Auberge du Choucas	Serre~Chevalier	+33 4 92 24 42 73
Romantik Hotel Beaucour Baumann	Strasbourg	+33 3 88 76 72 00
Château de L'Ile	Strasbourg – Ostwald	+33 3 88 66 85 00
Romantik Hotel L'Horizon	Thionville	+33 3 82 88 53 65
L'Assiette Champenoise	Tinqueux – Reims	+33 3 26 84 64 64
Les Demeures du Ranquet	Tornac-Anduze	+33 4 66 77 51 63
Domaine de Beauvois	Tours - Luynes	+33 2 47 55 50 11
Château d'Artigny	Tours - Montbazon	+33 2 47 34 30 30
Domaine de La Tortinière	Tours - Montbazon	+33 2 47 34 35 00
Ti Al Lannec	Trebeurden	+33 296 15 01 01
Hôtel Cantemerle	Vence	+33 4 93 58 08 18
La Tour du Roy	Vervins	+33 3 23 98 00 11
Château de Gilly	Vougeot	+33 3 80 62 89 98

Great Britain & Ireland

Amberley Castle	Amberley	+44 1798 831 992
Royal Marine Hotel	Brora	+44 1408 621252
Bovey Castle	Devon - Dartmoor National Park	+44 1647 445 016
Aberdeen Lodge	Dublin	+353 1 283 8155
Fawsley Hall	Fawsley	+44 1327 892000
Muckrach Lodge Hotel & Restaurant	Grantown~on~Spey	+44 1479 851257
Skeabost Country House	Highland	+44 1470 532202
The Carlton Tower	London	+44 20 7235 1234
The Cranley	London	+44 20 7373 0123
The Dorchester	London	+44 020 7629 8888
Draycott House Apartments	London	+44 20 7584 4659
The Lowndes Hotel	London	+44 20 7823 1234
Mayflower Hotel	London	+44 20 7370 0991
Pembridge Court Hotel	London	+44 20 7229 9977
The Royal Park	London	+44 20 7479 6600
Twenty Nevern Square	London	+44 20 7565 9555
The Peacock at Rowsley	Rowsley - Derbyshire	+44 1629 733518
Castle Venlaw Hotel	Scottish Borders	+44 1721 720384
The French Horn	Sonning on Thames	+44 1189 692204

Greece

Astir Palace Vouliagmeni	Athens	+30 210 890 2000
Hotel Pentelikon	Athens	+30 2 10 62 30 650
Athina Suites	Crete	+30 28210 20960
The Peninsula at Porto Elounda De Luxe Resort	Crete	+30 28410 68000
Pleiades Luxurious Villas	Crete	+30 28410 90450
St Nicolas Bay Hotel	Crete	+30 2841 025041
Apanema	Mykonos	+30 22890 28590
Tharroe of Mykonos	Mykonos	+30 22890 27370
Acquamarina Resort	Paros	+30 228404 3281

Italy

Castello di Leonina Relais	Asciano - Siena	+39 0577 716088
Albergo Al Sole	Asolo - Treviso	+39 0423 951 332
Romantik Hotel Le Silve di Armenzano	Assisi	+39 075 801 9000
Color Hotel	Bardolino - Lake Garda	+39 045 621 0857
Hotel Ca' Sette	Bassano del Grappa	+39 0424 383350
Villa Dal Pozzo d'Annone	Belgirate - Lake Maggiore	+39 0322 7255
Grand Hotel Villa Serbelloni	Bellagio - Lake Como	+39 031 950 216
Monte del Re	Bologna	+39 0542 678400
Grand Hotel Gardone Riviera	Brescia-Lake Garda	+39 0365 20261
Hotel Dominik am Park	Bressanone	+39 0472 830 144
Ciasa de Gahja	Budoia	+39 0434 654 897
Castello di Magona	Campiglia Marittima	+39 0565 851235
Castelbrando	Cison-Treviso	+39 0438 9761
Art Hotel Cappella	Colfosco - Corvara	+39 0471 836183
Romantik Hotel Villa di Monte Solare	Colle San Paolo - Perugia	+39 075 832376
Relais della Rovere	Colle Val d'Elsa - Siena	+39 0577 924696
Relais Villa Baldelli	Cortona	+39 0575 612406
Romantik Hotel Villa Novecento	Courmayeur - Mont Blanc	+39 0165 843 000
Park Hotel	Desenzano del Garda	+39 030 914 3494
Grand Hotel Diana Majestic	Diano Marina	+39 0183 402 727
Masseria Marzalossa	Fasano	+39 080 4413 780
Ripagrande Hotel	Ferrara	+39 0532 765250
Hotel Punta Est	Finale Ligure	+39 019 600611
Hotel Lorenzo Il Magnifico	Florence	+39 055 4630878
J and J Historic House Hotel	Florence	+39 055 26312
Marignolle Relais & Charme	Florence	+39 055 228 6910
Villa Montartino	Florence	+39 055 223520
Hotel Byron	Forte dei Marmi - Lucca	+39 0584 787 052

MINI LISTINGS EUROPE & THE MEDITERRANEAN

Condé Nast Johansens are delighted to recommend over 360 properties across Europe and The Mediterranean.
These properties can be found in *Recommended Hotels & Spas - Europe & The Mediterranean*.
Call 0800 269 397 or see the order forms on page 303 to order guides.

Villa Madrina	Garda - Lake Garda	+39 045 6270 144
Romantik Hotel Villa Pagoda	Genoa Nervi	+39 010 372 6161
Domina Palumbalza	Golfo di Marinella - Porto Rotondo	+39 0789 32005
Castello di Petroia	Gubbio	+39 075 92 02 87
Hotel Madrigale	Lake Garda	+39 045 627 9001
Park Hotel Brasilia	Lido di Jesolo	+39 0421 380851
Hotel Lorenzetti	Madonna di Campiglio	+39 0465 44 14 04
Romantik Hotel Oberwirt	Marling – Meran	+39 0473 22 20 20
Villa San Martino	Martina Franca	+39 080 485 7719
Park Hotel Mignon	Meran	+39 0473 230353
Country House Casa Cornacchi	Montebenichi	+39 055 998229
Dionora	Montepulciano - Siena	+39 0578 717 496
Hotel Monteriggioni	Monteriggioni – Siena	+39 0577 305009
Castel Pietraio	Monteriggioni – Strove	+39 0577 300020
Villa Sassolini	Montevarchi - Valdarno	+39 055 9702246
Hotel de la Ville	Monza - Milano	+39 039 382 581
Palazzo Terranova	Morra - Città di Castello	+39 075 857 0083
Posthotel Cavallino Bianco	Nova Levante	+39 0471 613113
Villa Ciconia	Orvieto	+39 0763 305582/3
La Posta Vecchia Hotel Spa	Palo Laziale – Rome	+39 0699 49501
Alla Corte del Sole Relais	Petrignano - Cortona	+39 075 9689008
Albergo Pietrasanta - Palazzo Barsanti Bonetti	Pietrasanta	+39 0584 793 727
Le Torri di Bagnara	Pieve san Quirico	+39 075 604 136
Relais La Suvera	Pievescola	+39 0577 960300
Hotel Relais Dell'Orologio	Pisa	+39 050 830 361
Il Pellicano Hotel & Spa	Porto Ercole	+39 0564 858111
Relais Fattoria Vignale	Radda in Chianti - Siena	+39 0577 738300
Hotel Villa Maria	Ravello	+39 089 857255
Hotel Posta Historical Residence	Reggio Emilia	+39 05 22 43 29 44
Hotel des Nations	Riccione	+39 0541 647878
Pieve di Caminino Historical Residence	Roccatederighi - Grosseto	+39 0564 569 737
The Duke Hotel	Rome	+39 06 367221
Hotel Aventino	Rome	+39 06 5745 231
Hotel dei Borgognoni	Rome	+39 06 6994 1505
Hotel dei Consoli	Rome	+39 0668 892972
Hotel Fenix	Rome	+39 06 8540 741
Hotel Giulio Cesare	Rome	+39 06 321 0751
Hotel Piranesi	Rome	+39 06328041
Hotel Bellerive	Salò - Lake Garda	+39 0365 520 410
Grand Hotel Miramare	Santa Margherita Ligure	+39 0185 287013
Masseria San Domenico	Savelletri di Fasano	+39 080 482 7769
Hotel Vis à Vis & Ristorante Olimpo	Sestri Levante	+39 0185 42661
Hotel des Etrangers et Miramare	Siracusa	+39 0931 62671
Grand Hotel Cocumella	Sorrento	+39 081 878 2933
Convento di Agghielli	Spoleto	+39 0743 225 010
Hotel San Luca	Spoleto	+39 0743 223 399
Hotel Villa Aminta	Stresa – Lake Maggiore	+39 0323 933 818
Grand Hotel Atlantis Bay	Taormina Mare	+39 0942 612111
Grand Hotel Mazzarò Sea Palace	Taormina Mare	+39 0942 612111
Baia Taormina Hotel & Spa	Taormina Riviera - Marina d'Agro	+39 0942 756292
Relais La Magioca	Valpolicella – Verona	+39 045 600 0167
Domina Prestige Giudecca	Venice	+39 041 2960 168
Hotel Giorgione	Venice	+39 041 522 5810
Hotel Londra Palace	Venice	+39 041 5200533
Albergo Quattro Fontane - Residenza d'Epoca	Venice – Lido	+39 041 526 0227
Grand Hotel Majestic	Verbania - Lake Maggiore	+39 0323 504305
Hotel Gabbia d'Oro Historical Residence	Verona	+39 045 8003060
Palazzo San Fermo	Verona	+39 045 800 3060
Hotel Plaza e de Russie	Viareggio - Lucca	+39 0584 44449

Altafiumara Hotel	Villa San Giovanni	+39 096 575 9804
Romantik Hotel Turm	Völs am Schlern	+39 0471 725014

Luxembourg

Hotel Saint~Nicolas	Remich	+352 2666 3

Monaco

Monte~Carlo Beach Hotel	Monte~Carlo	+377 92 16 25 25

The Netherlands

Ambassade Hotel	Amsterdam	+31 20 5550222

Norway

Fleischers Hotel	Voss	+47 56 52 05 00

Portugal

Grande Real Santa Eulália Resort & Hotel Spa	Albufeira	+351 289 598 000
Vila Joya	Albufeira	+351 289 59 1795
Quinta da Bela Vista	Funchal	+351 291 706400
Romantik Hotel Vivenda Miranda	Lagos	+351 282 763222
Villa Esmeralda	Lagos	+351 282 760 430
As Janelas Verdes	Lisbon	+351 21 39 68 143
Hotel Britania	Lisbon	+351 21 31 55 016
Lisboa Plaza Hotel	Lisbon	+351 213 218 218
Solar do Castelo	Lisbon	+351 218 870 909
Albatroz Palace, Luxury Suites	Lisbon - Cascais	+351 21 484 73 80
Vintage House	Pinhão	+351 254 730 230
Estalagem da Ponta do Sol	Ponta do Sol	+351 291 970 200
Convento de São Paulo	Redondo	+351 266 989 160
Casa da Alcáçova	Santarém	+351 343 304 030
Convento De São Saturnino	Sintra	+351 21 928 3192
Vidago Palace Hotel & Golf	Vidago	+351 276 990 900

Slovak Republic

Hotel Marrol's	Bratislava	+421 25 77 84 600

Spain

Tancat de Codorniu	Alcanar	+34 977 737 194
Amérigo	Alicante	+34 965 14 65 70
Hesperia Alicante Golf, Spa, Hotel	Alicante	+34 965 23 50 00
Hotel Sidi San Juan & Spa	Alicante	+34 96 516 13 00
Posada de la Casa del Abad de Ampudia	Ampudia	+34 979 768 008
Hacienda El Santiscal	Arcos de La Frontera	+34 956 70 83 13
El Milano Real	Ávila	+34 920 349 108
Hotel Puerta de la Luna	Baeza	+34 953 747 019
Claris Hotel	Barcelona	+34 934 87 62 62
Gallery Hotel	Barcelona	+34 934 15 99 11

MINI LISTINGS EUROPE & THE MEDITERRANEAN

Condé Nast Johansens are delighted to recommend over 360 properties across Europe and The Mediterranean. These properties can be found in *Recommended Hotels & Spas - Europe & The Mediterranean.* Call 0800 269 397 or see the order forms on page 303 to order guides.

Gran Hotel La Florida	Barcelona	+34 93 259 30 00
Hotel Casa Fuster	Barcelona	+34 93 255 30 00
Hotel Colón	Barcelona	+34 933 01 14 04
Hotel Omm	Barcelona	+34 93 445 40 00
Hotel Villa Padierna & Flamingos Golf Club	Benhavis - Marbella	+34 952 88 91 50
Hotel Urbisol	Calders	+34 93 830 9153
Hotel La Era	Casarabonela	+34 952 1125 25
Hotel Santa Marta	Costa Brava	+34 972 364 904
Rigat Park & Spa Hotel	Costa Brava	+34 972 36 52 00
Hotel Palacio de Los Granados	Écija	+34 955 905 344
Gran Hotel Elba Estepona & Thalasso Spa	Estepona	+34 952 809 200
Elba Palace Golf Hotel	Fuerteventura	+34 928 16 39 22
Gran Hotel Atlantis Bahía Real	Fuerteventura	+34 928 53 64 44
Mas Falgarona	Gerona	+34 972 54 66 28
Gran Hotel Costa Meloneras	Gran Canaria	+34 928 12 81 00
Hotel Casa Morisca	Granada	+34 958 221 100
Hotel La Bobadilla	Granada	+34 958 32 18 61
Hotel Palacio de Santa Inés	Granada	+34 958 22 23 62
Atzaró Agroturismo	Ibiza	+34 971 33 88 38
Can Curreu	Ibiza	+34 971 335 280
Can Lluc	Ibiza	+34 971 198 673

▼

Cas Gasi	**Ibiza**	**+34 971 197 700**
Gran Hotel Hesperia La Toja	Isla de La Toja	+34 986 73 00 25
Hesperia Isla de la Toja	Isla de La Toja	+34 986 73 00 50
Hotel Mas Passamaner	La Selva del Camp	+34 977 766 333
Hesperia Lanzarote Hotel	Lanzarote	+34 828 0808 00
Princesa Yaiza Suite Hotel*****	Lanzarote	+34 928 519 222
Antiguo Convento	Madrid	+ 34 91 632 22 20
Gran Meliá Fénix	Madrid	+34 91 431 67 00
Hotel Orfila	Madrid	+34 91 702 77 70
Hotel Quinta de los Cedros	Madrid	+34 91 515 2200
Hotel Villa Real	Madrid	+34 914 20 37 67
Mirasierra Suites Hotel	Madrid	+34 91 727 79 00
El Molino de Santillán	Málaga	+34 952 40 09 49
La Posada del Torcal	Málaga	+34 952 03 11 77
Agroturismo Es Puig Moltó	Mallorca	+34 971 18 17 58
Ca's Xorc	Mallorca	+34 971 63 82 80
Can Furiós	Mallorca	+34 971 51 57 51
Gran Hotel Son Net	Mallorca	+34 971 14 70 00
Hotel Dalt Murada	Mallorca	+34 971 425 300
Hotel Maricel	Mallorca	+34 971 707 744
La Moraleja Hotel	Mallorca	+34 971 534 010

Palacio Ca Sa Galesa	Mallorca	+34 971 715 400
Read's	Mallorca	+34 971 14 02 62
Sa Posada d'Aumallia	Mallorca	+34 971 58 26 57
Valldemossa Hotel	Mallorca	+34 971 61 26 26
Gran Hotel Guadalpin	Marbella	+34 952 899 400
Hotel Los Monteros	Marbella	+34 952 771 700
Vasari Vacation Resort	Marbella	+34 952 907 806
Hotel Byblos Andaluz	Mijas~Costa	+34 952 47 30 50
Santa Elena	Ontinyent	+34 96 291 16 56
Palacio Marqués de la Gomera	Osuna - Seville	+34 95 4 81 22 23
Hotel del Teatre	Regencós	+34 972 30 62 70
Romantic Villa - Hotel Vistabella	Roses	+34 972 25 62 00
Hotel Rector	Salamanca	+34 923 21 84 82
Hotel Cortijo el Sotillo	San José	+34 950 61 11 00
Hotel Las Casas Del Rey de Baeza	Sevilla	+34 954 561 496
Hotel Cortijo Águila Real	Seville	+34 955 78 50 06
Hotel Hacienda La Boticaria	Seville	+34 955 69 88 20
San Sebastian Playa Hotel	Sitges	+34 93 894 86 76
NH Almenara Golf Hotel & Spa	Sotogrande	+ 34 956 58 20 00
Hotel Torre Martí	St Julià de Vilatorta	+34 938 88 83 72
Cortijo el Aguilon	Tarifa	+34 637 424 251
Gran Hotel Bahía del Duque Resort	Tenerife	+34 922 74 69 00
Hotel Jardín Tropical	Tenerife	+34 922 74 60 11/2/3
Hotel La Quinta Roja	Tenerife	+34 922 13 33 77
Cerro de Hijar Hotel	Tolox	+34 952 11 21 11
Castillo de Buen Amor	Topas - Salamanca	+34 923 355 002
Palacio de la Rambla	Úbeda	+34 953 75 01 96
La Torre del Visco	Valderrobres	+34 978 76 90 15
Hotel Sidi Saler & Spa	Valencia	+34 961 61 04 11
Palau de la Mar	Valencia	+34 96 316 2884
Palacio de Cutre	Villamayor	+34 985 70 80 72

Sweden

Hestravikens Wärdshus	Hestra – Småland	+46 370 33 68 00

Switzerland

Park Hotel Weggis	Weggis - Lake Lucerne	+41 41 392 05 05

Turkey

Gloria Select Villas	Antalya	+90 242 715 2410
Olympos Lodge	Antalya	+90 242 825 7171
Renaissance Antalya Beach Resort & Spa	Antalya	+90 242 824 84 31
Tekeli Konaklari	Antalya	+90 242 244 54 65
Tuvana Residence	Antalya	+90 242 247 60 15
Ada Hotel	Bodrum	+90 252 377 5915
Divan Bodrum Palmira	Bodrum	+90 252 377 5601
Sacred House	Cappadocia - Ürgüp	+90 384 341 7102
Ürgüp Evi	Cappadocia - Ürgüp	+90 384 341 3173
Swissôtel Göcek Marina & Spa Resort	Göcek - Fethiye-Mugla	+90 252 645 2760
Sisus	İzmír	+90 232 724 0330
Tas Otel	İzmír	+90 232 716 7772
Hotel Villa Mahal	Kalkan	+90 242 844 32 68

www.hildon.com

MINI LISTINGS NORTH AMERICA

Condé Nast Johansens are delighted to recommend over 240 properties across North America, Mexico, Bermuda, The Caribbean, The Pacific. Call 0800 269 397 or see the order forms on page 303 to order guides.

ARIZONA - SEDONA

Canyon Villa Bed & Breakfast Inn

125 Canyon Circle Drive, Sedona, Arizona 86351
Tel: 1 928 284 1226
Fax: 1 928 284 2114

ARIZONA - SEDONA

L'Auberge De Sedona

301 L'Auberge Lane, Sedona, Arizona 86336
Tel: 1 928 282 1661
Fax: 1 928 282 1064

ARIZONA - SEDONA

The Lodge at Sedona - A Luxury Bed & Breakfast Inn

125 Kallof Place, Sedona, Arizona 86336
Tel: 1 928 204 1942
Fax: 1 928 204 2128

ARIZONA - TUCSON

Arizona Inn

2200 East Elm Street, Tucson, Arizona 85719
Tel: 1 520 325 1541
Fax: 1 520 881 5830

ARIZONA - TUCSON

Tanque Verde Ranch

14301 East Speedway, Tucson, Arizona 85748
Tel: 1 520 296 6275
Fax: 1 520 721 9426

ARIZONA - TUCSON

White Stallion Ranch

9251 West Twin Peaks Road, Tucson, Arizona 85743
Tel: 1 520 297 0252
Fax: 1 520 744 2786

ARKANSAS - EUREKA SPRINGS

The 1886 Crescent Hotel & Spa

75 Prospect Avenue, Eureka Springs, Arkansas 72632
Tel: 1 479 253 9766
Fax: 1 479 253 5296

ARKANSAS - LITTLE ROCK

The Empress of Little Rock

2120 South Louisiana, Little Rock, Arkansas 72206
Tel: 1 501 374 7966
Fax: 1 501 375 4537

ARKANSAS - LITTLE ROCK

The Peabody Little Rock

3 Statehouse Plaza, 72201 Arkansas
Tel: 1 501 375 5000
Fax: 1 501 375 4721

CALIFORNIA - BEL AIR

The Hotel Bel Air

701 Stone Canyon Road, Bel Air, California 90077
Tel: 1 310 472 1211
Fax: 1 310 909 1601

CALIFORNIA - BORREGO SPRINGS

La Casa del Zorro Desert Resort

3845 Yaqui Pass Road, Borrego Springs, California 92004
Tel: 1 760 767 5323
Fax: 1 760 767 5963

CALIFORNIA - CARMEL

Quail Lodge

8000 Valley Greens Drive, Carmel, California 93923
Tel: 1 831 624 2888
Fax: 1 831 624 3726

CALIFORNIA - CARMEL VALLEY

Bernardus Lodge

415 Carmel Valley Road, Carmel Valley California 93924
Tel: 1 831 658 3400
Fax: 1 831 659 3529

CALIFORNIA - CARMEL-BY-THE-SEA

Tradewinds Inn

Mission Street at Third, Carmel-by-the-Sea, California 93921
Tel: 1 831 624 2776
Fax: 1 831 624 0634

CALIFORNIA - EUREKA

Carter House

301 L Street, Eureka, California 95501
Tel: 1 707 444 8062
Fax: 1 707 444 8067

CALIFORNIA - FERNDALE

Gingerbread Mansion Inn

400 Berding Street, Ferndale, California 95536
Tel: 1 707 786 4000
Fax: 1 707 786 4381

CALIFORNIA - FORESTVILLE

Farmhouse Inn and Restaurant

7871 River Road, Forestville, California 95436
Tel: 1 707 887 3300
Fax: 1 707 887 3311

CALIFORNIA - GLEN ELLEN

The Gaige House

13540 Arnold Drive, Glen Ellen, California 95442
Tel: 1 707 935 0237
Fax: 1 707 935 6411

CALIFORNIA - HEALDSBURG

The Grape Leaf Inn

539 Johnson Street, Healdsburg, California 95448
Tel: 1 707 433 8140
Fax: 1 707 433 3140

CALIFORNIA - KENWOOD

The Kenwood Inn and Spa

10400 Sonoma Highway, Kenwood, California 95452
Tel: 1 707 833 1293
Fax: 1 707 833 1247

MINI LISTINGS NORTH AMERICA

Condé Nast Johansens are delighted to recommend over 240 properties across North America, Mexico, Bermuda, The Caribbean, The Pacific.
Call 0800 269 397 or see the order forms on page 303 to order guides.

CALIFORNIA - LA JOLLA

The Bed & Breakfast Inn At La Jolla

7753 Draper Avenue, La Jolla, California 92037
Tel: 1 858 456 2066
Fax: 1 858 456 1510

CALIFORNIA - LOS GATOS

Hotel Los Gatos & Spa

210 Main Street, Los Gatos, California 95030
Tel: 1 408 335 1700
Fax: 1 408 335 1750

CALIFORNIA - MENDOCINO

The Joshua Grindle Inn

44800 Little Lake Road, Mendocino, California 95460
Tel: 1 707 937 4143
Fax: 1 801 751 4998

CALIFORNIA - MENDOCINO

The Stanford Inn By The Sea

Coast Highway One & Comptche-Ukiah Road, Mendocino, California 95460
Tel: 1 707 937 5615
Fax: 1 707 937 0305

CALIFORNIA - MILL VALLEY

Mill Valley Inn

165 Throckmorton Avenue, Mill Valley, California 94941
Tel: 1 415 389 6608
Fax: 1 415 389 5051

CALIFORNIA - MONTEREY

Old Monterey Inn

500 Martin Street, California 93940
Tel: 1 831 375 8284
Fax: 1 831 375 6730

CALIFORNIA - NAPA

The Carneros Inn

4048 Sonoma Highway, California 94559
Tel: 1 707 299 4900
Fax: 1 707 299 4950

CALIFORNIA - NAPA

Milliken Creek

1815 Silverado Trail, Napa, California 94558
Tel: 1 707 255 1197
Fax: 1 707 255 3112

CALIFORNIA - NAPA VALLEY

1801 First Inn

1801 First Street, Napa, California 94559
Tel: 1 707 224 3739
Fax: 1 707 224 3932

CALIFORNIA - OLEMA

Olema Druids Hall

9870 Shoreline Highway One, Olema, California 94950
Tel: 1 415 663 8727
Fax: 1 415 663 1830

CALIFORNIA - PALM SPRINGS

Caliente tropics Resort

411 East Palm Canyon Drive, Palm Springs, California 92264
Tel: 1 760 327 1391
Fax: 1 760 318 1883

CALIFORNIA - PLAYA DEL REY

Inn At Playa Del Rey

435 Culver Boulevard Playa del Rey, Comer, California 90293
Tel: 1 310 574 1920
Fax: 1 310 574 9920

CALIFORNIA - RANCHO SANTA FE

The Inn at Rancho Santa Fe

5951 Linea del Cielo, Rancho Santa Fe, California 92067
Tel: 1 858 756 1131
Fax: 1 858 759 1604

CALIFORNIA - SAN FRANCISCO

Nob Hill Lambourne

725 Pine Street, San Francisco, California 94108
Tel: 1 415 433 2287
Fax: 1 415 433 0975

CALIFORNIA - SAN FRANCISCO

Union Street Inn

2229 Union Street, San Francisco, California 94123
Tel: 1 415 346 0424
Fax: 1 415 922 8046

CALIFORNIA - SAN FRANCISCO BAY AREA

Gerstle Park Inn

34 Grove Street, San Rafael, California 94901
Tel: 1 415 721 7611
Fax: 1 415 721 7600

CALIFORNIA - SAN JOSE

Hotel Valencia Santana Row

355 Santana Row, San Jose, California 95128
Tel: 1 408 551 0010
Fax: 1 408 551 05550

CALIFORNIA - SANTA BARBARA

Inn of the Spanish Garden

915 Garden Street, Santa Barbara, California 93101
Tel: 1 805 564 4700
Fax: 1 805 564 4701

CALIFORNIA - SANTA YNEZ

The Santa Ynez Inn

3627 Sagunto Street, Santa Ynez, California 93460-0628
Tel: 1 805 688 5588
Fax: 1 805 686 4294

CALIFORNIA - TIBURON

Waters Edge Hotel

25 Main Street, Tiburon, California 94920
Tel: 1 415 789 5999
Fax: 1 415 789 5888

Condé Nast Johansens are delighted to recommend over 240 properties across North America, Mexico, Bermuda, The Caribbean, The Pacific.

Call 0800 269 397 or see the order forms on page 303 to order guides.

CALIFORNIA - BIG SUR

Ventana Inn and Spa

Highway 1, Big Sur, California 93920
Tel: 1 831 667 2331
Fax: 1 831 667 2419

COLORADO - BEAVER CREEK

The Inn at Beaver Creek

10 Elk Track Lane, Beaver Creek Resort, Colorado, 81620
Tel: 1 970 845 5990
Fax: 1 970 845 5911

COLORADO - DENVER

The Brown Palace Hotel

321 17th Street, Denver, Colorado 80202
Tel: 1 303 297 3111
Fax: 1 303 297 2954

COLORADO - DENVER

Castle Marne

1572 Race Street, Denver, Colorado 80206
Tel: 1 303 331 0621
Fax: 1 303 331 0623

COLORADO - EAGLE

Inn & Suites at Riverwalk

27 Main Street, Edwards, Colorado 81632
Tel: 1 970 926 0606
Fax: 1 970 926 0616

COLORADO - ESTES PARK

Taharaa Mountain Lodge

3110 So. St. Vrain, Estes Park, Colorado 80517
Tel: 1 970 577 0098
Fax: 1 970 577 0819

COLORADO - MANITOU SPRINGS

The Cliff House at Pikes Peak

306 Cañon Avenue, Manitou Springs, Colorado 80829
Tel: 1 719 685 3000
Fax: 1 719 685 3913

COLORADO - STEAMBOAT SPRINGS

Vista Verde Guest Ranch

PO Box 770465, Steamboat Springs, Colorado 80477
Tel: 1 970 879 3858
Fax: 1 970 879 1413

DELAWARE - WILMINGTON

The Inn at Montchanin

Route 100 & Kirk Road, Montchanin, Delaware 19710
Tel: 1 302 888 2133
Fax: 1 302 888 0389

DELAWARE - REHOBOTH BEACH

Boardwalk Plaza Hotel

Olive Avenue & The Boardwalk, Rehoboth Beach, Delaware 19971
Tel: 1 302 227 7169
Fax: 1 302 227 0561

DISTRICT OF COLUMBIA - WASHINGTON D.C.

The Hay Adams

Sixteenth & H Streets N.W., Washington D.C. 20006
Tel: 1 202 638 6600
Fax: 1 202 638 2716

DISTRICT OF COLUMBIA - WASHINGTON D.C.

The Madison

15th and M Streets, N.W., Washington D.C. 20005
Tel: 1 202 862 1600
Fax: 1 202 587 2696

FLORIDA - KEY WEST

Simonton Court Historic Inn & Cottages

320 Simonton Street, Key West, Florida 33040
Tel: 1 305 294 6386
Fax: 1 305 293 8446

FLORIDA - LITTLE TORCH KEY

Little Palm Island Resort & Spa

28500 Overseas Highway, Little Torch Key, Florida 33042
Tel: 1 305 872 2524
Fax: 1 305 872 4843

FLORIDA - MIAMI BEACH

Fisher Island Hotel & Resort

One Fisher Island Drive, Fisher Island, Florida 33109
Tel: 1 305 535 6080
Fax: 1 305 535 6003

FLORIDA - MIAMI BEACH

The Tides

1220 Ocean Drive, Miami Beach, Florida 33139
Tel: 1 305 604 5070
Fax: 1 305 604 5180

FLORIDA - NAPLES

LaPlaya Beach & Golf Resort

9891 Gulf Shore Drive, Naples, Florida 34108
Tel: 1 239 597 3123
Fax: 1 239 597 8283

FLORIDA - ORLANDO

Celebration Hotel

700 Bloom Street, Celebration, Florida 34747
Tel: 1 407 566 6000
Fax: 1 407 566 6001

FLORIDA - ORLANDO

Portofino Bay Hotel

5601 Universal Boulevard, Orlando, Florida 32819
Tel: 1 407 503 1000
Fax: 1 407 503 1010

FLORIDA - ORLANDO

Villas of Grand Cypress

One North Jacaranda, Orlando, Florida 32836
Tel: 1 407 239 4700
Fax: 1 407 239 7219

Mini Listings North America

Condé Nast Johansens are delighted to recommend over 240 properties across North America, Mexico, Bermuda, The Caribbean, The Pacific.
Call 0800 269 397 or see the order forms on page 303 to order guides.

FLORIDA - PALM COAST

The Lodge at Ocean Hammock
105 16th Road, Palm Coast, Florida 32137
Tel: 1 386 447 4600
Fax: 1 386 447 4601

FLORIDA - SEAGROVE BEACH

WaterColor Inn & Resort
34 Goldenrod Circle, Seagrove Beach, Florida 32459
Tel: 1 850 534 5030
Fax: 1 850 534 5001

FLORIDA - ST. AUGUSTINE

Casablanca Inn
24 Avenida Menendez, St. Augustine, Florida 32084
Tel: 1 904 829 0928
Fax: 1 904 826 1892

FLORIDA - ST. PETE BEACH

Don CeSar Beach Resort
3400 Gulf Boulevard, St. Pete Beach, Florida 33706
Tel: 1 727 360 1881
Fax: 1 727 367 3609

GEORGIA - LITTLE ST. SIMONS ISLAND

The Lodge on Little St. Simons Island
PO Box 21078, Little St. Simons Island, Georgia 31522–0578
Tel: 1 912 638 7472
Fax: 1 912 634 1811

GEORGIA - PERRY

Henderson Village
125 South Langston Circle, Perry, Georgia 31069
Tel: 1 478 988 8696
Fax: 1 478 988 9009

GEORGIA - SAVANNAH

The Eliza Thompson House
5 West Jones Street, Savannah, Georgia 31401
Tel: 1 912 236 3620
Fax: 1 912 238 1920

HAWAII - HILO

Shipman House
131 Ka'iulani Street, Hilo, Hawaii 96720
Tel: 1 808 934 8002
Fax: 1 808 934 8002

HAWAII - HONOMU

The Palms Cliff House
28-3514 Mamalahoa Highway 19, PO Box 189, Honomu,
Hawaii 96728-0189
Tel: 1 808 963 6076
Fax: 1 808 963 6316

HAWAII - LAHAINA

Lahaina Inn
127 Lahainaluna Road, Lahaina, Maui, Hawaii 96761
Tel: 1 808 661 0577
Fax: 1 808 667 9480

HAWAII - LAHAINA

The Plantation Inn
174 Lahainaluna Road, Lahaina, Maui, Hawaii 96761
Tel: 1 808 667 9225
Fax: 1 808 667 9293

IDAHO - MCCALL

The Whitetail Club
501 West Lake Street, McCall, Idaho 83638
Tel: 1 208 634 2244
Fax: 1 208 634 7504

LOUISIANA - NAPOLEONVILLE

Madewood Plantation House
4250 Highway 308, Napoleonville, Louisiana 70390
Tel: 1 985 369 7151
Fax: 1 985 369 9848

LOUISIANA - NEW ORLEANS

Hotel Maison De Ville
727 Rue Toulouse, New Orleans, Louisiana 70130
Tel: 1 504 561 5858
Fax: 1 504 528 9939

LOUISIANA - NEW ORLEANS

The LaFayette Hotel
600 St. Charles Avenue, New Orleans, Louisiana 70130
Tel: 1 504 524 4441
Fax: 1 504 962 5537

LOUISIANA - ST. FRANCISVILLE

The Lodge at the Bluffs
Highland 965 at Freeland Road, 70748 Louisiana
Tel: 1 225 634 3410
Fax: 1 225 634 3528

MARYLAND - FROSTBURG

Savage River Lodge
1600 Mt. Aetna Road, Frostburg, Maryland 21536
Tel: 1 301 689 3200
Fax: 1 301 689 2746

MARYLAND - TANEYTOWN

Antrim 1844
30 Trevanion Road, Taneytown, Maryland 21787
Tel: 1 410 756 6812
Fax: 1 410 756 2744

MISSISSIPPI - JACKSON

Fairview Inn
734 Fairview Street, Jackson, Mississippi 39202
Tel: 1 601 948 3429
Fax: 1 601 948 1203

MISSISSIPPI - NATCHEZ

Dunleith
84 Homochitto Street, Natchez, Mississippi 39120
Tel: 1 601 446 8500
Fax: 1 601 446 8554

MINI LISTINGS NORTH AMERICA

Condé Nast Johansens are delighted to recommend over 240 properties across North America, Mexico, Bermuda, The Caribbean, The Pacific.
Call 0800 269 397 or see the order forms on page 303 to order guides.

MISSISSIPPI - NATCHEZ

Monmouth Plantation

36 Melrose Avenue At John A. Quitman Parkway, Natchez,
Mississippi 39120
Tel: 1 601 442 5852
Fax: 1 601 446 7762

MISSISSIPPI - VICKSBURG

Anchuca Historic Mansion & Inn

1010 First East Street, Vicksburg, Mississippi 39183
Tel: 1 601 661 0111
Fax: 1 601 661 0111

MISSOURI - ST. LOUIS

The Chase Park Plaza

212-232 North Kingshighway Boulevard, St. Louis, Missouri
63108
Tel: 1 314 633 3000
Fax: 1 314 633 1144

MISSOURI - KANSAS CITY

The Raphael Hotel

325 Ward Parkway, Kansas City, Missouri 64112
Tel: 1 816 756 3800
Fax: 1 816 802 2131

MONTANA - BIG SKY

The Big EZ Lodge

7000 Beaver Creek Road, Big Sky, Montana 59716
Tel: 1 406 995 7000
Fax: 1 406 995 7007

NEW ENGLAND / CONNECTICUT - ESSEX

Copper Beech Inn

46 Main Street, Ivoryton, Connecticut 06442
Tel: 1 860 767 0330
Fax: 1 860 767 7840

NEW ENGLAND / CONNECTICUT - GREENWICH

Delamar Greenwich Harbor Hotel

500 Steamboat Road, Greenwich, Connecticut 06830
Tel: 1 203 661 9800
Fax: 1 203 661 2513

NEW ENGLAND / CONNECTICUT - WESTPORT

The Inn at National Hall

2 Post Road West, Westport, Connecticut 06880
Tel: 1 203 221 1351
Fax: 1 203 221 0276

NEW ENGLAND / MAINE - GREENVILLE

The Lodge At Moosehead Lake

Upon Lily Bay Road, Box 1167, Greenville, Maine 04441
Tel: 1 207 695 4400
Fax: 1 207 695 2281

NEW ENGLAND / MAINE - KENNEBUNKPORT

The Captain Lord Mansion

6 Pleasant Street, Kennebunkport, Maine 04046-0800
Tel: 1 207 967 3141

NEW ENGLAND / MAINE - NEWCASTLE

The Newcastle Inn

60 River Road, Newcastle, Maine 04553
Tel: 1 207 563 5685
Fax: 1 207 563 6877

NEW ENGLAND / MASSACHUSETTS - BOSTON

The Charles Street Inn

94 Charles Street, Boston, Massachusetts 02114–4643
Tel: 1 617 314 8900
Fax: 1 617 371 0009

NEW ENGLAND / MASSACHUSETTS - BOSTON

The Lenox

61 Exeter Street at Boylston, Boston, Massachusetts 02116
Tel: 1 617 536 5300
Fax: 1 617 267 1237

NEW ENGLAND / MASSACHUSETTS - CAPE COD

Wequassett Inn Resort and Golf Club

On Pleasant Bay, Chatham, Cape Cod, Massachusetts 02633
Tel: 1 508 432 5400
Fax: 1 508 430 3131

NEW ENGLAND / MASSACHUSETTS - LENOX

Cranwell Resort, Spa & Golf Club

55 Lee Road, Route 20, Lenox, Massachusetts 01240
Tel: 1 413 637 1364
Fax: 1 413 637 4364

NEW ENGLAND / MASSACHUSETTS - MARTHA'S VINEYARD

Hob Knob Inn

128 Main Street, Edgartown, Massachusetts 02539
Tel: 1 508 627 9510
Fax: 1 508 627 4560

NEW ENGLAND / MASSACHUSETTS - MARTHA'S VINEYARD

The Victorian Inn

24 South Water Street, Edgartown, Massachusetts 02539
Tel: 1 508 627 4784

NEW ENGLAND / MASSACHUSETTS - MARTHA'S VINEYARD

The Winnetu Inn & Resort at South Beach

31 Dunes Road, Edgartown, Massachusetts 02539
Tel: 1 978 443 1733
Fax: 1 978 443 0479

NEW ENGLAND / MASSACHUSETTS - ROCKPORT

Seacrest Manor

99 Marmion Way, Rockport, Massachusetts 01966
Tel: 1 978 546 2211

NEW ENGLAND / NEW HAMPSHIRE - ASHLAND

The Glynn House Inn

59 Highland Street, Ashland, New Hampshire 03217
Tel: 1 603 968 3775
Fax: 1 603 968 9415

MINI LISTINGS NORTH AMERICA

Condé Nast Johansens are delighted to recommend over 240 properties across North America, Mexico, Bermuda, The Caribbean, The Pacific. Call 0800 269 397 or see the order forms on page 303 to order guides.

NEW ENGLAND / NEW HAMPSHIRE - JACKSON

The Wentworth
Jackson Village, New Hampshire 03846
Tel: 1 603 383 9700
Fax: 1 603 383 4265

NEW ENGLAND / RHODE ISLAND - BLOCK ISLAND

The Atlantic Inn
Po Box 1788, Block Island, Rhode Island 02807
Tel: 1 401 466 5883
Fax: 1 401 466 5678

NEW ENGLAND / RHODE ISLAND - NEWPORT

The Agincourt Inn
120 Miantonomi Avenue, Newport, Rhode Island 02842
Tel: 1 401 847 0902
Fax: 1 401 848 6529

RHODE ISLAND - NEWPORT

The Chanler at Cliff Walk
117 Memorail Boulevard, Newport, Rhode Island 02840
Tel: 1 401 847 1300
Fax: 1 401 847 3620

NEW ENGLAND / VERMONT - KILLINGTON

Fox Creek Inn
49 Dam Road, Chittenden, Vermont 05737
Tel: 1 802 483 6213
Fax: 1 802 483 2623

NEW ENGLAND / VERMONT - KILLINGTON

Mountain Top Inn & Resort
195 Mountain Top Road, Chittenden, Vermont 05737
Tel: 1 802 483 2311
Fax: 1 802 483 6373

NEW ENGLAND / VERMONT - KILLINGTON

Red Clover Inn
Woodward Road, Mendon, Vermont 05701
Tel: 1 802 775 2290
Fax: 1 802 773 0594

NEW ENGLAND / VERMONT - MANCHESTER CENTER

Inn at Ormsby Hill
Route 7A, 1842 Main Street, Manchester Center, Vermont 05255
Tel: 1 802 362 1163
Fax: 1 802 362 5176

NEW ENGLAND / VERMONT - STOWE

The Green Mountain Inn
18 Main Street, Stowe, Vermont 05672
Tel: 1 802 253 7301
Fax: 1 802 253 5096

NEW ENGLAND / VERMONT - STOWE

The Mountain Road Resort At Stowe
PO Box 8, 1007 Mountain Road, Stowe, Vermont 05672
Tel: 1 802 253 4566
Fax: 1 802 253 7397

NEW ENGLAND / VERMONT - WOODSTOCK

Woodstock Inn & Resort
Fourteen The Green, Woodstock, Vermont 05091-1298
Tel: 1 802 457 1100
Fax: 1 802 457 6699

NEW MEXICO - SANTA FE

The Bishop's Lodge Resort & Spa
PO Box 2367, Santa Fe, New Mexico 87504
Tel: 1 505 983 6377
Fax: 1 505 989 8739

NEW MEXICO - SANTA FE

Hotel St. Francis
210 Don Gaspar Avenue, Santa Fe, New Mexico 87501
Tel: 1 505 983 5700
Fax: 1 505 989 7690

NEW MEXICO - SANTA FE

Inn of the Anasazi
113 Washington Avenue, Santa Fe, New Mexico 87501
Tel: 1 505 988 3030
Fax: 1 505 988 3277

NEW MEXICO - SANTA FE

The Inn of The Five Graces
150 E Devargas Street, Santa Fe, New Mexico 87501
Tel: 1 505 992 0957
Fax: 1 505 955 0549

NEW MEXICO - SANTA FE

Inn of the Turquoise Bear
342 E. Buena Vista Street, Santa Fe, New Mexico 87505-2623
Tel: 1 505 983 0798
Fax: 1 505 988 4225

NEW YORK - AURORA

The Aurora Inn
391 Main Street, Aurora, new York 13026
Tel: 1 315 364 8888
Fax: 1 315 364 8887

NEW YORK - CAZENOVIA

The Brewster Inn
6 Ledyard Avenue, Cazenovia, New York 13035
Tel: 1 315 655 9232
Fax: 1 315 655 2130

NEW YORK - DOVER PLAINS

Old Drovers Inn
196 East Duncan Hill Road, Dover Plains, New York 12522
Tel: 1 845 832 9311
Fax: 1 845 832 6356

NEW YORK - EAST AURORA

Roycroft Inn
40 South Grove Street, East Aurora, New York 14052
Tel: 1 716 652 5552
Fax: 1 716 655 5345

Condé Nast Johansens are delighted to recommend over 240 properties across North America, Mexico, Bermuda, The Caribbean, The Pacific.
Call 0800 269 397 or see the order forms on page 303 to order guides.

NEW YORK - GENEVA

Geneva On The Lake
1001 Lochland Road (Route 14), Geneva, New York 14456
Tel: 1 315 789 7190
Fax: 1 315 789 0322

NEW YORK - LAKE GEORGE

The Sagamore
110 Sagamore Road, Bolton Landing, New York 12814
Tel: 1 518 644 9400
Fax: 1 518 644 2851

NEW YORK - LAKE PLACID

Lake Placid Lodge
Whiteface Inn Road, New York 12946
Tel: 1 518 523 2700
Fax: 1 518 523 1124

NEW YORK - LONG ISLAND

Inn at Great Neck
30 Cutter Mill Road, Great Neck, New York 11021
Tel: 1 516 773 2000
Fax: 1 516 773 2020

NEW YORK - LONG ISLAND

The Mill House Inn
31 North Main Street, East Hampton New York 11937
Tel: 1 631 324 9766
Fax: 1 631 324 9793

NEW YORK - MOUNT TREMPER

The Emerson Inn & Spa
146 Mount Pleasant Road, Mount Tremper, New York 12457
Tel: 1 845 688 7900
Fax: 1 845 688 2789

NEW YORK - NEW YORK CITY

The Benjamin
125 East 50th Street, New York, New York 10022
Tel: 1 212 320 8002
Fax: 1 212 465 3697

NEW YORK - NEW YORK CITY

Hotel Plaza Athenee
37 East 64th Street, New York 10021
Tel: 1 212 734 9100
Fax: 1 212 772 0958

NEW YORK - NEW YORK CITY

The Inn at Irving Place
56 Irving Place, New York, New York 10003
Tel: 1 212 533 4600
Fax: 1 212 533 4611

NEW YORK - SARANAC LAKE

The Point
Saranac Lake, New York 12983
Tel: 1 518 891 5674
Fax: 1 518 891 1152

NORTH CAROLINA - BEAUFORT

The Cedars Inn
305 Front Street, Beaufort, North Carolina 28516
Tel: 1 252 728 7036
Fax: 1 252 728 1685

NORTH CAROLINA - BLOWING ROCK

Gideon Ridge Inn
202 Gideon Ridge Road, Blowing Rock, North Carolina 28605
Tel: 1 828 295 3644
Fax: 1 828 295 4586

NORTH CAROLINA - CASHIERS

Millstone Inn
119 Lodge Lane, Highway 64 West, Cashiers, North Carolina 28717
Tel: 1 828 743 2737
Fax: 1 828 743 0208

NORTH CAROLINA - CHARLOTTE

Ballantyne Resort
10000 Ballantyne Commons Parkway, Charlotte, North Carolina 28277
Tel: 1 704 248 4000
Fax: 1 704 248 4099

NORTH CAROLINA - CHARLOTTE

The Park
2200 Rexford Road, Charlotte, North Carolina 28211
Tel: 1 704 364 8220
Fax: 1 704 365 4712

NORTH CAROLINA - HENDERSONVILLE

Claddagh Inn
755 North Main Street, Hendersonville, North Carolina 28792
Tel: 1 828 697 7778
Fax: 1 828 697 8664

NORTH CAROLINA - HIGHLANDS

Old Edwards Inn and Spa
445 Main Street, Highlands, North Carolina 28741
Tel: 1 828 526 8008
Fax: 1 828 526 8301

NORTH CAROLINA - NEW BERN

Aerie Inn
509 Pollock Street, New Bern, North Carolina 28562
Tel: 1 252 636 5553
Fax: 1 252 514 2157

NORTH CAROLINA - RALEIGH - DURHAM

The Siena Hotel
1505 E Franklin Street, Chapel Hill, North Carolina 27514
Tel: 1 919 929 4000
Fax: 1 919 968 8527

NORTH CAROLINA - ROBBINSVILLE

Snowbird Mountain Lodge
275 Santeetlah Road, Robbinsville, North Carolina 28771
Tel: 1 828 479 3433
Fax: 1 828 479 3473

Condé Nast Johansens are delighted to recommend over 240 properties across North America, Mexico, Bermuda, The Caribbean, The Pacific. Call 0800 269 397 or see the order forms on page 303 to order guides.

NORTH CAROLINA - TRYON

Pine Crest Inn
85 Pine Crest Lane, Tryon, North Carolina 28782
Tel: 1 828 859 9135
Fax: 1 828 859 9136

NORTH CAROLINA - WILMINGTON

Graystone Inn
100 South Third Street, Wilmington, North Carolina 28401
Tel: 1 910 763 2000
Fax: 1 910 763 5555

OHIO - CINCINNATI

The Cincinnatian Hotel
601 Vine Street, Cincinnati, Ohio 45202-2433
Tel: 1 513 381 3000
Fax: 1 513 651 0256

OKLAHOMA - BARTLESVILLE

Inn at Price Tower
510 Dewey Avenue, Bartlesville, Oklahoma 74003
Tel: 1 918 336 1000
Fax: 1 918 336 7117

OREGON - ASHLAND

The Winchester Inn & Restaurant
35 South Second Street, Ashland, Oregon 97520
Tel: 1 541 488 1113
Fax: 1 541 488 4604

OREGON - EUGENE

The Campbell House
252 Pearl Street, Eugene, Oregon 97401
Tel: 1 541 343 1119
Fax: 1 541 343 2258

OREGON - GOLD BEACH

Tu Tu' Tun Lodge
96550 North Bank Rogue, Gold Beach, Oregon 97444
Tel: 1 541 247 6664
Fax: 1 541 247 0672

OREGON - PORTLAND

The Benson Hotel
309 Southwest Broadway, Portland, Oregon 97205
Tel: 1 503 228 2000
Fax: 1 503 471 3920

OREGON - PORTLAND

Portland's White House
1914 North East 22nd Avenue, Portland, Oregon 97212
Tel: 1 503 287 7131
Fax: 1 503 249 1641

PENNSYLVANIA - HANOVER

Sheppard Mansion
117 Frederick Street, Hanover, Pennsylvania 17331
Tel: 1 717 633 8075
Fax: 1 717 633 8074

PENNSYLVANIA - LEOLA

Leola Village Inn & Suites
38 Deborah Drive, Route 23, Leola, Pennsylvania 17540
Tel: 1 717 656 7002
Fax: 1 717 656 7648

PENNSYLVANIA - NEW BERLIN

The Inn at New Berlin
321 Market Street, New Berlin, Pennsylvania 17855-0390
Tel: 1 570 966 0321
Fax: 1 570 966 9557

PENNSYLVANIA - PHILADELPHIA

Rittenhouse Square European Boutique Hotel
1715 Rittenhouse Square, Philadelphia, Pennsylvania 19103
Tel: 1 215 546 6500
Fax: 1 215 546 8787

PENNSYLVANIA - SKYTOP

Skytop Lodge
One Skytop, Skytop, Pennyslvania 18357
Tel: 1 800 345 7759
Fax: 1 570 595 8917

SOUTH CAROLINA - CHARLESTON

The Boardwalk Inn at Wild Dunes Resort
5757 Palm Boulevard, Isle of Palms, South Carolina 29451
Tel: 1 843 886 6000
Fax: 1 843 886 2916

SOUTH CAROLINA - CHARLESTON

Vendue Inn
19 Vendue Range, Charleston, South Carolina 29401
Tel: 1 843 577 7970
Fax: 1 843 577 2913

SOUTH CAROLINA - KIAWAH ISLAND

The Sanctuary at Kiawah Island
1 Sanctuary Beach Drive, Kiawah Island, South Carolina 29455
Tel: 1 843 768 6000
Fax: 1 843 768 5150

SOUTH CAROLINA - PAWLEYS ISLAND

Litchfield Plantation
Kings River Road, Box 290, Pawleys Island, South Carolina 29585
Tel: 1 843 237 9121
Fax: 1 843 237 1041

SOUTH CAROLINA - TRAVELERS REST

La Bastide
10 Road Of Vines, Travelers Rest, South Carolina 29690
Tel: 1 864 836 8463
Fax: 1 864 836 4820

TEXAS - AUSTIN

The Mansion at Judges' Hill
1900 Rio Grande, Austin, Texas 78705
Tel: 1 512 495 1800
Fax: 1 512 691 4461

Mini Listings North America

Condé Nast Johansens are delighted to recommend over 240 properties across North America, Mexico, Bermuda, The Caribbean, The Pacific.
Call 0800 269 397 or see the order forms on page 303 to order guides.

TEXAS - GLEN ROSE
Rough Creek Lodge
PO Box 2400, Glen Rose, Texas 76043
Tel: 1 254 965 3700
Fax: 1 254 918 2570

TEXAS - SAN ANTONIO
Hotel Valencia Riverwalk
150 East Houston Street, San Antonio, Texas 78205
Tel: 1 210 227 9700
Fax: 1 210 227 9701

TEXAS - SAN ANTONIO SAN ANTONIO
Beauregard House
215 Beauregard Street, San Antonio, Texas 78204
Tel: 1 210 222 1198
Fax: 1 210 222 9338

VIRGINIA - CHARLOTTESVILLE
200 South Street Inn
200 South Street, Charlottesville, Virginia 22902
Tel: 1 434 979 0200
Fax: 1 434 979 4403

VIRGINIA - CHARLOTTESVILLE
The Clifton Inn
1296 Clifton Inn Drive, Charlottesville, Virginia 22911
Tel: 1 434 971 1800
Fax: 1 434 971 7098

WASHINGTON - BELLINGHAM
The Chrysalis Inn & Spa
804 10th Street, Bellingham, Washington 98225
Tel: 1 360 756 1005
Fax: 1 360 647 0342

WASHINGTON - FRIDAY HARBOR
Friday Harbor House
130 West Street, Washington 98250
Tel: 1 360 378 8455
Fax: 1 360 378 8453

WASHINGTON - SEATTLE
Sorrento Hotel
900 Madison Street, Seattle, Washington 98104-1297
Tel: 1 206 622 6400
Fax: 1 206 343 6155

WASHINGTON - SEATTLE
Woodmark Hotel on Lake Washington
1200 Carillon Point, Kirkland, Washington 98033
Tel: 1 425 822 3700
Fax: 1 425 822 3699

WASHINGTON - SPOKANE
The Davenport Hotel
10 South Post Street, Spokane, Washington 99201
Tel: 1 509 455 8888
Fax: 1 509 624 4455

WASHINGTON - UNION
Alderbrook Resort & Spa
10 East Alderbrook Drive, Union, Washington 98592
Tel: 1 360 898 2200
Fax: 1 360 898 4610

WASHINGTON - WOODINVILLE
The Herbfarm
14590 North East 145th Street, Woodinville, Washington 98072
Tel: 1 425 485 5300
Fax: 1 425 424 2925

WASHINGTON - WOODINVILLE
Willows Lodge
14580 N.E. 145th Street, Woodinville, Washington 98072
Tel: 1 425 424 3900
Fax: 1 425 424 2585

WYOMING - CHEYENNE
Nagle Warren Mansion
222 East 17Th Street, Cheyenne, Wyoming 82001
Tel: 1 307 637 3333
Fax: 1 307 638 6879

WYOMING - JACKSON
The Rusty Parrot Lodge
175 North Jackson Street, Jackson, Wyoming 83001
Tel: 1 307 733 2000
Fax: 1 307 733 5566

WYOMING - JACKSON HOLE
Spring Creek Ranch
1800 Spirit Dance Road, Wyoming 83001
Tel: 1 307 733 8833
Fax: 1 307 733 1524

WYOMING - MORAN
Jenny Lake Lodge
Inner Park Loop Road, Grand Teton National Park, Wyoming 83013
Tel: 1 307 543 3300
Fax: 1 307 543 3358

MEXICO - ACAPULCO
Quinta Real Acapulco
Paseo de la Quinta 6, Desarrollo Turistico Real Diamante, Acapulco, Guerrero 39907
Tel: 52 744 469 1500
Fax: 52 744 469 1516

MEXICO - AGUASCALIENTES
Quinta Real Aguascalientes
Av. Aguascalientes Sur 601, Jardines de la Asuncion, Aguascalientes, Aguascalientes 20070
Tel: 52 449 978 5818
Fax: 52 449 978 5616

MEXICO - BAJA CALIFORNIA
Casa Natalia
Blvd Mijares 4, San Jose Del Cabo, Baja California Sur 23400
Tel: 52 624 14 251 00
Fax: 52 624 14251 10

Condé Nast Johansens are delighted to recommend over 240 properties across North America, Mexico, Bermuda, The Caribbean, The Pacific.
Call 0800 269 397 or see the order forms on page 303 to order guides.

MEXICO - CANCUN

Villas Tacul Boutique Hotel
Boulevard Kukulkan, KM 5.5, Cancun, Quintana Roo 77500
Tel: 52 998 883 00 00
Fax: 52 998 849 70 70

MEXICO - NUEVO VALLARTA

Grand Velas All Suites & Spa Resort
Av. Cocoteros 98 Sur, Nuevo Vallarta, Nayarit 63735
Tel: 52 322 226 8000
Fax: 52 322 297 2005

MEXICO - GUADALAJARA

Quinta Real Guadalajara
Av. Mexico 2727 Fraccionamiento Monraz, Guadalajara, Jalisco 44680
Tel: 52 33 3669 0600
Fax: 52 33 3669 0601

MEXICO - OAXACA

Casa Cid de Leon
Av. Morelos 602, Centro, Oaxaca, Oaxaca 68000
Tel: 52 951 514 1893
Fax: 52 951 514 7013

MEXICO - GUANAJUATO

Quinta Las Acacias
Paseo de la Presa 168, Guanajuato, Guanajuato 36000
Tel: 52 473 731 1517
Fax: 52 473 731 1862

MEXICO - OAXACA

Casa Oaxaca
Calle García Vigil 407, Centro, Oaxaca, Oaxaca 68000
Tel: 52 951 514 4173
Fax: 52 951516 4412

MEXICO - GUANAJUATO

Quinta Real Casa de Sierra Nevada
Hospicio 35, San Miguel de Allende, Guanajuato 37700
Tel: 52 415 152 7040
Fax: 52 415 152 1436

MEXICO - OAXACA

Hacienda Los Laureles - Spa
Hildago 21, San Felipe del Agua, Oaxaca 68020
Tel: 52 951 501 5300
Fax: 52 951 501 5301

MEXICO - HUATULCO

Quinta Real Huatulco
Paseo Benito Juarez Lote 2, Bahia de Tangolunda, Huatulco, Oaxaca 70989
Tel: 52 958 58 10428
Fax: 52 958 58 10429

MEXICO - PUERTO VALLARTA

Las Alamandas Resort
Carretera Barra de Navidad - Puerto Vallarta km 83.5, Col. Quemaro, Jalisco 48980
Tel: 52 322 285 5500
Fax: 52 322 285 5027

MEXICO - ISLA MUJERES

Secreto
Sección Rocas, Lote 11, Punta Norte, Isla Mujeres, Quintana Roo 77400
Tel: 52 998 877 1039
Fax: 52 998 877 1048

MEXICO - PUERTO VALLARTA

Quinta Real Puerto Vallarta
Pelicanos 311, Fracc. Marina Vallarta, Puerto Vallarta, Jalisco 48354
Tel: 52 322 226 6688
Fax: 52 322 226 6699

MEXICO - MÉRIDA

Hacienda Xcanatun & Casa de Piedra
Carretera Mérida-Progreso, Km 12, Mérida, Yucatán 97300
Tel: 52 999 941 0273
Fax: 52 999 941 0319

MEXICO - SALTILLO

Quinta Real Saltillo
Colosio 1385, Saltillo, Coahuila, 25205
Tel: 52 844 485 0471
Fax: 52 844 485 0470

MEXICO - MONTERREY

Quinta Real Monterrey
Diego Rivera 500, Fracc. Valle Oriente, Monterrey, Nuevo León 66260
Tel: 52 81 83 68 1000
Fax: 52 81 83 68 1070

MEXICO - SONORA

Hacienda de los Santos Resort & Spa
Calle Molina 8, Alamos, Sonora 85760
Tel: 52 647 428 0222
Fax: 52 647 428 0367

MEXICO - MORELIA

Hotel Los Juaninos
Morelos Sur 39, Centro, Morelia, Michoacán 58000
Tel: 52 443 312 00 36
Fax: 52 443 312 00 36

MEXICO - ZACATECAS

Quinta Real Zacatecas
Av. Ignacio Rayon 434, Centro, Zacatecas, Zacatecas 98000
Tel: 52 492 92 29104
Fax: 52 492 922 8440

MEXICO - MORELIA

Villa Montaña Hotel & Spa
201 Patzimba Vista Bella, Morelia, Michoacán 58090
Tel: 52 443 314 02 31
Fax: 52 443 315 14 23

MEXICO - ZIHUATANEJO

Hotel Villa Del Sol
Playa La Ropa S/N, Zihuatanejo, Guerrero 40880
Tel: 52 755 555 5500
Fax: 52 755 554 2758

Condé Nast Johansens are delighted to recommend over 240 properties across North America, Mexico, Bermuda, The Caribbean, The Pacific.
Call 0800 269 397 or see the order forms on page 303 to order guides.

BAHAMAS - HARBOUR ISLAND

Pink Sands
Chapel Street, Harbour Island, Bahamas
Tel: 1 242 333 2030
Fax: 1 242 333 2060

BERMUDA - DEVONSHIRE

Ariel Sands
34 South Shore Road, Devonshire, Bermuda
Tel: 1 441 236 1010
Fax: 1 441 236 0087

BERMUDA - HAMILTON

Rosedon Hotel
P.O. Box Hm 290, Hamilton Hmax, Bermuda
Tel: 1 441 295 1640
Fax: 1 441 295 5904

BERMUDA - PAGET

Fourways Inn
PO Box Pg 294, Paget Pg Bx, Bermuda
Tel: 1 441 236 6517
Fax: 1 441 236 5528

BERMUDA - SOMERSET

Cambridge Beaches
Kings Point, Somerset, MA02 Bermuda
Tel: 1 441 234 0331
Fax: 1 441 234 3352

BERMUDA - SOUTHAMPTON

The Reefs
56 South Shore Road, Southampton, SN02 Bermuda
Tel: 1 441 238 0222
Fax: 1 441 238 8372

BERMUDA - WARWICK

Surf Side Beach Club
90 South Shore Road, Warwick, Bermuda
Tel: 1 441 236 7100
Fax: 1 441 236 9765

CARIBBEAN - ANGUILLA

Cap Juluca
Maundays Bay, Anguilla, Leeward Islands, British West Indies
Tel: 1 264 497 6666
Fax: 1 264 497 6617

CARIBBEAN - ANTIGUA

Blue Waters
PO BOX 256, ST. JOHN'S, ANTIGUA, WEST INDIES
Tel: 1 870 360 1245
Fax: 1 870 360 1246

CARIBBEAN - ANTIGUA

Curtain Bluff
P.O. Box 288, Antigua, West Indies
Tel: 1 268 462 8400
Fax: 1 268 462 8409

CARIBBEAN - ANTIGUA

Galley Bay
Five Islands, PO Box 305, St. John's, Antigua, West Indies
Tel: 1 268 462 0302
Fax: 1 268 462 4551

CARIBBEAN - ANTIGUA

The Inn at English Harbour
Po Box 187, St. John's, Antigua, West Indies
Tel: 1 268 460 1014
Fax: 1 268 460 1603

CARIBBEAN - BARBADOS

Coral Reef Club
St. James, Barbados, West Indies
Tel: 1 246 422 2372
Fax: 1 246 422 1776

CARIBBEAN - BARBADOS

The House at Tamarind Cove
Paynes Bay, St. James, Barbados, West Indies
Tel: 1 246 432 5525
Fax: 1 246 432 5255

CARIBBEAN - BARBADOS

Little Arches
Enterprise Beach Road, Christ Church, Barbados, West Indies
Tel: 1 246 420 4689
Fax: 1 246 418 0207

CARIBBEAN - BARBADOS

Lone Star Hotel
Mount Standfast, St. James, Barbados, West Indies
Tel: 1 246 419 0599
Fax: 1 246 419 0597

CARIBBEAN - BARBADOS

The Sandpiper
Holetown, St. James, Barbados, West Indies
Tel: 1 246 422 2251
Fax: 1 246 422 0900

CARIBBEAN - BRITISH VIRGIN ISLANDS (TORTOLA)

Long Bay Beach Resort & Villas
Long Bay, Tortola, British Virgin Islands
Tel: 1 954 481 8787
Fax: 1 954 481 1661

CARIBBEAN - CURAÇAO

Avila Beach Hotel
Penstraat 130, Willemstad, Curaçao, Netherlands Antilles, West Indies
Tel: 599 9 461 4377
Fax: 599 9 461 1493

CARIBBEAN - GRENADA

Spice Island Beach Resort
Grand Anse Beach, Box 6, St. George's, Grenada, West Indies
Tel: 1 473 444 4423/4258
Fax: 1 473 444 4807

Condé Nast Johansens are delighted to recommend over 240 properties across North America, Mexico, Bermuda, The Caribbean, The Pacific. Call 0800 269 397 or see the order forms on page 303 to order guides.

CARIBBEAN - JAMAICA

Half Moon
Montego Bay, Jamaica, West Indies
Tel: 1 876 953 2211
Fax: 1 876 953 2731

CARIBBEAN - JAMAICA

Round Hill Hotel and Villas
P.O. Box 64, Montego Bay, Jamaica, West Indies
Tel: 1 876 956 7050
Fax: 1 876 956 7505

CARIBBEAN - JAMAICA

The Tryall Club
PO Box 1206, Montego Bay, Jamaica, West Indies
Tel: 1 800 238 5290
Fax: 1 876 956 5673

CARIBBEAN - JAMAICA

Sans Souci Resort & Spa
PO Box 103, Ocho Rios, St. Ann, Jamaica, West Indies
Tel: 1 876 994 1206
Fax: 1 876 994 1544

CARIBBEAN - NEVIS

The Hermitage
Figtree Parish, PO Box 497, Charlestown, Nevis, West Indies
Tel: 1 869 469 3477
Fax: 1 869 469 2481

CARIBBEAN - NEVIS

Montpelier Plantation Inn
Montpelier Estate, PO Box 474, Nevis, West Indies
Tel: 1 869 469 3462
Fax: 1 869 469 2932

CARIBBEAN - NEVIS

Nisbet Plantation Beach Club
St. James Parish, Nevis, West Indies
Tel: 1 869 469 9325
Fax: 1 869 469 9864

CARIBBEAN - ST. KITTS

Ottley's Plantation Inn
P.o. Box 345, Basseterre, St. Kitts, West Indies
Tel: 1 869 465 7234
Fax: 1 869 465 4760

CARIBBEAN - SAINT-BARTHÉLEMY

Carl Gustaf Hotel
BP 700, Rue des Normands, Gustavia, 97099 Saint-Barthélemy, French West Indies
Tel: 1 590 590 297 900
Fax: 1 590 590 278 237

CARIBBEAN - ST. LUCIA

Anse Chastanet
SoufriÈre, St. Lucia, West Indies
Tel: 1 758 459 7000
Fax: 1 758 459 7700

CARIBBEAN - ST. LUCIA

The Body Holiday at LeSport
Cariblue Beach, Castries, St. Lucia, West Indies
Tel: 1 758 457 7800
Fax: 1 758 450 0368

CARIBBEAN - ST. LUCIA

Windjammer Landing Villa Beach Resort & Spa
Labrelotte Bay, Castries, St. Lucia, West Indies
Tel: 1 954 481 8787
Fax: 1 954 481 1661

CARIBBEAN - THE GRENADINES (MUSTIQUE)

Firefly
Mustique Island, St. Vincent & The Grenadines
Tel: 1 784 488 8414
Fax: 1 784 488 8514

CARIBBEAN - THE GRENADINES (PALM ISLAND)

Palm Island
St. Vincent & The Grenadines, West Indies
Tel: 1 954 481 8787
Fax: 1 954 481 1661

CARIBBEAN - TURKS & CAICOS

Point Grace
P.O. Box 700, Providenciales, Turks & Caicos Islands, British west indies
Tel: 1 649 946 5096
Fax: 1 649 946 5097

CARIBBEAN - TURKS & CAICOS

Turks & Caicos Club
PO Box 687, Providenciales, Turks & Caicos, British West Indies
Tel: 1 649 946 5800
Fax: 1 649 946 5858

PACIFIC - FIJI ISLANDS (LABASA)

Nukubati Island
P.O. Box 1928, Labasa, Fiji Islands
Tel: 61 2 93888 196
Fax: 61 2 93888 204

PACIFIC - FIJI ISLANDS (LAUTOKA)

Blue Lagoon Cruises
183 Vitogo Parade, Lautoka, Fiji Islands
Tel: 1 679 6661 622
Fax: 1 679 6664 098

PACIFIC - FIJI ISLANDS (QAMEA ISLAND)

Qamea Resort & Spa
P.A. Matei, Tajeuni, Fiji Islands
Tel: 679 888 0220
Fax: 679 888 0092

PACIFIC - FIJI ISLANDS (SAVU SAVU)

Jean-Michel Cousteau Fiji Islands Resort
Lesiaceva Point, Savu Savu, Fiji Islands
Tel: 415 788 5794
Fax: 415 788 0150

Condé Nast Johansens are delighted to recommend over 240 properties across North America, Mexico, Bermuda, The Caribbean, The Pacific. Call 0800 269 397 or see the order forms on page 303 to order guides.

The International Mark of Excellence

For further information, current news,
e-club membership, hotel search, Preferred Partners,
online bookshop and special offers visit:

www.johansens.com

Annually Inspected for the Independent Traveller

INDEX BY PROPERTY

INDEX BY LOCATION

England

INDEX BY LOCATION

"THE WORLD MAKES WAY FOR THE MAN WHO KNOWS WHERE HE IS GOING."

RALPH WALDO EMERSON

CONDÉ NAST JOHANSENS PREFERRED PARTNER

JOHNNIE WALKER

INDEX BY ACTIVITY

🔔 Licensed for wedding ceremonies

M75 Conference facilities for 75 delegates or more

Grand Heritage members

Relais & Châteaux members

Ireland's Blue Book

NORTH WEST ENGLAND

Hotel location shown in red (hotel) or purple (spa hotel) with page number

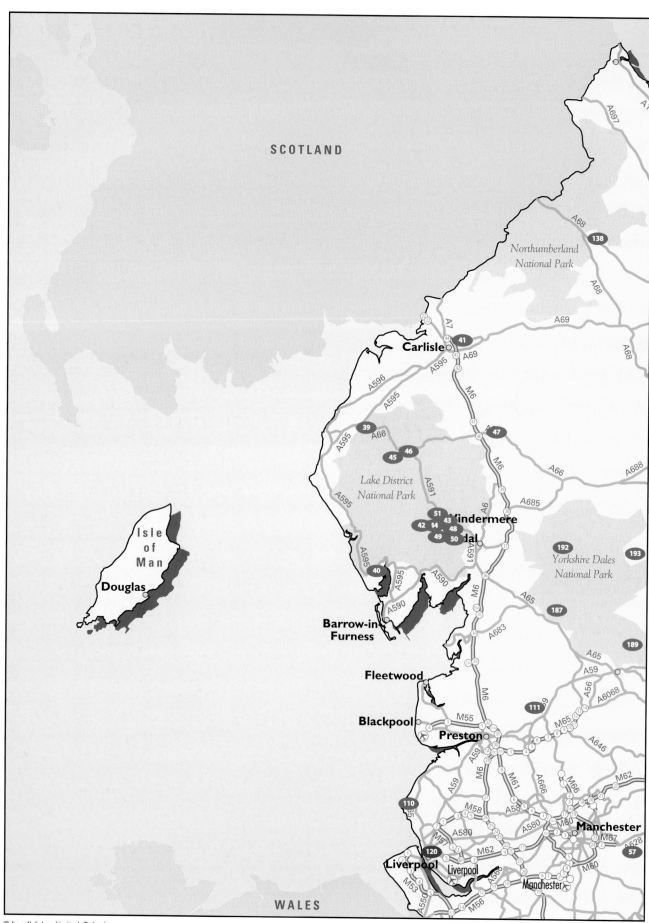

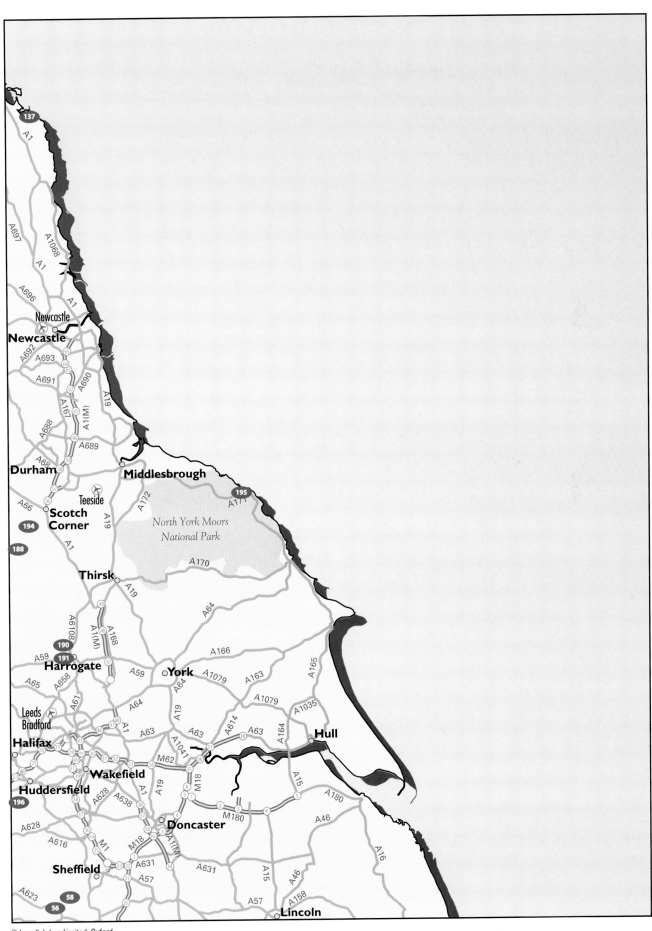

Central England

Hotel location shown in red (hotel) or purple (spa hotel) with page number

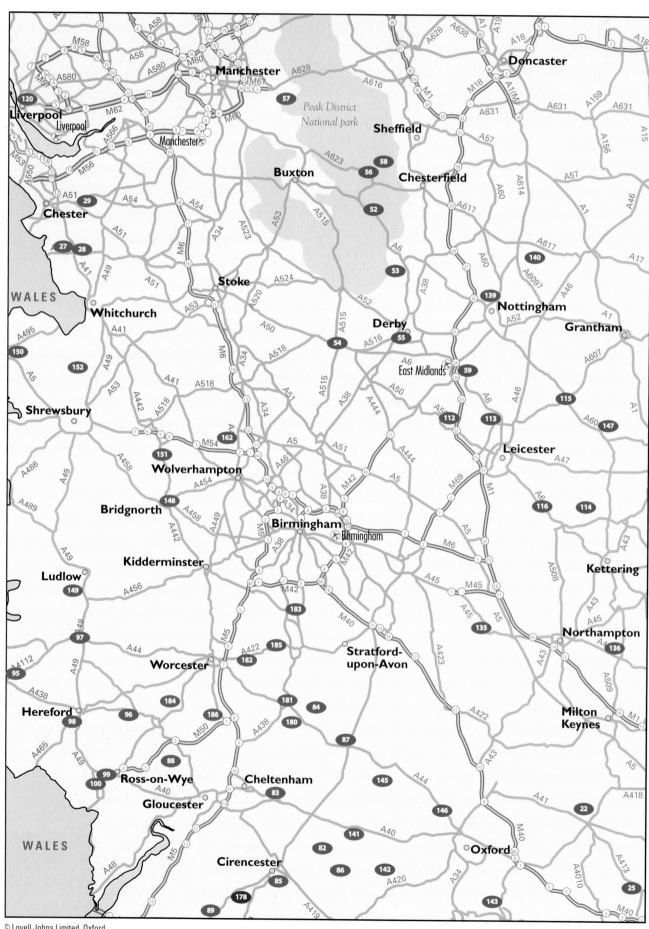

© Lovell Johns Limited, Oxford

EASTERN ENGLAND

Hotel location shown in red (hotel) or purple (spa hotel) with page number

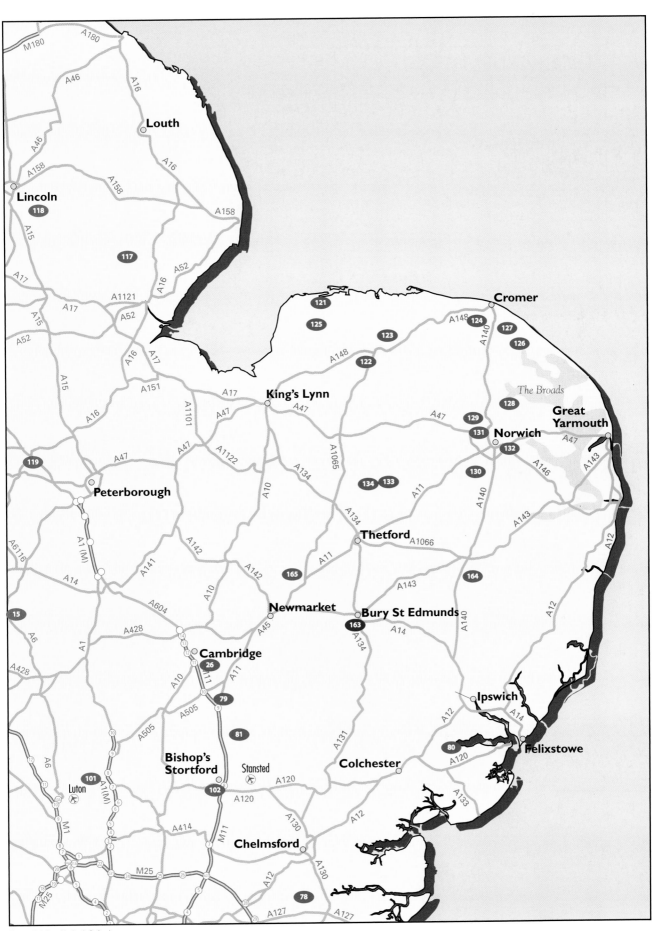

Louth

Lincoln
118

117

Cromer
121
125
123
A148 124 127
126
122
The Broads
King's Lynn
128
A47 129
131 Norwich
Great Yarmouth
132
119
130
Peterborough
134 133

Thetford
165
164

Newmarket
Bury St Edmunds
163

15
26 Cambridge
79
81
Ipswich
80 Felixstowe
Bishop's Stortford
Stansted
101
102
Colchester
Luton
Chelmsford
78

© Lovell Johns Limited, Oxford

295

CHANNEL ISLANDS & SOUTH WEST ENGLAND

Hotel location shown in red (hotel) or purple (spa hotel) with page number

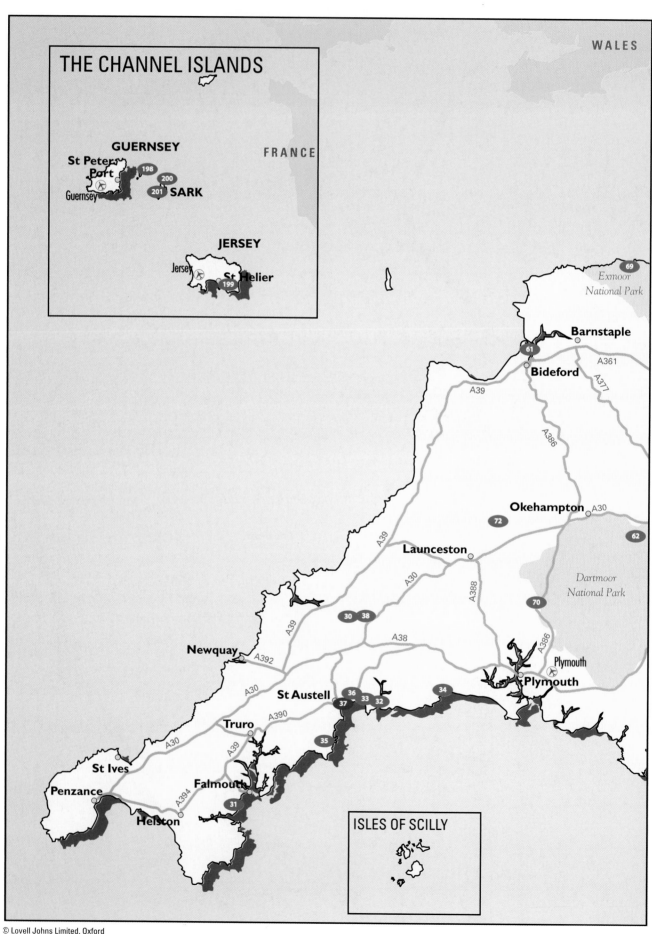

THE CHANNEL ISLANDS

WALES

GUERNSEY

FRANCE

St Peter Port

198

200

Guernsey

201

SARK

JERSEY

Jersey

St Helier

199

Exmoor
National Park

69

Barnstaple

61

Bideford

A361

A377

A39

A386

Okehampton

A30

72

62

Launceston

A39

A30

A388

Dartmoor
National Park

70

A386

30

38

A38

Newquay

A392

Plymouth

A30

St Austell

36

33

34

Plymouth

A39

37

32

A390

Truro

A38

35

A39

St Ives

Penzance

A394

Falmouth

31

ISLES OF SCILLY

Helston

© Lovell Johns Limited, Oxford

296

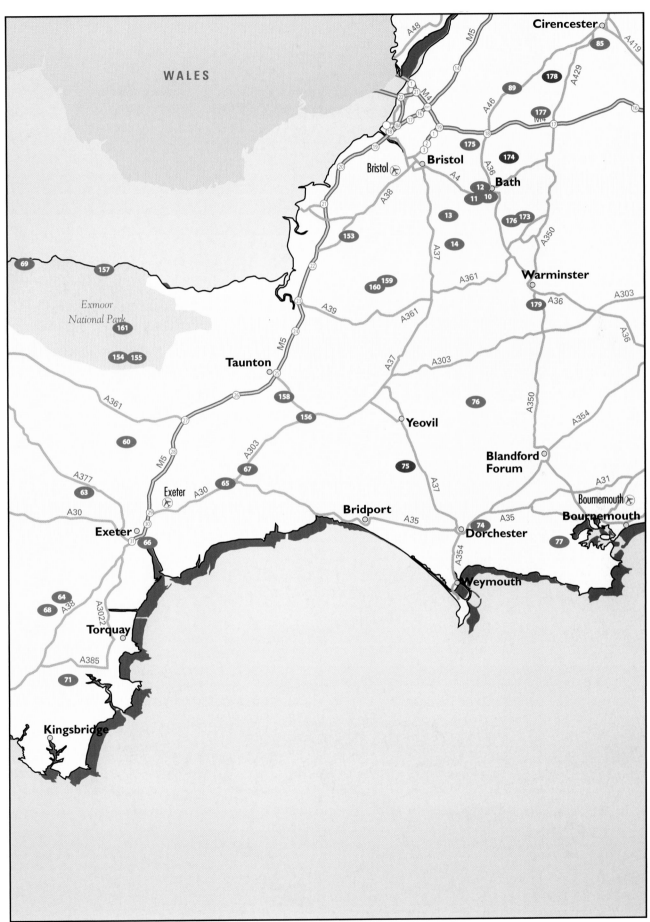

SOUTH WEST ENGLAND

Hotel location shown in red (hotel) or purple (spa hotel) with page number

WALES

Cirencester

Bristol

Bristol

Bath

Warminster

Exmoor
National Park

Taunton

Yeovil

Blandford
Forum

Bournemouth

Bournemouth

Exeter

Exeter

Bridport

Dorchester

Weymouth

Torquay

Kingsbridge

SOUTHERN ENGLAND

Hotel location shown in red (hotel) or purple (spa hotel) with page number

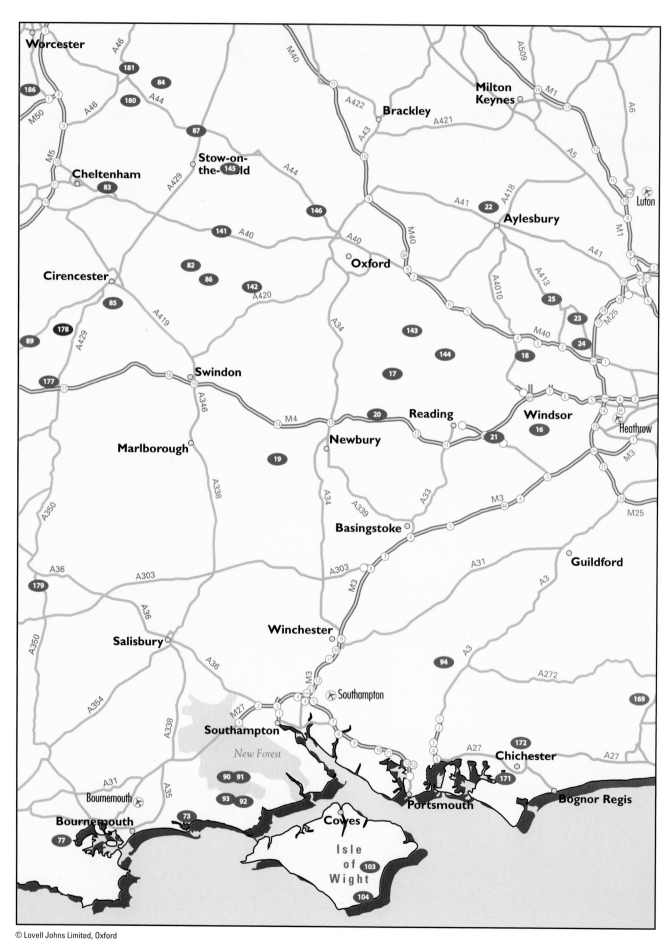

© Lovell Johns Limited, Oxford

SOUTH EAST ENGLAND

Hotel location shown in red (hotel) or purple (spa hotel) with page number

IRELAND

Hotel location shown in red (hotel) or purple (spa hotel) with page number

SCOTLAND

Hotel location shown in red (hotel) or purple (spa hotel) with page number

Thurso

Stornoway

Ullapool

Fraserburgh

Uig

Inverness
(Dalcross)
226
Inverness

Aberdeen
Aberdeen

214

229

Mallaig
228
227

225
Fort William
233

219
218
216

215
Dundee

217
232
Perth
St Andrews

231
230
221

234

Glasgow
Glasgow
Edinburgh
Edinburgh

235

Prestwick
Ayr

220
223
224

Campbeltown

Dumfries

NORTHERN
IRELAND
Stranraer
222

ENGLAND

© Lovell Johns Limited,

WALES

Hotel location shown in red (hotel) or purple (spa hotel) with page number

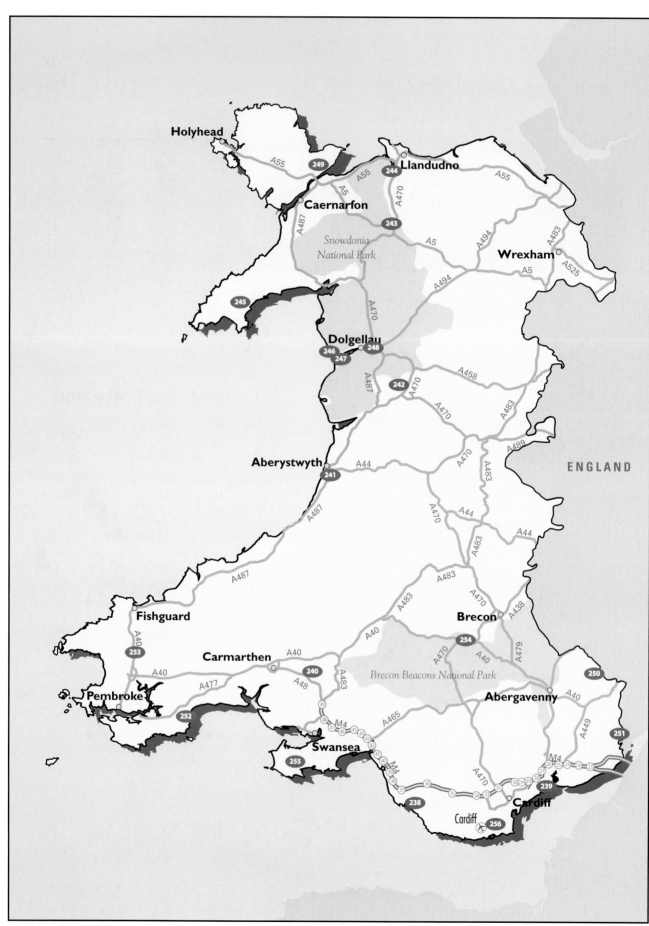

© Lovell Johns Limited, Oxford

ORDER FORM

Choose from our wide range of titles below

Up to £20 off when you order more than one guide...

Order 4 guides get £20 off, 3 guides get £10 off, 2 guides £5 off

Hotels & Spas
Great Britain & Ireland
£19.95

Country Houses
Great Britain & Ireland
£16.95

Hotels & Spas
Europe & Mediterranean
£16.95

Hotels, Inns & Resorts
N. America, Caribbean
£14.95

Business Venues
(published Feb 2005)
£25.00

Save over £40 when you order the **The International Collection...**

a boxed presentation set of the four leisure guides,

PLUS the Business Venues Guide,

PLUS our exclusive silver plated luggage tag.

A great offer for only £70 (RRP £113.80)

(Silver plated luggage tag RRP £15, presentaion box RRP£5)

The International Collection
£70.00

QUANTITY £

DISCOUNT - Discount does not apply to the International Collection   2 Guides = £5 off ☐   3 Guides = £10 off ☐   4 Guides = £20 off ☐

PACKING & DELIVERY - All UK Orders add £4.90. (Outside UK add £6 (per Guide) or £25 for The International Collection)   £

GRAND TOTAL - Don't forget to deduct your discount   £

☐ Please charge my Visa/Mastercard/Amex/Switch   ☐ I enclose a cheque payable to Condé Nast Johansens

Card No.:   Exp. Date: Issue No. (Switch only):   Start Date:

Name: Signature:

Address:

Postcode: Tel: E-mail:

Mail to Condé Nast Johansens, FREEPOST (CB264), Eastbourne, BN23 6ZW (no stamp required)
or fax your order on 01323 649 350 or register online at www.cnjguides.co.uk quoting reference below

OR CALL OUR HOTLINE NOW ON FREEPHONE 0800 269 397, quote ref: G007

GUEST SURVEY REPORT

Evaluate your stay in a Condé Nast Johansens Recommendation

Dear Guest,

Following your stay in a Condé Nast Johansens recommendation, please spare a moment to complete this Guest Survey Report. This is an important source of information for Johansens, to maintain the highest standards for our recommendations and to support the work of our team of inspectors.

It is also the prime source of nominations for Condé Nast Johansens Awards for Excellence, which are made annually to those properties worldwide that represent the finest standards and best value for money in luxury, independent travel.

Thank you for your time and I hope that when choosing future accommodation Condé Nast Johansens will be your guide.

Yours faithfully,

Andrew Warren
Managing Director

p.s. Guest Survey Reports may also be completed online at www.johansens.com

1. Your details

Your name: ....

Your address: ....

....

....

Postcode: ....

Telephone: ....

E-mail: ....

2. Hotel details

Name of hotel: ....

....

Location: ....

Date of visit: ....

3. Your rating of the hotel

Please tick one box in each category below (as applicable)

	Excellent	Good	Disappointing	Poor
Bedrooms	○	○	○	○
Public Rooms	○	○	○	○
Food/Restaurant	○	○	○	○
Service	○	○	○	○
Welcome/Friendliness	○	○	○	○
Value For Money	○	○	○	○

4. Any other comments

If you wish to make additional comments, please write separately to the Publisher, Condé Nast Johansens Ltd, 6-8 Old Bond Street, London W1S 4PH

....

....

....

....

Please return to **Condé Nast Johansens, FREEPOST (CB264), EASTBOURNE BN23 6ZW** (no stamp required)
or alternatively send by fax on 01323 649350